Linking LANs

A Micro Manager's Guide

Linking LANs
A Micro Manager's Guide

Stan Schatt

Windcrest®/McGraw-Hill

FIRST EDITION
SECOND PRINTING

© 1991 by **Windcrest Books,** an imprint of TAB Books.
TAB Books is a division of McGraw-Hill, Inc.
The name "Windcrest" is a registered trademark of TAB Books.

Library of Congress Cataloging-in-Publication Data

Schatt, Stanley.
    Linking LANs : a micro manager's guide / by Stan Schatt.
      p.   cm.
    Includes index.
    ISBN 0-8306-8755-6   ISBN 0-8306-3755-9 (pbk.)
    1. Local area networks (Computer networks)   I. Title.
    TK5105.7.S36   1991
    004.6'8—dc20   91-11407
                                          CIP

TAB Books offers software for sale. For information and a catalog, please contact
TAB Software Department, Blue Ridge Summit, PA 17294-0850.

Acquisitions Editor: Stephen Moore
Technical Editor: Sandra L. Johnson
Production: Katherine G. Brown
Series Design: Jaclyn J. Boone

WT1

This book is dedicated to my wife, Jane.
She's making sure that the children currently at
the Flora Vista School in Encinitas, California,
will be able to read the network manuals
and solve the enterprise networking problems
of the next decade.

Contents

Chapter 8. Local routers and brouters   171

Chapter 9. Wide area networks   183

Chapter 10. ISDN 211

Chapter 11. Gateways to the mainframe world 221

Introduction

I wrote this book for anyone who needs to understand how different networks can be linked together. In a very short time, an entirely new industry has developed with its own language—terms like *brouters*, *source routing*, *enterprise networking*, and *management network protocols*. Companies are beginning to look at their enormous investments in mainframe and LAN hardware and software and demanding that someone (perhaps you) come up with some answers on how these incompatible resources can be made to communicate effectively with each other. As if that were not a large enough assignment, corporate computing resources often include remote sites as well as LANs that use different network operating systems.

The first section of this book shows the hardware and software required for a local area network. I examine the different types of file servers and network interface cards now available as well as specific features to look for when selecting a network workstation. You also look at a number of operating systems including DOS, OS/2, and Unix as well as network operating systems including NetWare and LAN Manager. Finally, I show you the client-server model that is bound to play an increasingly important role in network design and system integration.

This book's second section focuses on network protocols, the software that must be understood in order to link together different networks. I discuss the OSI model, TCP/IP, and the problems associated with migrating from TCP/IP to OSI model protocols. In order to understand the problems associated with bridging and routing LANs, I show specific protocols associated with Ethernet and Token Bus as well as Token Ring and FDDI. I also examine the suite of protocols associated with AppleTalk and Arcnet.

This book's third section concentrates on internetwork operability by examining bridges, brouters, and routers. You will see how the incompatible routing schemes used by Ethernet and Token Ring can be reconciled as well as how a new class of brouters can solve problems that plague many large companies.

The book's fourth section provides a global perspective on linking together networks. It looks at the specific requirements for a metropolitan area network (MAN), how T-1 lines can be used as part of a wide area network (WAN), and how networks can be linked to packet switched networks (X.25).

It is becoming increasingly necessary for a network manager or systems integrator to understand telecommunications as well as data communications. I show the Integrated Services Digital Network (ISDN), which promises to integrate voice and data transmission over the public telephone network. You will see how gateways and LANs can be linked to host computers. This chapter will examine AppleTalk links to both IBM and DEC computers in addition to different methods of linking Token Ring networks to these computers.

Chapter 12 examines some key systems integration issues that are critical when networks are to be linked together. This section also covers the movement toward an international standard for electronic mail (X.400) and a global directory (X.500).

One area of growing importance is network management. I give you the different approaches taken by IBM, AT&T, and DEC, as well as the current battle of network management protocols between Simple Network Management Protocol (SNMP) and Common Information Network Management (CIMP). One of these protocols will probably play an important part in your network sometime in the future.

I have included an annotated list of books that belong on the shelf of the network manager as well as a discussion of seminars available on "cutting edge" topics such as network management and bridges, routers, and gateways. I have also included an extensive glossary that defines all the key terms that appear in the text.

I sincerely hope this book helps you understand the bewildering world of enterprise networking and the problems associated with integrating different network components. This book assumes no prior knowledge of networking or specific LANs. No book can answer all the questions you probably have about the very fast changing field, but I hope this book will help you formulate the questions you need to ask and the answers you need to find in order to solve your company's enterprise networking problems.

1
CHAPTER

LAN hardware basics

In this chapter, you will explore the role of

- Local area network workstations.
- Network interface cards.
- File servers.
- Media.
- Network architecture.

Introduction

A *local area network* (LAN) is a group of computers that share hardware and software resources at the same physical location. This chapter examines a LAN's hardware building blocks. I describe the types of LAN workstations, the role of a disk server or file server, and the key functions performed by the network interface cards. Because LANs can be designed a variety of different ways to perform a wide range of different functions, you will explore some of the criteria network designers use when selecting the appropriate cabling or media as well as the network's architecture or topology.

This book assumes that you do not have any previous LAN experience. If you already have a solid background in local area network hardware and software, you might want to skip ahead to chapter 3, which discusses protocols and the Open Systems Interconnect model for linking different computer networks.

1

Centralized and distributed processing

The first and second generations of computers developed during the 1950s and 1960s illustrate the principle of centralized processing. Mainframe computers and minicomputers used their powerful *central processing units* or *CPUs* to process all the work required by users connected by terminals. The number of users accessing the host computer has a direct correlation to the response time, so that more users resulted in slower computer response time.

The microcomputer revolution

The development of microcomputers in the 1970s and 1980s meant that processing could be distributed rather than centralized. It is true that local area networks permit users to share the cost of expensive resources such as laser printers. Equally important, though, is that a distributed processing environment can be inherently more efficient. Figure 1-1 illustrates the key difference between centralized and distributed processing. Each workstation is a microcomputer with its own processing power so that users need not wait for a host computer to share some of its valuable processing time. A LAN is often faster than a minicomputer with the same number of terminals because the processing workload is distributed among several workstations.

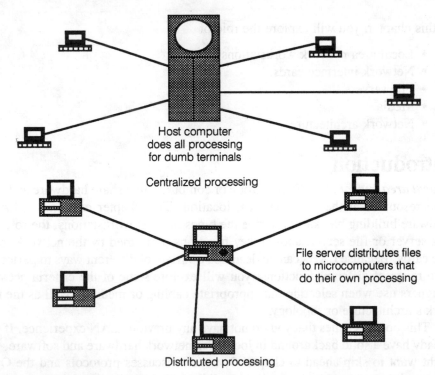

Host computer does all processing for dumb terminals

Centralized processing

File server distributes files to microcomputers that do their own processing

Distributed processing

1-1 Distributed processing and centralized processing.

With powerful new software such as LAN Manager version 2.0 and NetWare 386 and powerful new hardware such as Intel 80486 based file servers, local area networks are beginning to approach mainframe-like performance.

The network workstation

Network workstations, also sometimes referred to as network *nodes*, provide each network user with a display, a keyboard, and a microprocessor capable of running network programs. Today some *diskless workstations* utilize a computer chip known as an autoboot ROM to load programs directly from the network's file server into its own *random access memory* (RAM), meaning that it holds information as long as the computer is turned on The lack of disk drives makes these nodes more secure because users cannot download network files to a floppy disk. Learning some of the terminology about workstation features will help you distinguish one workstation from another.

One of the problems a systems integrator faces is that with so many potential network workstations on the market it is necessary to establish a product matrix and do some careful comparisons and contrasts. In addition to raw processing speed, the type of workstation architecture and RAM can be very significant.

The workstation architecture

One major limitation of the original IBM PC was that while it contained a microprocessor capable of handling 16 bits at one time (a 16-bit word), it only utilized an 8-bit data bus, a data highway for moving the information from CPU to RAM or external devices. Perhaps an example will clarify this problem. Assume that during rush hour a Tokyo subway station utilizes sixteen turnstiles. In effect the station is processing sixteen people at a time. These sixteen people move to the train, which will carry them to their ultimate destinations. Unfortunately, though, these trains have only eight doors. A bottleneck probably will occur during rush hour as people have to wait their turns to enter through one of the eight doors.

The very same process occurred with the original IBM PC. The Intel 8088 microprocessor handled 16 bits of information while the data bus that was responsible for taking this information to the appropriate RAM or external location could not keep up with the flow of information from the microprocessor.

Network workstations also have an address bus and a control bus. The *address bus* serves as a highway of sorts through which travels the address (location in memory) of the next instruction to be executed or the next piece of data to be accessed. The *control bus* consists of a highway used for all timing and controlling function sent from the control unit to other parts of the computer system.

Micro Channel architecture

IBM's upper-range of PS/2 microcomputers feature a *Micro Channel Architecture* (MCA), an intelligent bus or data highway capable of handling high-speed traffic.

As network software begins to tap the potential speed of 32-bit machines, this new type of bus might become a very significant factor in network workstation and file server selection. A Micro Channel bus has a number of advantages, including the ability to move 128 bytes of information in a continuous block. A level-sensitive interrupt system ensures that signals remain active in a queue until they can be serviced. This approach results in far less chance of losing a request when two interrupts occur at the same time than the traditional PC architecture approach known as an edge-triggered interrupt system.

The Micro Channel bus also offers improved *Direct Memory Access* (DMA). Rather than the three DMA devices permitted under PC architecture, MCA permits up to 15 DMA devices. The result is that the number of processor interrupts required is reduced significantly. In addition to improved DMA, Micro Channel provides hardware-mediated channel arbitration which determines which subsystems or processor obtains access to system assets and for how long. This means that changeovers of channel control can take place four times faster than is possible with a PC architecture.

EISA architecture

The success of the IBM PC and AT causes dozens of manufacturers to produce machines that imitated IBM's products, usually offered some additional features, and always (with the exception of Compaq Computer Corporation's models) sold for lower prices. These *clones* caused a significant drop in IBM's market share of the growing microcomputer market, and they caused it to release a new family of microcomputers (the PS/2) with the patented Micro Channel architecture.

Many clone manufacturers did not want to license IBM's technology, yet they needed a higher performance architecture to compete with the PS/2 models. The result was that Compaq and eight other clone manufacturers (known in the industry as the "Gang of Nine") announced *Extended Industry Standard Architecture* (EISA), a 32-bit bus structure that retains compatibility with the circuit cards developed for IBM's AT and PC models.

EISA appeals to many customers because they can continue to use their existing peripheral controller circuit cards. EISA's flexibility permits access by 8-bit, 16-bit, and 32-bit circuit cards. EISA peripherals can do 32-bit transfers of information up at up to 32 megabytes/second; this speed makes EISA competitive with Micro Channel architecture for the type of distributed processing functions that characterize local area network operations.

Random access memory

Network workstations need random access memory (RAM), temporary memory used for storing data and instructions while the computer is running. While the first microcomputers features anywhere from 16 kilobytes to 64 kilobytes of

RAM, today's models often feature several megabytes (millions of bytes) of RAM. As chapter 2 indicates, when you look at operating systems such as OS/2, today's sophisticated operating systems often demand several megabytes of RAM.

Just as important as the amount of RAM a microcomputer has is the type of RAM inside the machine. Today's faster machines often use the very fastest dynamic RAM chips, those with 80-nanosecond access time. A *nanosecond* is a billionth of a second. No matter how fast the microprocessor, it has to wait until the RAM chips have refreshed themselves and are ready for new information. Some manufacturers offer static RAM chips. While these chips are more expensive than the dynamic variety, they do offer speeds as fast as 30 nanoseconds to handle clock speeds up to 24 MHz. The data in static RAM does not have to be refreshed 200–500 times a second, as is the case with the dynamic RAM chips.

Some RAM management techniques

Some workstations manufacturers use a technique known as *two-way memory interleave* to speed up their dynamic RAM chips. They break their RAM chips down into even and odd banks so that immediately after a CPU accesses an even bank of chips, it can access the odd bank, which does not need time to recover.

Finally, a number of workstation manufacturers are using a technique called *cache memory*. Very high-speed RAM chips with 45-nanosecond access time is used to keep a copy of the information last accessed from disk by the microprocessor; the assumption made is that a program will probably need this information again shortly. A second assumption often made is that related information might be requested shortly. Some built-in cache programs will bring related information into cache in addition to the requested data. When the computer requests previously requested material or related information, the turnaround time is much faster because the data is already in the cache. Figure 1-2 illustrates how caching works.

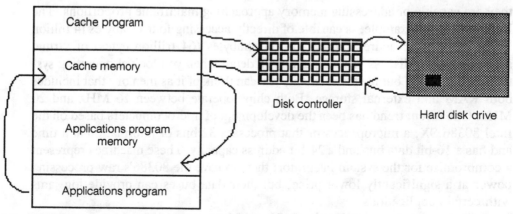

1-2 RAM caching.

Intel offers an 82385 32-bit cache controller chip to help manufacturers design effective caching techniques. Some network operating systems such as NetWare cache several different types of information including directories as well as files to speed up the lowest part of network operations, disk drive access.

The microprocessor

The *microprocessor* is the "brains" of a network workstation, the mainframe equivalent of a central processing unit. IBM's original PC utilized an Intel 8088 microprocessor that was capable of handling 16-bits of information at a time. Because microprocessors can perform tasks in millionths of a second, they need a clock that is very accurate. These computer chips use a crystal that generates frequencies (pulses) that are recorded in megahertz (MHz) or millions of beats/second. Rather than the Apple's II's Mostek 6502 microprocessor that utilized a machine cycle built around one million pulses per second, the Intel 8088 had a "clock speed" of 4.77 MHz, which meant that it was capable of scheduling tasks during the 4.77 million beats that its clock pulsed during one second. The actual instructions that are executed by the microprocessing chip might take several cycles to complete. Because some RAM chips are not able to perform at the same level of speed as the microprocessor, some manufacturers build *wait states* into its PC so that the unit did not really perform at 4.77 MHz. Certain pulses were used to let the slower RAM "keep up" with the microprocessor. Today some companies offer microcomputers advertised with "zero wait states," which means that they are utilizing fast enough RAM chips to allow their microprocessors to operate at full speed without forcing the microprocessors to wait for the RAM chips to complete the process of placing data in temporary storage.

With the release in 1986 of the Compaq 386 based on the Intel 80386 chip and the unveiling in 1987 of the Macintosh II based on the Motorola 68020, many of the traditional distinctions between microcomputer, minicomputer, and mainframe computer blur. Because both chips handle 32-bits of information at a time, they are capable of addressing memory approaching mainframe proportions. The Intel 80386, for example, is capable of directly accessing four gigabytes (4 billion bytes) of physical address space and 64 terabytes (64 trillion bytes) of virtual address space. I discuss virtual memory in detail when you look at operating systems in chapter 2, but for the moment, you can think of it as memory that includes both RAM and external storage. Both chips operate between 16 MHz and 20 MHz. One recent trend has been the development of microcomputers based on the Intel 80386 SX, a microprocessor that processes 32 bits of information at a time and has a 16-bit data bus and a 24-bit address capacity. These machines represent a compromise for the system integrator; they do have the 80386's raw processing power at a significantly lower price, but their data buses can provide log jams with certain applications.

Microcomputers using Intel's 80486 and Motorola's 68030 chips are starting to appear and are capable of running close to 50 MHz. These numbers are almost meaningless unless a user ensures that his or her software is capable of utilizing this speed. The major use of these very fast microprocessing chips will be for file servers, a topic I return to later in this chapter.

Video adapter cards

In addition to each workstation having its own processor and RAM, it also has its own monitor and video adapter circuit card. A network program running on a particular workstation must contain the correct video graphics program or *driver* so that the video adapter card can ensure that the information will be displayed on the monitor. While this might seem like a straightforward enough task, it can become very difficult if there are dozens of network workstations with different types of monitors and video graphics adapters. Some major network application programs might not even have a driver for an occasional "oddball" adapter. Figure 1-3 illustrates some of the different IBM PC standards that have evolved over two generations. Even if drivers exist, the network supervisor will have to write special batch programs to make sure that a workstation loads the appropriate drivers prior to loading a particular program.

Standard	Resolution pixels	Total colors	Colors/screen
Hercules MDA	720 × 348	N/A	N/A
CGA	640 × 200	16	4
EGA	640 × 350	64	16
PGA	640 × 480	4096	256
MCGA			
CGA mode	640 × 200	4096	256
Text mode	640 × 480	16	2
VGA			
CGA mode	640 × 200	4096	256
Text mode	720 × 400	16	2

1-3 IBM microcomputer video standards.

Why purchase a specialized LAN workstation

While any compatible microcomputer can serve as a network workstation, many LAN manufacturers offer their own specialized network workstations, machines that have been optimized for LAN use. Examine a couple of 3Com workstations that illustrate why in some cases they might be preferable to less expensive clones. 3Com's 3Station will serve as one example of this new class of LAN workstations, microcomputers designed specifically for network use and not as stand-alone personal computers. It features an 8 MHz 80286 microprocessor, EGA graphics (see Fig. 1-3), up to 4 megabytes of RAM, and an Ethernet connection to 3Com's network. Ethernet will be discussed in chapter 4.

3Station does not contain any expansion slots, fan, or disk drives because it is optimized for network use only. Because of this very specific purpose, 3Station occupies only 25% of the space of a standard IBM PC or compatible and consumes only 10% of the power. Figure 1-4 illustrates the 3Station printed circuit board. It contains only five custom *Application-Specific Integrated Circuits* (ASICs). Note that the network interface card is already built-in as is the video circuitry.

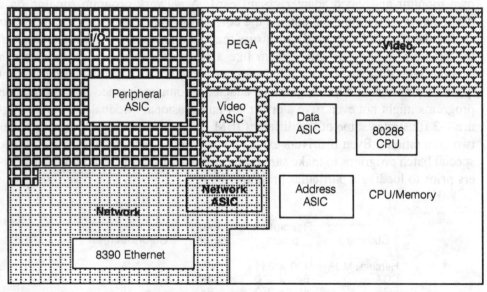

1-4 3Station as an example of a network workstation.

An even more specialized network workstation is 3Com's 3Station/2ED. The 3Station/2ED combines the ability of a Digital Equipment Corporation color graphics terminal with a diskless network workstation. Utilizing the Intel 80286 microprocessor, this workstation/terminal supports both 3Com's Ethernet software and DEC's Local Area Transport protocol. Users can switch among applications running simultaneously on a DEC VAX as well as on the workstation.

One of the major reasons to look at such a specialized workstation/terminal would be for a situation that required regular file transfers from the DEC to the PC environments. The workstation has built-in file transfer support and can emulate several DEC terminals from a no-frills VT52 to a VT340 with 132 column resolution and an 800×500 pixel display.

This example illustrates why it is so essential for a systems integrator to examine specialized solutions for specialized situations. The alternative to this workstation would be to have a PC serving as a workstation and then add a terminal server to coordinate communications with the DEC VAX.

The network interface card

The *network interface card* contains the brains of a local area network, the key information required for proper addressing, reading, and transmitting of information to be carried over the LAN. It is able to determine if there is a collision on the network, and it is then able to take corrective action and retransmit its information. Just as network workstations vary considerably by vendor, network interface cards also differ considerably even though they might share a common designation as an Ethernet card or a Token Ring card. Among features you might want to consider are the card's processing power, the amount of RAM on the card, the card's use of a half or full-slot, and the ease with which switches on the card can be changed. 3Com's EtherLink card will serve as an example of this key network component. Designed to fit into an IBM PC or compatible's half-slot, this circuit card contains a single coaxial cable connector and many jumpers. These jumpers are used to change the card's address (which must be unique), its interrupts, or its Direct Memory Access (DMA) channel.

3Com also markets an EtherLink Plus card designed for the PC AT bus. This is a full-sized card with its own Intel 80186 microprocessor and RAM. While this card is more expensive, it also can provide higher performance because it can respond to the faster interrupts generated by the Intel 80286-based PC AT. The EtherLink card provides an 8 kilobyte buffer, while the EtherLink Plus card provides a buffer of 64 kilobytes. A workstation that rarely needs to access the network can probably get by with a small buffer while a network file server responsible for supplying information for all network users should have a large buffer. Generally, though, a larger buffer does provide higher network performance.

The disk server

When local area networks first appeared, they were designed to save users money by permitting them to share expensive hardware and not necessarily the same software or data. Most of the programs available at that time were designed for single users. If two users tried to use the same program at the same time, the result would be the loss of valuable data.

The network operating system and programs were stored on a *disk server*, a computer with a hard disk that took responsibility for "serving" the programs and data files requested by network users. As Fig. 1-5 indicates, each network user had a volume reserved on the disk server for programs and data files. A public volume contained information that could be shared because it normally was read-only and did not permit users to change anything. As an example, this volume might contain a department's final budget or a company's monthly newsletter. It might even contain a listing of current openings with detailed job descriptions.

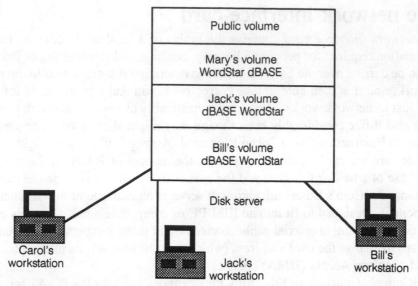

Public volume
Mary's volume WordStar dBASE
Jack's volume dBASE WordStar
Bill's volume dBASE WordStar
Disk server

Carol's workstation

Jack's workstation

Bill's workstation

1-5 A disk server in action.

Each network user on a disk server based LAN logs on to the network by providing a login name and password. The disk server matches this information with a table it keeps and then sends the user's workstation a copy of the *file allocation table* (FAT) so that the user can use directory commands to see which files are available to be requested. This FAT resides in the workstation's RAM until it is turned off.

The file server

Local area networks can be *centralized* or *peer-to-peer*. A peer-to-peer network such as Sun Systems TOPS enables workstations to share resources with each other. Two PCs with their own hard disks can share directories containing files with each other. In a similar way, the two workstations can share other resources with each other including printers. Today a centralized network is built around a *file server*, usually a dedicated fast microcomputer with a large hard disk drive containing files for all workstations on the network. This file server contains the application programs for the network as well as special network software to manage network resources.

File servers are found in more recent LANs based on MS-DOS 3.1 or later versions. The reason is that these newer versions of DOS provide commands that enable programmers to offer record locking in their programs. *Record locking* means that multiple users are able to access a particular program at the same time but are unable to access a particular record simultaneously. This means that two users can access the same inventory program and make changes as they add and delete items, but they cannot change figures for the same inventory item at precisely the same time. MS-DOS 3.1 provided this ability through its SHARE program.

A file server only needs to keep one copy of a networkable program. Also, it does not bother to provide each workstation with a copy of its FAT because it keeps sole track of this table. Workstations request files but need not concern themselves with where these files are located because there are no volumes on a file server. File servers have their own software which performs many tasks including managing files and directories, monitoring users, controlling print functions, and optimizing network efficiency. Figure 1-6 illustrates a file server in operation.

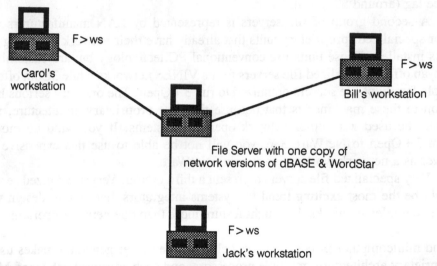

1-6 A file server in operation.

Selecting a file server has become a much more complicated task recently with the release of several very specialized models. For small LANs virtually any reliable 80386-based microcomputer with sufficient RAM might do the job. Many companies now are offering 80386 and 80486 based micros that are designed specifically as generic file servers. While they are not designed for a particular network operating system such as NetWare or LAN Server, they do offer several built-in hardware features that help them perform efficiently regardless of the software they are running. Features you might want to look for in a generic file server include extra expansion slots, a large RAM capacity, a significantly larger power supply than a standard PC, built-in backup hardware and software, and an uninterruptible power supply.

These generic file servers have limitations, though, particularly if you are designing a network that will grow and perhaps include more than one network operating system. Many of these micros are still based on traditional PC architecture or *Industry Standard Architecture* (ISA). Unlike units designed around EISA or micro channel architecture, these low-cost file servers do not have the ability to eliminate some of the traffic bottlenecks bound to occur on a LAN. They can represent a short-range solution, particularly if you plan to replace them eventually with faster models and then use them for specialized and less demanding jobs such as serving as print servers or asynchronous remote communications servers.

Some of these generic file servers do use the newer EISA or micro channel architecture standards. One popular choice for systems integrators is Compaq's Deskpro 486/25. It will serve as an example of how a standard PC has been optimized by its manufacturer for file server use. This unit supports up to 1.3 gigabytes of internal disk storage and 100 megabytes of RAM and carries a very hefty price tag (around $20,000).

A second group of file servers is represented by LAN manufacturers who offer specialized, proprietary units that already have their network operating systems installed. These units use conventional PC technology but are customized. Banyan offers specialized file servers for its VINES networks while 3Com offers a whole family of file servers optimized to run 3+Open. The one very serious limitation to these machines is that because they use proprietary architecture, they cannot be used with other network operating systems. If you wind up moving from 3+Open to NetWare 386, you will not be able to use this expensive file server as a network workstation running NetWare.

Very specialized file servers represent a third option. Very specialized servers might be the most exciting trend for systems integrators that have to design very large, complex networks that might feature more than one network operating system. These very specialized servers approach mainframe performance and command minicomputer prices. This new class of file server generally makes use of proprietary architecture, multiple processors, and such advanced EISA and MCA features as *bus mastering*. Bus mastering is a technique that enables the file server to move information from network adapter cards to the host without use of the host's processor. Freeing the host's processor from these chores vastly improves the network's efficiency. While present LANs might not really test these machines' capabilities, new versions of LAN Manager and NetWare 386 as well as new uses for file servers such as client-servers (discussed in chapter 2) could make these units very attractive for systems integrators. Two examples, Compaq's SystemPro and NetFrame Systems' NetFrame, illustrate the features you can expect from this class of file server.

The Compaq SystemPro is built around two Intel 80386 processors running at 33 MHz. It has seven 32-bit EISA slots, a maximum of 256 megabytes of RAM, and the ability to address 840 megabytes of disk storage that can consist of separate drives that it views as one device.

Compaq's SystemPro uses two processors that both run the same network operating system (such as NetWare) and both share the same main system memory space and memory bus. While the SystemPro can run industry-standard software applications, it does so with only one processor. To use both processors, an application must be written specifically to take advantage of this feature. That means you should be sure you have a version of NetWare, VINES, or LAN Manager written specifically for the unique architecture of this machine if you want it to run efficiently.

NetFrame, on the other hand, is much more of a radical break with the present file server architecture than SystemPro. It uses its own proprietary architecture rather than conforming to EISA or MCA standards. NetFrame uses a number of mainframe I/O techniques to speed up operations including a hierarchical bus structure. This means that data can be sent out via one network interface while a query is being read in via another interface. NetFrame's buses grow wider and faster as they move away from their interface with a LAN and toward the server's main memory and processors so that internal speed begins to approach mainframe proportions. An I/O server board rides on the server's main board and provides access for Ethernet, Token Ring, AppleTalk, RS-232, and SCSI inputs.

NetFrame's Intel 80486 microprocessor can support multiple application servers. This means that it is possible, for example, with the right software written for this server and the installation of a special board, to support different network operating systems such as NetWare 386 and LAN Manager running simultaneously. One vexing problem for system integrators is that if you need a special board or interface, you have to wait for NetFrame Systems to design it; it is, after all, a proprietary platform.

In many ways, SystemPro represents the end of the present evolutionary scale for conventional PC architecture. It is open architecture in the sense that it uses standard buses, but it does require a machine-specific version of a network operating system in order to use both coprocessors. NetFrame, on the other hand, represents what likely will be the future type of file server for very large, complex networks. It is minicomputer-like with its hierarchical bus structure, numerous optimizing and error-checking features, and proprietary nature.

Disk drive technology jargon

Pity the poor new systems integrator who thought selecting a generic, plain vanilla file server would be relatively painless. With so many different types of disk drive technology available today, it is necessary to translate the jargon in order to understand just what the vendor is offering. Asking for what was best used to be simply a matter of asking for the most affordable drive with the fastest access time. Matters are far more complex today.

Seagate originated a disk drive interface standard that has become known as the ST-506. Originally modified from a floppy drive interface, the venerable and low-cost ST-506 is still the most commonly found model. When the ST-506 uses *Modified Frequency Modulation* (MFM) models have a data transfer rate of around 5 megabits/second while models using *Run Length Limited* coding (RLL) transfer data at around 7.5 megabits/second. RLL technology packs more data on each track, but it also can result in the loss of information, particularly if you mix and match controllers and drives without ensuring that the manufacturer has certified its product for RLL. *Enhanced Small Disk Interface* (ESDI) is more expensive, but can provide much greater capacity (at least 3 times that of ST-506 MFM) and faster data transfer rates (up to around 15 megabytes/second). Matching controllers and drives with ESDI is much easier because it is an integral part of the drive and not the controller.

The Small Computer Subsystem Interface (SCSI) can provide data transfer rates up to eight times faster than the ST-506. Several SCSI devices can be daisy chained together to provide massive storage capacity. Expensive but far advanced in technology, these SCSI devices are becoming the file servers of choice on larger networks. They provide data transfer rates up to 40 megabits/second and data storage capacities approaching the gigabyte range.

Another advantage of the SCSI drive is that up to seven devices can be attached to a single SCSI bus. (ESDI imposes a two drive limit.) The current ESDI specification tops out at 760 megabytes while the SCSI storage can reach 4 megabytes.

The optical disk as file server

Slowly, almost without much fanfare, optical disk technology has been evolving to the point where it is not just possible but practical in some cases to use an optical disk as a file server. Novell, in fact, now certifies optical disks for its NetWare operating system. Microsoft's High Sierra format (ISO-9660) makes an optical disk look like a standard MS-DOS drive with standard DOS directory and subdirectory structure. The limitation at present is access time. Generally current CD-ROM drives have an average disk access time of about 90 milliseconds, much slower than conventional hard disk technology. This number is deceiving, however, because special mirrors can be adjusted on the optical drive to speed up access time and make it competitive with hard drive technology.

Optical disks used to be available only in read only (CD-ROM) or write once and read many times (WORM) versions, neither of which is practical for a file server. The new erasable optical disk technology has changed this situation while the availability of optical disk removable cartridges has also opened up new opportunities to use this exciting technology. Optical disk servers are immune to the head crashes that can cripple a conventional hard disk file server.

Even if your clients are not ready to commit to an optical disk server yet, one possibility worth exploring is to connect one or more CD-ROM drives to be used as special purpose file servers. They can be used for network users who want to access some of the libraries and encyclopedias now available on CD-ROM. They also can be used to archive information that is not needed on a regular basis. Libraries are drawn to systems such as those offered by Meridian Data, Inc., which offers a dedicated file server which can accommodate up to 14 optical drives in one cabinet and run either NetWare or 3Com's network operating systems.

Network media

Local area networks can be connected together using a variety of different type of media or cabling. The three major types of cabling include twisted pair wire, coaxial cable, and optic fiber, each with its own set of advantages and disadvantages.

Twisted pair

Many LAN managers like twisted pair wire because of its low cost. Older facilities often have been wired prior to divestiture by the telephone company with many extra unused twisted pair. A company's telephone system required two wires to carry the electrical signal, one for the "outbound" current and one for the "returning" current. The two wires are twisted to prevent the mutual inductance of a wire from developing a secondary signal in its neighbor. Each wire is covered with a layer of insulation to keep it from touching the other wire and making electrical contact. Cables carry many pairs (color coded) and surround these pairs with a layer of protective material. The standard used is 22-, 24- and 26-gauge copper wire. The smaller the gauge number, the larger the wire.

If your facility already has been wired with twisted pair, some labels should indicate each pair's function. The twisted pairs are color coded. The color code consists of 10 different colors. Usually only 25 combinations for the 25 pairs are used in 25 pair cables. If a cable has more than 25 pairs, the first 25 pairs are wrapped in a blue ribbon within the cable, while the second 25 pairs are wrapped in an orange ribbon, repeating the color B code used for the wires in the color of the binding ribbons. For cables over 100 pairs, two-colored ribbons are used to group each bundle of 100 pairs. Figure 1-7 illustrates the standard color coding format.

Today LAN vendors offer proprietary as well as standard twisted pair cabling schemes. 3Com, for example, offers both a proprietary one twist pair approach as well as a standard (10BaseT) product. The proprietary schemes offer certain

Color A	Color B	Pair #	Wire colors	Body stripe
White	Blue	1	White-blue	Blue-white
Red	Orange	2	White-orange	Orange-white
Black	Green	3	White-green	Green-white
Yellow	Brown	4	White-brown	Brown-white
Violet	Slate	5	White-slate	Slate-white
		6	Red-blue	Blue-red
		7	Red-orange	Orange-red
		8	Red-green	Green-red
		9	Red-brown	Brown-red
		10	Red-slate	Slate-red
		11	Black-blue	Blue-black
		12	Black-orange	Orange-black
		13	Black-green	Green-black
		14	Black-brown	Black-brown
		15	Black-slate	Slate-black
		16	Yellow-blue	Blue-yellow
		17	Yellow-orange	Orange-yellow
		18	Yellow-green	Green-yellow
		19	Yellow-brown	Brown-yellow
		20	Yellow-slate	Slate-yellow
		21	Violet-blue	Blue-yellow
		22	Violet-orange	Orange-violet
		23	Violet-green	Green-violet
		24	Violet-brown	Brown-violet
		25	Violet-slate	Slate-violet

1-7 Twisted pair color code.

advantages. As an example, look at 3Com's one twisted pair product before examining the new twisted pair standard. Up until recently, the LAN industry standard for twisted pair has been 1 megabit/second transmission speed. Recently an IEEE (Institute for Electrical and Electronics Engineers) task force in charge of standardizing Ethernet over unshielded twisted pair has developed a new standard known as *10BaseT*. This standard describes a 10 megabit/second transmission speed over baseband twisted pair wire.

A proprietary twisted pair approach

3Com has developed a method of achieving 10 megabit/second transmission speed on its local area networks using a single twisted pair. Because most offices are wired with three or more pairs of unshielded copper wire and only use one pair for telephone service, 3Com's ability to use a single pair almost ensures cable availability. An additional benefit to 3Com's twisted pair solution is that it permits users to mix twisted pair, coaxial, and fiber-optic cable on a single network.

The 3Com approach features an adapter called a PairTamer that connects to 3Com EtherLink network interface cards. The PairTamer contains both a coaxial connector for thin coaxial cable and a modular connector for twisted pair wire. Generally because twisted pair wiring runs from a desktop to a central wiring closet and not from desktop to desktop, PairTamers are used to link together Ethernet nodes of as many as 25 network workstations connected by thin coaxial cable.

3Com's MultiConnect Repeater resides in a wiring closet and ties the entire network together. It is able to accept transceiver modules for several different types of cabling. Figure 1-8 illustrates how this approach works.

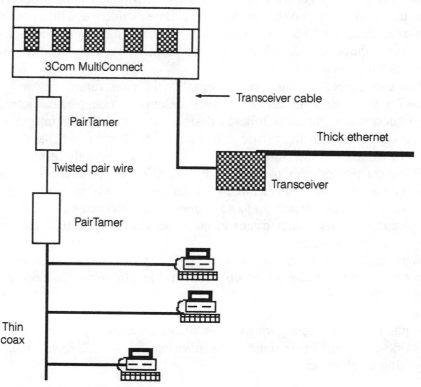

1-8 3Com's proprietary approach to twisted pair cabling.

10BaseT, the new IEEE standard for unshielded twisted pair wiring on a LAN, requires two twisted pairs, a transmit pair and a receive pair. The two pairs form a logical circuit for collision detection. This new approach utilizes centralized hubs, which are often referred to as *multiport repeaters* or *concentrators*. These hubs regenerate signals before transmitting them over untwisted wire cabling to network adapter cards installed in each node. Hubs can be linked together within wiring closets or between wiring closets by a variety of cabling including thin and thick coaxial cabling, optic fiber, and untwisted pair. The 10BaseT system requires that workstations be located no more than 328 feet from a phone closet although the standards committee is defining repeaters that can be used to extend this distance.

One additional 10BaseT feature is known as a *link test*, a function that constantly scans lines between nodes and hubs as well as lines between hubs for evidence of electrical activity to ensure the line is still functioning. This network management feature monitors a LAN's health and ensures its continued efficiency.

One problem you might have as a system integrator is linking together pre-10BaseT networks with standard 10BaseT networks. It is critical that all ports be labeled appropriately (pre-10BaseT or 10BaseT). Modular hubs probably will permit the coexistence of older cabling with 10BaseT cabling and then connect the two over an Ethernet backplane in the hub. Workstation network interface cards might come equipped with switches that will permit the turning off or turning on of the link function unique to 10BaseT.

You can expect a variety of products in the near future that will make 10BaseT even easier to install and monitor. 3Com, for example, has introduced two products that might make 10BaseT designs easier for a system integrator who has to grapple with existing twisted pair installations. It offers a 10BaseT adapter for micro channel architecture workstations. More importantly, it also offers a MultiConnect twisted pair module for its MultiConnect repeater. This module plugs into one of 15 slots to link three workstations over twisted pair wiring to the hub. The system can support up to 45 connections to twisted pair wiring in one MultiConnect chassis, which means it can accommodate up to 1024 connections through multiple repeaters.

What makes this module particularly appealing for systems integrators is that it can be plugged into the same hub with existing MultiConnect modules; this means that the same hub can support thick and thin coaxial cabling, shielded and unshielded twisted pair wiring, IBM's own Token Ring network cabling, and fiber-optic media. By configuring the MultiConnect hubs in a star configuration, each workstation will have a direct link to a wiring closet which should make troubleshooting much easier.

Disadvantages of twisted pair

While there are a number of advantages to the use of twisted pair wire on a local area network, there also are some disadvantages. The bandwidth is limited compared to other media. It is not ideal when video images are an integral part of a LAN for this reason. Emanations are susceptible to interception, which means that it is not a good medium if security is a concern. Despite industry advances and the ability to limit electrical interference, twisted pair is still subject to some crosstalk between adjacent wires. Also, it must be protected against lightning if used as external cabling. Finally, a network manager must keep in mind that there must be sufficient extra twisted pair available to replace telephone cabling that might go bad. Because it is normal practice to cut only one termination point of a damaged twisted pair, what appears to be surplus cabling might not really be any good. AT&T's *Premises Distribution System* (PDS) is widespread. It provides a minimum of two spare twisted pair wires that can be pulled to work locations and terminated at telephone distribution frames. Generally, three wire pairs are pulled to each work location; unfortunately this might not be enough for future data needs. You might want to pull an additional two pair to ensure adequate capacity in the future. Even with all these limitations, however, the ability to achieve 10 megabit/second transmission speed with this low-cost medium makes it worthy of serious consideration when designing a local area network.

Coaxial cable

Coaxial cable consists of a single strand of wire (the central conductor) surrounded by a second conductor in the form of a solid tube or braided wire. This shield reflects the magnetic field back to the central conductor as well as shielding the primary conductor from outside interference. Its shielding makes it much less susceptible to electrical interference than twisted pair wire.

Today many local area networks utilize both thick and thin coaxial cabling. The standard Ethernet coaxial cable (RG-11 with 0.4 inch diameter) provides greater immunity to noise and less signal loss than thin coaxial cable (RG-58 cable with 0.2 inch diameter).

Arcnet uses RG-62 coaxial cabling, the same medium used for IBM's 3270 terminals; this is one reason that Arcnet is such a popular choice in sites where a number of 3270 terminals are already installed. Thick coaxial cable requires an external transceiver and a cable to connect the transceiver with the network interface card, but it provides a greater distance and allows the network workstation to be located up to 164 feet (50 meters) from the network cable. This thick variety is highly reliable. The maximum length of a single trunk segment is 1640 feet. Up to 5 trunk segments can be connected by using 4 repeaters and the maximum length of an entire network trunk is 8200 feet. Thin Ethernet coaxial cabling is connected directly to the BNC connector on a network interface card. It does, however, limit the length of a trunk segment to 607 feet and the length of the entire network trunk to 3035 feet. There is a maximum of 30 workstations per trunk permitted. The thick Ethernet coaxial cabling is more difficult and expensive to install. Thin Ethernet coaxial cabling must be run to every workstation; furthermore, a break in the cable will result in the breakdown of the entire network.

Perhaps the best of both worlds can be achieved by mixing and matching the two types of cabling. Thick and thin Ethernet coaxial cabling can be combined on a local area network with some limitations. Using 3Com equipment as an example, the total length of the combined network should not exceed 1000 meters or the length as defined by the expression:

$$(3.28 \times T) + E \searrow < 1000 \text{ meters}$$

where T = length of Thin Ethernet cable in meters

E = length of thick Ethernet cable in meters

There should be a minimum of 7.5 feet (2.5 meters) between any two computers on thick Ethernet cabling and 3 feet (1 meter) on thin Ethernet cabling.

Repeaters can be used with coaxial cabling. Repeaters link separate segments together to form a larger multi-branch network. Each repeater has the electrical characteristics of a single transceiver, so that the combined number of repeaters and computers cannot exceed 100 on any cable segment. No more than two repeaters can be in the path between any two computers. Figure 1-9 displays several workstations connected with thin Ethernet coaxial cabling and reflecting the use of repeaters.

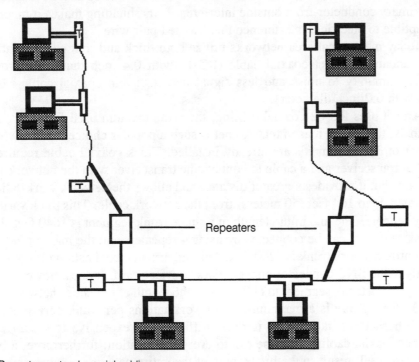

1-9 Repeaters extend coaxial cabling.

The type of coaxial cabling discussed so far is known as *baseband*. You might want to think of it as a large hose or channel through which data can flow very quickly. A second type of coaxial cabling, *broadband*, features several different channels (up to 50), each with its own unique frequency. Narrow bands of frequency known as guardbands keep information flowing on these channels from interfering with each other. One advantage of broadband in factory environments where electrical noise is a significant factor, is that noise tends to be below 5 MHz while broadband broadcasts at frequencies significantly above this. The IEEE 802.3 broadband standard (10Broad36) stipulates broadcast frequencies in the 36 to 54 MHz range. IBM's first local area network, PC Network, used this broadband medium.

While broadband local area networks are more expensive than their baseband cousins, they offer greater distance, reliability, and security. The reliability issue is significant. On a baseband Ethernet network, data collisions are detected by transceivers by sensing an unusually high level of DC voltage on the coaxial cable. On a broadband Ethernet network, however, RF modems reserve a separate collision enforcement frequency which provides a much more efficient method of notifying workstations of data collisions.

Broadband coaxial cabling makes an excellent backbone. Backbones in network terms serve much the same purpose as a human backbone. Network backbones serve as the central spine connecting together different networks, sort of like the network's central nervous center and switching station. Broadband networks can cover up to 20 kilometers, far more than baseband cabling. This ability to cover significant distances without the cost considerations of fiber optic is important in backbone design, particularly since multi-building and multi-floor networks easily can stretch beyond baseband cabling's limitations.

Optic-fiber cable

Optic-fiber cable consists of very thin glass fiber of high purity. The glass core provides the transmission carrying capability. It is surrounded by another type of glass called cladding, which is reflective. The outside of the cable consists of protective plastic material. Optic fiber is immune to electrical interference and offers greater security than coax or twisted pair.

While the actual fiber-optic cabling is not much more expensive than coaxial cabling, the other elements associated with it are very expensive. Fiber-optic technology requires the use of skilled personnel for installation. It requires the use of LEDs or lasers to provide the light and special network interface cards as well as transducers to convert electrical energy into light energy.

Fiber-optic cabling might prove attractive to a network manager because of some of its special characteristics. It is relatively easy using devices such as 3Com's MultiConnect Repeater to mix and match different media. Fiber-optic cabling might be appropriate for a span between two repeaters or between a network interface card and a hub. Fiber-optic cabling can be used on an FDDI network (discussed in chapter 5) to achieve transmission speeds of 100 megabits/second. On an Ethernet network, fiber optics would not increase the speed beyond 10 megabits/second, but it would provide the maximum distance, security, and protection against electrical interference. Fiber optics generally is installed *point-to-point*, that is between two specific units. The fiber-optic cabling installed could be linked to the rest of the network using a device such as the MultiConnect Repeater.

Structured vs. unstructured cabling

Most systems integrators spend much of their design time trying to balance larger initial capital expenditures versus long-term lower life-cycle costs. Cabling is one area where more money wisely spent initially in a structured cabling design will provide significant long-term cost savings. An unstructured cabling design consists of pulling cable from termination points to the individual workstations. A structured approach tries to anticipate future growth for the LAN as well as the possible need for additional cabling for future technology. Using a structured cabling approach, a systems integrator would design wiring closets with outlets installed at locations where future workstations likely would be placed. Cable drops extend from distribution frames in wiring closets to data outlets at work sites and patch cables connect outlets to the desired workstations.

Data communications can learn much from standard telecommunications procedures. The use of wiring closets and modular jack connections is standard procedure for telephone company installations; Ma Bell designed this approach years ago to make moves and changes more economical. System integrators are learning that it still makes sense to listen to Ma.

A structured cabling design makes it much easier to troubleshoot media problems and also much easier to reconfigure a network. It is much easier to work on a problem at a wiring closet site than to have to disrupt office operations by opening ceilings.

LAN topologies

Different types of local area networks might have different network architectures or topologies. This section will examine the star, bus, and ring topologies.

The star

A *star topology* consists of a central computer with cabling radiating from it to the other network workstations as seen in Fig. 1-10. It is the oldest network architecture, and it still offers a number of significant advantages. Because a cable goes from each workstation to the central computer or hub, it is possible to provide greater cable reliability and maintenance. It is relatively easy to isolate a cable break and, equally important, a single cable break will not bring down the entire network. Similarly, it is relatively easy to make moves and changes as workstations are moved and need to be recabled. The entire network is not affected by such management tasks.

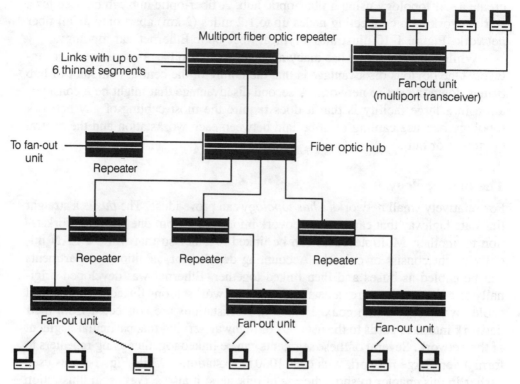

1-10 A typical fiber optic Ethernet star topology.

Because information flows from a sending workstation to a central computer and then to the destination workstation, it is easy to maintain detailed records on each workstation's network use. A log can be kept of which files a workstation requests as well as what types of reports are printed.

A variation of the star topology is the *cascaded stars structure* that permits running the traditional non-star architecture Ethernet with a variety of different media including twisted pair and coaxial cable, even thick coaxial cabling. A network composed of thick Ethernet coaxial cabling can be configured in a star topology. To accomplish this task requires the use of a multiport transceiver (*fanout box*). This unit allows up to eight Ethernet workstations to be connected from one cable tap. It is possible to use this fanout box in conjunction with a multiport repeater. A multiport repeater can connect up to six thin Ethernet segments with one or two thick Ethernet cable systems. It also becomes a handy tool for isolating faulty segments from the rest of the network. Several of these fanout boxes can be linked together in a wiring closet. The connections between the wire closet and the workstations is made with Ethernet transceiver cable, a special nine-conductor cable. It is also possible to use fiber-optic cabling with Ethernet to create a star topology using a fiber-optic hub. A fiber-optic hub can be used for a star network with connecting nodes up to 1.2 miles (2 km) apart onto an all fiber network. Figure 1-10 illustrates a typical fiber-optic Ethernet star topology.

While a star topology has many advantages, it also has a couple of disadvantages. One obvious disadvantage is that the failure of the central computer or hub brings down the entire network. A second disadvantage that might be a consideration in a large facility is that it does require the most cabling of any network topology because cabling must be laid between each workstation and the central computer or hub.

The bus topology

For relatively small networks a *bus topology* can prove ideal. The *bus* is a straight line data highway that carries the network information from one network workstation to another. Multiple buses can be linked together so that while a LAN initially might consist of only the Accounting department, additional departments can be cabled as buses and then linked together. Ethernet was developed originally as a bus architecture, a data highway with workstations linked to this coaxial cable. With today's thin coaxial cabling, workstations are connected from their network interface cards to the data bus or highway serving that particular segment of the network. Several of these segments can be linked together using repeaters to form a very large network with over 1000 workstations. While Fig. 1-9 was used earlier in this chapter to show the use of repeaters, it also serves as an illustration of a bus topology linking together three separate segments.

As Figure 1-9 also illustrates, a bus topology results in information being broadcast to all workstations on the network. Each workstation examines the address on the packet of information and determines whether or not there is a match. This approach differs from a star topology where the central computer or hub ensures that a packet is directed only to the destination workstation.

Ring topology

The *ring topology* has gained popularity because IBM chose it as its major LAN architecture. A closed ring generally uses a token, a specific bit pattern that indicates that a workstation has permission to send information. Chapter 5 takes a close look at IBM's Token Ring Network and shows how traffic control is maintained. Rings can be bidirectional as well as unidirectional; the newest fiber-optic networks take advantage of bidirectional cabling to achieve data transmission speeds of over 100 megabits/second. Figure 1-11 illustrates a typical ring network with workstations numbered in sequential order.

It is possible to have a physical bus network that functions logically (electrically) like a true token ring. This means that the workstations are cabled in seg-

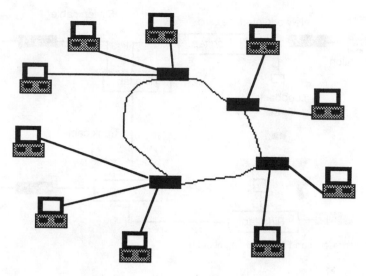

1-11 A ring network.

ments in a typical bus configuration but operates like a ring network sending information sequentially (by address) down the ring.

3Com's Token Ring Network will illustrate how it is possible to have the best of both worlds, the ease of installation found in a bus network, and compatibility with IBM's own Token Ring Network.

The 3Com RingTaps are connected to Token Ring network interface cards installed in the network workstations or servers. 3Com offers its own network interface card called the TokenLink Plus. This card has an Intel 80186 microprocessor and on-board RAM to offload work from the workstation's own processor. This card can also be used on a PC AT and can use this machine's faster interrupts. A Station Extension Cable can be used to extend the distance between the station and the RingTap. Multiple RingTaps are connected with Trunk Cables. Trunk Barrel Connectors are used to link multiple Trunk Cables. A special loopback device at the end of each segment routes the messages back down the cable to provide the same kind of service normally provided by movement around a ring. This arrangement permits the connection of the TokenPlus cabling system with IBM's own IBM Cabling System MultiStation Access Unit. Figure 1-12 displays a group of workstations that are physically arranged in a bus topology but (because of the 3Com RingTap and Token Plus Cabling System) are connected together in a logical ring topology.

A special solenoid in each RingTap provides information on whether the workstation is active or not. If the workstation is turned off or the cable is damaged, the RingTap passes the message straight on down the network bypassing this particular unit.

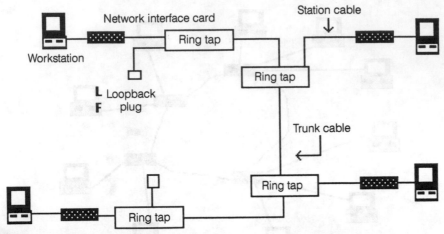

1-12 A physical bus and a logical ring network.

Summary

An understanding of local area networks begins with an understanding of its hardware including its file servers and media. File servers vary according to the microprocessor, architecture, and type of RAM used. SCSI drives are becoming more popular for use as file servers with optical disk drives now certified and available. Most LANs use twisted pair, thin or thick coaxial cable, or fiber-optic cable as their medium. Twisted pair wire has grown in popularity the past few years and should grow in the future because of the development of the 10BaseT standard. A number of network topologies are available for the systems integrator, but the most popular continue to be the star, bus, and ring.

2
CHAPTER

LAN software basics

This chapter explores the role of

- MS-DOS and PC-DOS.
- OS/2.
- NetWare.
- LANs running under UNIX.
- Client servers.

Introduction

Chapter 1 examined some of the basic building blocks of a local area network from a hardware perspective. You saw how workstations are connected by their network interface cards to physical media such as twisted pair or coaxial cable to a local area network and, if desired, to a centralized file server. This chapter looks at the operating system software required for each workstation to manage its hardware resources as well as some other significant network software. This chapter also examines the key differences that distinguish MS-DOS and PC-DOS from OS/2 and why these differences require different LAN software.

Operating systems have programming interfaces, software programs that make it easier for programmers to write application programs that require operating system resources. This chapter takes a look at some of these interfaces to see why they are so important on a network.

To make matters even more confusing, local area networks also require a very special program called a *network operating system* (NOS). The network operating system manages network resources. I show in this chapter how a NOS such as Novell's NetWare works in conjunction with a workstation's operating system such as MS-DOS. Figure 2-1 illustrates some of the leading products in each of these categories that this chapter explores.

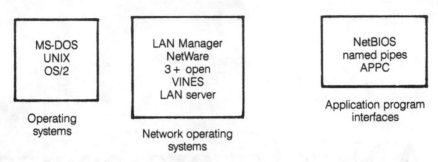

2-1 The software building blocks of a network.

Local area network vendors make it very difficult to understand their products because of the vast number of confusing buzz words associated with network software. Among the many terms in this chapter are NetBIOS, Named Pipes, Client-Servers, and NetWare's OS/2 Redirector. This chapter explains these terms as well as many others and provides a foundation for a later look at the software issues involved in linking together networks with routers and gateways.

The role of an operating system

An *operating system* is a group of programs that manage all computer system resources and operations to make your job as a computer user easier. Its responsibilities include managing both internal memory (RAM) and the auxiliary storage resources such as a floppy disk drive or hard disk drive. It is responsible for scheduling the performance of tasks, handling input/output requests, and monitoring system security to ensure that users are authorized to view certain files and use specific programs. An operating system also includes utility programs that help the user perform key tasks such as preparing a new disk for use with a specific computer (formatting) and placing some key system files on a disk that enable the user to copy files and delete material.

Operating system programs facilitate communication among the computer user, the computer's hardware and software, and any peripherals. Most business users are more concerned with the end product their computers produce than with how they produce it. Rather than knowing precisely how information flows from computer to printer when they must print reports, most people simply want the assurance that the command PRINT will result in professional-quality output.

Similarly, when an administrator wants to save a lengthy report onto a hard disk, his or her major concern is that the document be available for future retrieval rather than with how the computer locates available areas on the disk and parcels out sections of the document wherever it finds room. An operating system therefore serves as a key link between the computer user and the machine's hardware and software—a silent, trustworthy assistant that performs complex tasks involving possibly several dozen steps, even though they are initiated by one-word commands such as LOAD, SAVE, DIR, and PRINT.

The MS-DOS operating system

In 1981 Microsoft published MS-DOS, an operating system for the new IBM PC and all other compatibles that used the Intel 8088 or 8086 microprocessor. Microcomputers based on later versions of this chip including the Intel 80286, 80386, and 80486 chips continue to run MS-DOS, but it is very much like running a jet with only a single propeller functioning. I return to this issue of MS-DOS's limitations a bit later in this chapter.

IBM sold a version of the operating system labeled PC-DOS. Both operating systems were developed for one user performing one task at a time (single user/single-tasking).

MS-DOS added a number of handy utility programs not found under older operating systems such as CP/M. The new operating system also provided the ability to address the additional internal memory (RAM) and external memory (disk storage) available because of the powerful Intel microprocessing chip. The ability to manage files more efficiently included a tree-like hierarchical file structure making it possible to organize hundreds or even thousands of files efficiently, an essential feature for the fixed disk (hard disk) user.

The utility programs accompanying MS-DOS enabled users to perform such useful tasks as comparing the contents of one disk to another disk (DISCOMP) and recovering data stored on damaged areas of a disk (RECOVER). Finally, MS-DOS was able to address up to 640K of RAM and 32 megabytes of fixed disk storage. In 1981 this seemed like more memory than anyone could possibly ever use.

You can generalize about the different parts of an operating system using MS-DOS as an example. The major parts of MS-DOS can be described as the supervisor, the input/output manager, the file manager, and the command processor. As illustrated in Fig. 2-2, the supervisor is responsible for scheduling and coordinating the activities of all programs running under the operating system. The input/output manager is responsible for all information transferred to and from all peripheral devices, including printers, bar code readers, disk drives, and so on. The file manager's responsibility includes all areas of file management, such as saving, loading, deleting, copying, naming, and renaming files. The command processor checks commands from the keyboard before forwarding the requests to

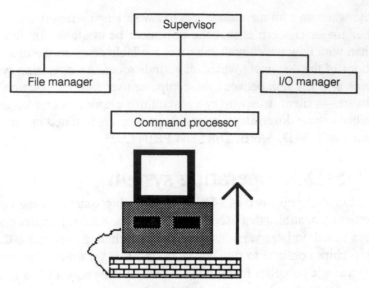

2-2 The role of a Supervisor in an operating system.

the supervisor. Think of this part of the operating system as a very efficient secretary. Before bothering Ms. Supervisor, the command processor wants to ensure that the command is correct. If a user types DIT instead of DIR, for example, the command processor will indicate that DIT represents a Bad command or file name; in other words, this command is not on a list of acceptable words and the user must try again.

The command processor receives messages back from other parts of the operating system and translates them into language that the user can understand. If the file manager discovers that a request to make a second copy of a file named BUDGET and name the new file BUDGET1 is impossible because there is no room on the disk for this additional file, it will convey this information to the command processor, which in turn will indicate to the user that there is Insufficient space on disk.

MS-DOS and IBM's NetBIOS

When IBM announced its first local area network in 1984, it also announced an important network software interface called the *NetBIOS*. The NetBIOS or Network Input/Output System contains some critical software that functions as an interface between a program and network software.

The NetBIOS has a number of management functions. It can use a system interrupt (INT "5C") to issue commands to provide data transfer, routing of information, flow control error checking and recovery, and establishment and termination of a session. Figure 2-3 illustrates the relationship of NetBIOS, application programs, and MS-DOS.

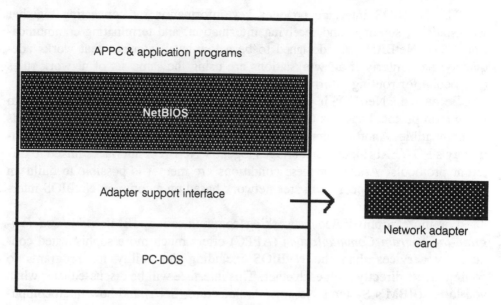

2-3 The relationship of NetBIOS, application programs, and PC-DOS.

Suppose that you need to have a data transfer from workstation 10 to workstation 20. Workstation 10's network software issues a command for MS-DOS that is intercepted by a program called the *Redirector*. The Redirector packages this command as well as instructions in a packet known as a *Message Control Block* (MCB) which tells the NetBIOS program which of its 19 different functions needs to be performed. The instructions specify that a data transfer needs to take place between workstation 10 (source) and workstation 20 (destination). The NetBIOS interface that ensures that this job is accomplished is an integral part of the IBM PC's operating system; in fact, on IBM's PC Network the NetBIOS was placed on a ROM chip on a workstation's network interface card.

While the NetBIOS was developed for use in conjunction with IBM's PC Network and its network operating system program known as PC LAN Program, other vendors soon realized that they could be "IBM network compatible" by writing code that addressed the NetBIOS. Several publishers issued programs that were NetBIOS compatible and capable of sharing hardware and software resources. To visualize this process, imagine a special delivery service. You take your report, place it in a special envelope (the MSB) and hand it to a messenger. The messenger stops whatever else he was doing (he is interrupted), and follows the delivery instructions on the envelope. Any company (program) that uses this special delivery envelope, can use this messenger's services. The NetBIOS is a very simple software interface for a relatively simple operating system (MS-DOS). You might liken it to the old switchboard operator who has only a limited number of connections she can make.

The NetBIOS interface provides key information on connecting together workstations, sending, and receiving information, and terminating communications. The NetBIOS was designed to be a low-level interface that works adequately, particularly if all workstations are using the same set of network rules (protocols) for routing information. Chapter 3 examines these rules.

Because the NetBIOS is just a low-level data interface, it needs to be linked to a common protocol such as OSI or TCP/IP to ensure that network adapter cards are compatible. Another alternative is to use a product such as Performance Technology's POWERbridge II that bridges together NetBIOS interfaces linked to different protocols. Assuming these conditions are met, it is possible to build an inexpensive peer-to-peer local area network based on a common NetBIOS interface.

For more sophisticated networking communication, IBM's *Advanced Program-to-Program Communication* (APPC) offers much more sophisticated connectivity services than the NetBIOS including the ability for programs to communicate directly with each other. This interface will be discussed later when you look at IBM's Systems Network Architecture (SNA) and how microcomputers will communicate directly with host computers in the near future.

MS-DOS and the Redirector program

I have already mentioned the Redirector program in conjunction with the NetBIOS. Microsoft provided this Redirector program with its MS-DOS 3.1 and with all subsequent versions. As previously illustrated in Fig. 2-3, this operating system and the Redirector program serve as an interface between NetBIOS and application programs. Rather than write code to NetBIOS, it is possible and usually desirable to use the Redirector program to address the NetBIOS. As an example, an application program that normally under single-user conditions would want to use a local disk drive would have that request rerouted by the Redirector to a network drive.

The Redirector program requires LAN manufacturers writing to this interface to use file servers rather than disk servers. I/O requests from network workstations are routed to the file server by the Redirector; consequently as you saw in chapter 1, a file server requires only a single file allocation table.

The Redirector communicates with a file server by transmitting blocks of information called *Server Message Blocks* (SMBs). As an example, 3Com's 3+ Share LAN software uses the Redirector to intercept DOS Input/Output calls and then reroutes them to a file server using SMBs. The 3+ Share file server has the necessary software to process these SMBs and then send information in the appropriate format back to the Redirector as well as back to the application programs generating these requests for services. In order to provide full IBM compatibility, 3Com's file server software also emulates NetBIOS function calls whenever necessary in conjunction with the SMBs packets traveling over the network.

The limitations of MS-DOS on a local area network

As noted earlier in this chapter, MS-DOS was developed at a time when computer hardware was much less sophisticated than it is today. Most microcomputers present before the introduction of the IBM PC used 8-bit microprocessors and contained a maximum of 64K of RAM. Application programs were forced to be written very tightly so that they would take up little room and leave RAM for the actual processing of information. Disk drive technology was still in its infancy, and these secondary storage devices were still very expensive.

The years following the introduction of the IBM PC saw tremendous advances in hardware technology. As pointed out in chapter 1, microcomputers jumped from 8-bit microprocessors to 32-bit technology. Disk drives leaped from 10 megabyte storage units to over 500 megabyte devices; some manufacturers even developed compact disk units that provided over a gigabyte (a billion bytes) of storage.

Along with these hardware advances came more and more sophisticated application programs. Users began to demand such memory-intensive features as graphic interfaces and terminate-and-stay-resident utilities that resided in memory and were available by pressing a single key (called the *hot key*).

MS-DOS can take up anywhere from 30K to 50K depending upon the version used, and sophisticated application programs today are routinely demanding at least 320K of RAM. When end-users add the network operating software (such as NetWare or 3+ Share), they often have virtually no room in RAM left to process information. This "RAM cram" phenomenon illustrates how MS-DOS's ability to address only 640K of RAM is forcing some companies to look at the possibility of running their local area network under an operating system such as OS/2 which can address up to 16 megabytes of RAM.

Another major limitation of MS-DOS is that it was designed originally for a single-user, single-tasking environment. While local area networks superimpose their own network software to process user requests very quickly, the file server is still limited in its operations. Microsoft's new OS/2 operating system facilitates multitasking by providing the means for programs to communicate with other programs.

The release of Microsoft's OS/2

Microsoft's 1987 release of Operating System 2 (OS/2) heralded a quantum leap in the efforts of software companies like Microsoft to keep up with the tremendous hardware advances the previous five years. This new operating system featured a graphic interface similar to Apple's Macintosh, the multitasking ability to enable programs to interact with other programs, the significant increases in the amount of addressable RAM (16 megabytes) and addressable secondary storage (virtually limited only by the amount available).

As illustrated in Fig. 2-4, there were actually two distinctly different versions of OS/2 published by Microsoft and IBM. The Standard Edition is the generic operating system without IBM's proprietary features. IBM's Extended Edition featured a built-in relational database as well as enhanced communications with IBM's complete computer family. IBM built its own network software (LAN Server) on the OS/2 Extended Edition platform. This chapter focuses on generic features of OS/2.

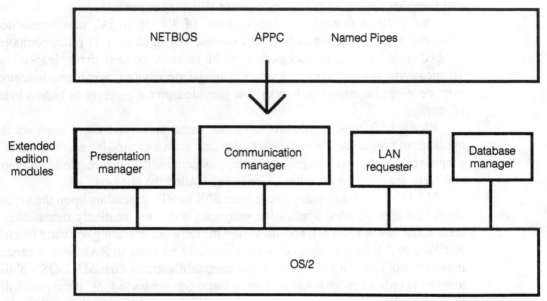

2-4 OS/2 Extended Edition adds several modules.

OS/2's several other significant features that will be discussed in this chapter did come at a price, however. This new operating system required at least an Intel 80286 microprocessor-based microcomputer and several megabytes of RAM for optimum performance. Unfortunately, Microsoft's release of OS/2 coincided with a tremendous jump in the price of RAM chips. At a minimum of $500 per each megabyte of RAM, PC managers were reluctant to jump quickly aboard the OS/2 bandwagon. An even more serious issue for prospective OS/2 buyers was that this operating system required a complete rewrite of all existing MS-DOS software because it utilizes a different way of handling the way programs communicate with computer hardware as well as with each other.

Initial sales of OS/2 were disappointing because most companies did not see an immediate benefit in converting to this new operating system. Over the past three years, though, OS/2-based software products such as Borland's Paradox have begun to appear and, more importantly, local area network operating system software such as 3Com's 3+ Open and IBM's LAN Server have begun to appear.

In the area of distributed processing in general and local area networks in particular is where OS/2 offers the greatest promise. This chapter examines many of the features that make this operating system an ideal platform for a local area network.

Major OS/2 features

Before looking at how OS/2 functions in a network environment, it is useful to examine several of its features that help distinguish it from MS-DOS. These features illustrate why this software requires the much more powerful Intel 80286 or 80386 microprocessors.

Real and protected mode

OS/2 offers a *real mode* and a *protected mode*. The real mode provides a special window, or compatibility box, that permits an MS-DOS program to run. Microsoft provided this option presumably because companies have so very much money invested already in MS-DOS software. The problem with real mode, however, is that this solution results in OS/2 emulating or imitating the older operating system with all its inherent limitations. This means that the program is restricted to single-user, single- tasking status. It is limited to addressing 640K of RAM and 32 megabytes of secondary storage. While a program is running in real mode, the multitasking capability of OS/2 is eliminated even though other programs in the computer might be written for the OS/2 operating system. In other words, real mode is an option, but would you really want to take a brand new, powerful sports car and use it to drive over dirt roads at 25 mph to deliver newspapers?

Under OS/2's protected mode displayed in Fig. 2-5, several programs can run simultaneously. The operating system protects a computer from failing if one program happens to freeze or "bomb" by isolating each running program in a separate portion of memory and then providing each program with access to its own registers as well as RAM.

Virtual memory

OS/2 is able to utilize *virtual memory*. This means that it can draw upon the resources of its secondary storage to handle very large programs that cannot reside entirely in RAM. Even though OS/2 can address a maximum of 16 megabytes of RAM, with virtual memory it can also fool an application program into thinking it has much more memory.

Under virtual memory a special table (a descriptor table) indicates to the operating system whether a particular segment of a program is actually in physical memory (RAM) or somewhere else (such as on a hard disk). Up to one gigabyte of virtual memory can be mapped using OS/2 tables.

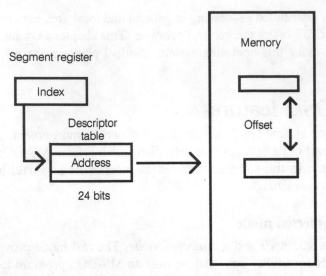

Segment register

Index

Descriptor
table

Address

24 bits

Memory

Offset

2-5 OS/2's protected mode.

The computer's microprocessor notifies OS/2 through an interrupt that a certain task requires the use of a segment of a program not found in RAM. The operating system then swaps this segment from the hard disk with a segment no longer needed. This entire process is transparent to the large application program which thinks that everything it needs in RAM actually is in RAM. This feature, displayed in Fig. 2-6, is characteristic of mainframe computers and minicomputers and illustrates a new level of sophistication in microcomputer operating systems.

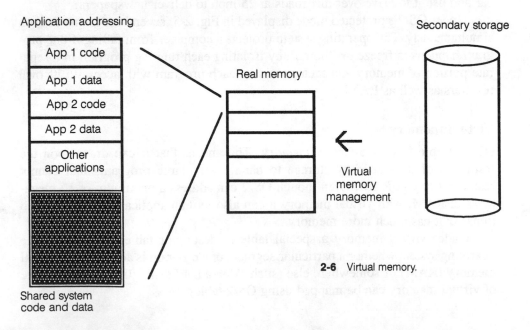

Application addressing

| App 1 code |
| App 1 data |
| App 2 code |
| App 2 data |
| Other applications |

Shared system
code and data

Real memory

Virtual
memory
management

Secondary storage

2-6 Virtual memory.

OS/2 version 2.0

Microsoft's newer editions of OS/2 (versions 2.0 and above) are specifically for Intel's 80386 and 80486 chips while they still provide full binary compatibility with current versions of OS/2. What makes it beneficial to network users is its ability to support 32-bit instructions and a 32-bit data path. The 32-bit addressing capability of this new OS/2 version will support a more efficient use of virtual memory. OS/2 for the Intel 80386 supports up to 15 virtual machines running DOS sessions; users are also able to switch from one DOS application to another.

Presentation Manager

OS/2 includes a completely new version of Presentation Manager. It features multiple overlapping windows, access to a Session Manager, the ability to run graphics-oriented programs, and enhanced mouse and keyboard control. Equally important, it is consistent with IBM's *Systems Application Architecture* (SAA).

A couple of years ago, IBM announced a long-range plan known as Systems Application Architecture (SAA), which provided some specifications for a common user interface (CUA or common user access), a common system interface (CCS or common communication support), and a common programmer interface (CPI or common programmer interface). The graphics-oriented interface reflecting the SAA set of specifications eventually will be found on all IBM computers from its largest mainframes to its microcomputers running under OS/2. Some of the OS/2-based local area network operating systems such as 3Com's 3+ Open feature full compliance with SAA guidelines. This means that the look and feel of programs running on a network workstation will closely resemble the appearance of programs running on IBM mainframe and minicomputers. Training time will be reduced for personnel who need to use different types of IBM computers. Perhaps even more important, programmers will find it relatively easy to develop communications between programs running on different SAA compliant IBM computers. In other words, programs running on mainframe computers will communicate more efficiently with programs running on a local area network.

The Session Manager

From the windows environment, an OS/2 user requests access to the Session Manager by pressing the [SysReq] key. At this point it is possible to start or terminate any process. It also has the ability to switch between different screen groups. The Session Manager ensures that different application programs are able to send information to different windows on the screen without disrupting each other. Users can switch from window to window and even transfer data back and forth between applications running in different windows.

The major components of OS/2

One of the major characteristics of OS/2 is its emphasis on modularity. Because it is a multitasking environment, this operating system must break programs down to smaller, more manageable units for the operating system to process. This section examines some of these basic OS/2 building blocks.

Processes

OS/2 divides applications into one or more processes. A *process* can comprise a single program and all the computer resources required to run it including memory areas, descriptor tables, and system support. If an application is composed of many different processes, the main program is called the backbone process while all other related processes are known as child processes. While OS/2 implements the backbone process, it in turn is responsible for its own children.

Threads

A *thread* represents an execution path within a process. The OS/2 Scheduler concerns itself with scheduling these different threads and does not care about processes. These threads can be time critical, which will cause the Scheduler to give them the highest priority. The three priority classes for OS/2 threads include time critical, regular, and idle time. OS/2 can support up to 255 threads at any given time.

The kernel

The Scheduler and a number of other key programs responsible for managing resources reside in the OS/2 kernel. The Scheduler uses a preemptive time slicing technique which permits a thread to execute for a short time before the Scheduler reasserts its control. If it decides that another thread needs to run at that time, it preempts the currently running thread by saving its state and then schedules the other thread. The *kernel* is the key administrative center for OS/2 and handles file management, memory management, and overall system coordination.

Device drivers

All hardware devices communicate with the kernel through *device drivers*. OS/2 maintains a library of these drivers for communication with graphics boards, memory management boards, printers, plotters, and so on. Because OS/2 maps virtual ports to its actual device ports, its drive drivers are directed toward a virtual port. To a program, this virtual port might seem to be the physical printer port to which it normally sends information, but is the operating system and not the program that now controls when and where the information will go to be printed. Unlike MS-DOS where an application program could assume control of a printer or other device, OS/2's multitasking environment requires these device drivers which permit only one program to control a driver (and resource) at a time. Figure 2-7 illustrates the OS/2 environment including the kernel, device drivers, and hardware.

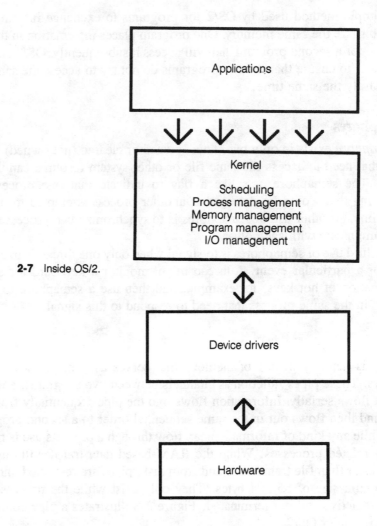

2-7 Inside OS/2.

Interprocess communications under OS/2

Often the processes and threads described in the previous section need to communicate with each other under OS/2. This section explores several different means of communication available to them. This section has descriptions of such techniques as shared memory, semaphores, pipes, and queues. These methods of communication for OS/2 processes and this chapter's subsequent discussion of how OS/2's LAN Manager works will help you understand how a local area network such as 3Com's 3+Open LAN functions under an OS/2 platform.

Shared memory

One simple method used by OS/2 for programs to exchange information is for them to share the same memory. One program places information in this memory location for a second program that will access it subsequently. OS/2 acts as a traffic officer to ensure that the two programs do not try to access the same memory at precisely the same time.

Semaphores

A *semaphore* exists in only two states, owned or cleared (not-owned). Two processes that need to access the same file or other system resource can use a semaphore. The semaphore acts like a flag to indicate that one process is using something that would be damaged if another process attempted to use it at the same time. Another use of semaphores is to synchronize two processes that need to communicate with each other.

A third use of semaphores is to signal when only one thread is in a position to monitor a particular event. A thread might monitor a keyboard for a particular combination of hot keys, for example, and then use a semaphore to alert other threads in the same process that need to respond to this signal.

Pipes

A *pipe* is actually a part of memory that serves as a buffer with in and out pointers. These pipes function as channels between two programs, and the information flows serially. Information flows into the pipe sequentially from one program and then flows out in the same sequential order to a second program.

While any kind of information can flow through a pipe, its use is restricted to closely related processes. While the RAM-based data transfer through pipes is much faster than file transfers to and from disk, pipes are restricted under OS/2 to a maximum size of 65,504 bytes. They only exist while the processes creating them are active and not terminated. Figure 2-8 illustrates a pipe connecting two programs under OS/2.

Named Pipes

While pipes represent a simple but effective means for two programs to have interprocess communications under OS/2, *Named Pipes* are a much more sophisticated extension of this technique designed for network communications under OS/2. Named Pipes provide full duplex (two-way) traffic within a computer and

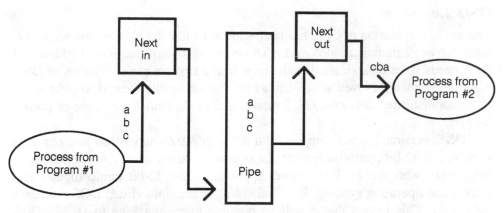

2-8 A pipe connects two programs.

between two computers. This interface program creates a virtual session between two computers with an unlimited number of such sessions on the network.

Microsoft's LAN Manager contains this Named Pipes application program interface. This means that all the companies such as AT&T, 3Com, and Hewlett-Packard that license the product and sell their own versions support Named Pipes. Until recently, Novell's NetWare did not use Named Pipes. After a good deal of complaints from NetWare users, Novell announced Named Pipes support. Named Pipes can be accessed like any sequential file; the information goes through once in sequential order.

Queues

Queues function very much like pipes. Information is placed in these memory locations by a program. A second program can then access this information that has been queued up, but it can do so in any order. Queues do not require the sequential exchange of information.

While queues are much slower than pipes, they also are far more powerful and flexible. Any process can open and write to a queue, and its size is limited only by the amount of free memory plus swap space on a disk. Each record in a queue may be as large as 65,536 bytes.

Named mailslots

OS/2 also supplies a "quick and dirty" method for two processes to communicate without the need for a full duplex, error-free channel. Named mailslots are ideal for quick messages because they lack the overhead associated with pipes. They are much faster than pipes or semaphores because once created, they do not have to be opened each time they are to be used. Once they exist on a network, remote processes can send information to them simply by name, hence the name mailslots.

OS/2 2.0

The gradual evolution of OS/2 has been somewhat like the old Chinese water torture. Network managers looking for an operating system that would address all their needs were disappointed in the gaps in the first couple of releases of OS/2 and leaned toward Novell's NetWare as an alternative that seemed to offer much more sophisticated services. OS/2 version 2.0 might shift the balance of power, however.

OS/2 version 2.0 will support both the Intel 80386 and 80486 microprocessors. A full 32-bit operating system platform will make it much more appealing to developers who are used to writing applications for 32-bit minicomputer and mainframe operating systems. It will also feature multiple virtual DOS machines (MVDM). This means that it will be possible to multitask up to 16 MS-DOS applications in separate sessions with each DOS application able to access up to 624K of RAM and 32K of hard disk memory.

Network operating systems

A local area network needs a network operating system (NOS) to manage its network resources.

Microsoft's MS-Net and Novell NetWare

Microsoft developed a network operating system called MS-Net which worked in conjunction with MS-DOS. MS-Net was a program that was licensed to companies that added their own enhancements and then sold it under their own brand names. IBM's PC LAN Program and 3Com's 3+ Server are both network operating systems based on MS-Net.

Other companies have chosen to develop their own network operating systems rather than use MS-Net as a foundation. The most notable example is Novell's NetWare, a product that captured the lion's share of the network operating system market by offering far more functionality than MS-Net.

LAN Manager

LAN Manager is Microsoft's network operating system that uses OS/2 rich collection of commands to perform its varied duties. It is composed of two major components, a Redirector and a Server. Because OS/2 permits file servers to be non-dedicated, in some cases the two components could reside on the same machine. In most cases, though, the *Redirector* portion of LAN Manager resides in each workstation where it intercepts and redirects input/output operating system calls to the network where they can be managed. The Redirector also is responsible for the starting and stopping of network operations and the configuration of a workstation's use of network resources.

A *Server* portion of LAN Manager assumes responsibility for file management, printer service, scheduling, and security. It also maintains network statistics, monitors the network and issues alerts if something goes wrong, and enables users to execute commands on remote computers. Several companies license LAN Manager as the foundation of their own network operating systems running under OS/2.

LAN Manager uses the same application programming interfaces (APIs), such as Named Pipes and semaphores, discussed in previous sections when examining OS/2 running on one machine to link together applications running on different network workstations. Specific APIs utilized by the LAN Manager reflecting its job include error logging, printer support, network statistics, security, remote program execution, and several different server functions. Figure 2-9 illustrates LAN Manager's relationship to OS/2, NetBIOS, and the application programs running on the network.

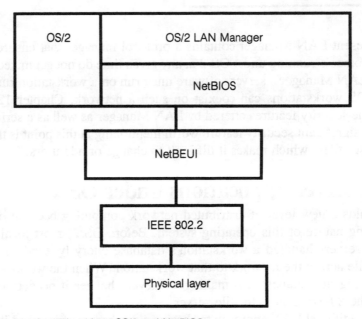

2-9 LAN Manager's relationship to OS/2 and NetBIOS.

In effect, LAN Manager is a platform that can be used by a LAN manufacturer to mount its own network operating system. LAN Manager supports a number of standard protocols such as NetBIOS, which you already have examined. At the present time, the NetBIOS interface serves as the major application program interface (API) for LAN Manager. Figure 2-10 illustrates the protocols supported by LAN Manager.

```
┌─────────────────────────────────────┐
│        OS/2 LAN manager             │
├─────────────────────────────────────┤
│      Server message block           │
├─────────────────────────────────────┤
│           NetBIOS                   │
├─────────────────────────────────────┤
│           NetBEUI                   │
├─────────────────────────────────────┤
│           TokREUI                   │
├─────────────────────────────────────┤
│      Data link control              │
│      Token Ring/Ethernet            │
├─────────────────────────────────────┤
│      Twisted pair/coaxial           │
└─────────────────────────────────────┘
```

2-10 Protocols supported by LAN Manager.

At present LAN Manager contains a protocol manager that ensures that the various protocols running under OS/2 at any given time do not get mixed together.

The LAN Manager's server software must run on a workstation running OS/2, but DOS workstations can coexist on such a network. Chapter 12 explores many of the security features offered by LAN Manager as well as a serious weakness. One significant security feature worth mentioning at this point is that it does encrypt user files, which makes it difficult to change or add users.

Client-server applications under OS/2

OS/2 heralds a new level of distributed network computing because of the true multitasking nature of this operating system. Before OS/2, most local area network file servers handled a workstation's database query by sending the entire database file across the network to that workstation. When the workstation completed sorting the database and making whatever changes it needed to make, it returned the information to the file server.

This traditional LAN approach to sharing a database program and its files has several problems associated with it. Network congestion increases as more and more workstations request that the program and its files be sent and then send information back to the file server. Network overhead also can become a problem with this approach because a database program might need to create several different processes to permit multiuser operations. Data integrity also might be an issue with so many files traveling through the network.

A number of new programs that utilize this approach are beginning to appear using the Structured Query Language (SQL) that IBM developed several years ago. SQL-based LAN database servers will be able to communicate with SQL databases running on mainframe and minicomputers using SQL commands. A LAN user on a client machine will be able to issue an SQL command such as:

SELECT INVOICE NUMBER FROM CUSTOMERS WHERE LAST NAME = "ABRAMOVITZ"

The server will locate the ABRAMOVITZ record and deliver it to the client machine. Oracle has published Oracle Server while Microsoft and Ashton-Tate have developed a structured query language (SQL) server program called SQL Server. SQL Server running on a file server under OS/2 is able to provide database management service to applications running on network workstations.

This example where a user located information on a customer named ABRA-MOVITZ illustrates the power of client-server databases. When a workstation queries an SQL database, the SQL Server "back end" program receives the request, finds the information desired residing on a database and then forwards the specific information requested and not the entire database file back to the workstation where it can do its own processing. The end user's "front-end" application program uses APIs to make these queries and requests in a manner that is transparent to the user. It really does not matter where the database is physically located. Figure 2-11 illustrates this process.

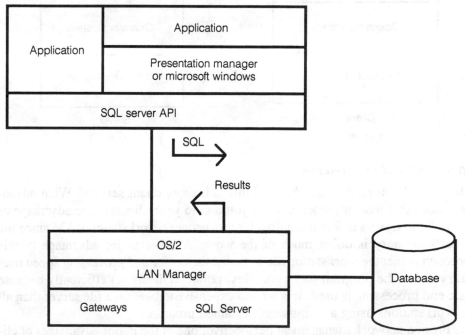

2-11 Client-server operations.

We call this type of distributed processing "client-server" computing because two distinctly different types of activities are taking place. A "front-end" client application program accesses a "back-end" server, in this case a database server. Several different types of client front-end applications (spreadsheets, accounting programs, project management programs, etc.) can access the back-end server. The front-end application program processes the information it requested and displays it on its screen; meanwhile, the back-end server program maintains the database's integrity and ensures the network functions with optimum efficiency.

Figure 2-12 illustrates a typical client-server relationship on a local area network. Client workstations will have a graphics interface that will simplify many of today's complex database requests. A special program running on the client manipulates data from the server. The server has software to sort records as well as perform other server-related functions such as communicating with other database servers.

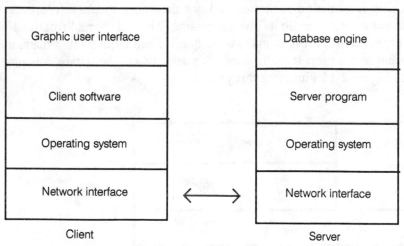

Graphic user interface	Database engine
Client software	Server program
Operating system	Operating system
Network interface	⟷	Network interface
Client	Server

2-12 A client and a server.

Advantages of client-servers

Why should you really care about all this talk about client servers? What advantages does this new approach offer to you and to your clients? One advantage of using client-servers is that it requires far less network workstation RAM since the server's memory is doing much of the work. Another major advantage of this approach is that the workstations do not need the power and processing speed necessary to run the program (say a complex, powerful database) efficiently because back-end processing is used. It is far less expensive to beef up a file server than all the workstations using a client-server database program.

From a network management perspective, one of the major advantages of client-server architecture is that it reduces network traffic significantly. Rather than sending records individually to a network workstation, a client-server will process records and send a data set which is smaller and less likely to congest the network. These smaller chunks of information from the server mean faster response time than conventional network database operations.

From a systems integration point of view, a major advantage of client-server architecture is that it is easier for developers to write a client-server application and then simply write new front ends and use appropriate remote procedure calls (RPCs) to link the front end with the client-server. Oracle and Gupta Technologies both offer database programs that have interfaces to IBM's DB2 program. In the not too distant future, clients will expect distributed databases on mainframes, minicomputers, and LANs to exchange information transparently; the user will view a graphics interface front-end screen and not know or care about the source or pathway of the data requested.

Client-servers using OS/2

One very important point to keep in mind with regard to client-server software running under OS/2 is that while the server needs to run OS/2, client workstations can run MS-DOS or OS/2. The next section examines how a typical client-server database, ORACLE Server, works.

ORACLE's server software is installed on a workstation running OS/2. It makes use of OS/2 virtual memory feature because it uses a substantial amount of memory for its memory structures, memory caches for high speed transfer of information. ORACLE's memory structures include *Program Global Areas* (PGAs), memory areas that hold information linked to a specific Structured Query Language (SQL) SELECT database command. ORACLE also sets aside one memory area known as a *System Global Area* (SGA). The SGA is shared by several different client processes (programs) and holds transactions during the interval between the time clients have initiated them and the time these transactions are written to the server's hard disk. On the server, a special database known as the *Redo log* keeps track of data that has to be written to the actual database. It is used for error recovery because it contains a step-by-step listing of all changes made to the database since the last Redo log was written to disk. Figure 2-13 illustrates how ORACLE Server handles communications between client and server.

Client-servers and the future

Imagine, if you will, a time not too far in the future when many different network applications are built around relational databases able to use SQL servers. Because these servers will support comprehensive user-level security on their databases, the individual client applications will not have to worry about implementing security procedures. These applications would be able to access each other's files residing on a wide range of different types of machines connected to a

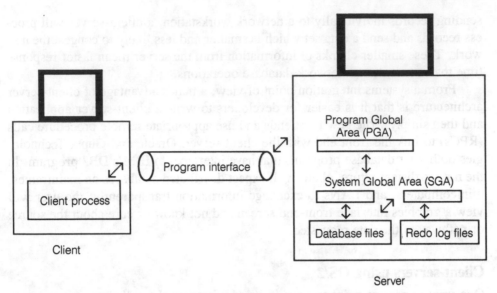

2-13 Client-server communications under OS/2 with Oracle Server.

network including microcomputers, minicomputers, and even mainframes. Programs will talk to programs running on different machines in a way that is transparent to the human users. Need information on John Q. Customer? You could ask for the information with an English-like request, and the information would be fetched for you, perhaps from a database running on a mainframe server in another city.

Novell NetWare

Depending upon whose figures you accept, Novell's NetWare dominates the network operating system market with somewhere between 60% and 70% of this growing market. NetWare is a multi-tasking operating system that requires two sets of programs to run it, a set of programs running on the file server and a set of programs running as a "shell" on each workstation. If network programs require NetBIOS calls, then a NetBIOS emulation program must also be run.

NetWare uses its shell program to grab MS-DOS input/output calls such as requests to print or requests to save a file. NetWare then provides the necessary queuing directions for effective file management and printer operations. It would create chaos if several workstations were permitted to try to print documents at the same time on the same printer. NetWare's shell intercepts these printer commands and sends them to a printer server program where the requests are queued up and handled in an orderly fashion.

Under MS-DOS, the Redirector program discussed earlier in this chapter receives interrupts from MS-DOS and then formats the message blocks for the

NetBIOS for transmission over the network. With NetWare, all interrupts are intercepted by the NetWare shell program that runs on each network workstation. The shell passes on to MS-DOS all commands that are not network related. The network-related commands are formatted according to NetWare's own set of rules or protocols (remember that word protocol?) into a NetWare format known as *NetWare Core Protocol* (NCP). The packet of information now in the form of a Network Core Protocol request packet goes through an internetwork packet exchange software layer as illustrated in Fig. 2-14 where it is encapsulated into IPX format.

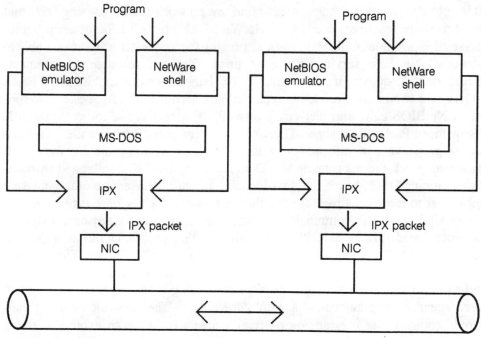

2-14 NetWare translates MS-DOS commands.

The packet now contains the original data as well as such key information as its source and destination. Control information is also part of this packet, and it includes such data as the length of the packet, error checking parameters, and transport instructions. Figure 2-15 illustrates a typical IPX packet, which can carry from 0 to 546 bytes of data along with the control information.

Control information	Destination network	Destination host	Destination socket	Source network	Source host	Source socket	Data 0 – 546 bytes

2-15 A typical IPX packet.

The IPX formatted packet is now directed by a special program known as a *network driver*. This program ensures that the packet is transmitted over the network's physical media (twisted pair, coax, etc.) to a network file server. This file server will receive the packet and begin processing it. When chapter 3 examines protocol more fully, you can see that the IPX packet is broken down by software running on this server workstation so that the data can be processed and used by appropriate programs. The file server then sends a response back to the workstation that first submitted the request.

NetWare and OS/2

It is not unusual in large companies to find several workstations running OS/2 that need to share resources found on a NetWare LAN. Novell's Requester program makes this possible. OS/2 workstations running the Requester program are able to share all NetWare services including print, file, and resource management. Because the Requester includes support for Named Pipes, it enables OS/2 based SQL client-server software to run on a NetWare network. The Requester also supports NetBIOS calls and NetWare's own IPX (Internetwork Protocol) and SPX (Sequenced Packet Exchange). These options mean that a NetWare file server can exchange packets of information with workstations running the NetWare shell program, workstations running MS-DOS and using NetBIOS calls, and workstations running OS/2. Much like a tri-lingual translator, the Redirector might take a bit longer to translate a message and then to translate the response it receives, but the flexibility of such communication more than makes up for any degradation in network speed. Figure 2-16 illustrates how an OS/2 program would send a message to the OS/2 kernel and then through the Requester software. The message would be encapsulated in NetWare's own IPX/SPX format. It would be transmitted to a workstation's network interface card using a special network interface card specific program called a *LAN card driver*. The network interface card would transmit the message over network media (cabling) to another network workstation or network resource such as a printer.

Novell's vision of the future

In its earliest days, Novell tried to be all things for all people. It sold hardware including network interface cards and file servers and software. Now, the company has made a long-term commitment to focus on being a network software company and free itself of any particular hardware platform. Let Apple, IBM, and Sun battle over who supplies the network workstations—Novell will be happy to supply one and all with network software.

With this goal of a truly open NetWare system in mind, Novell has issued several public announcements the past couple of years concerning a policy of "NetWare Open Systems." Consistent with this policy has been Novell's development of NetWare for DEC's VAX/VMS computer operating system, NetWare for

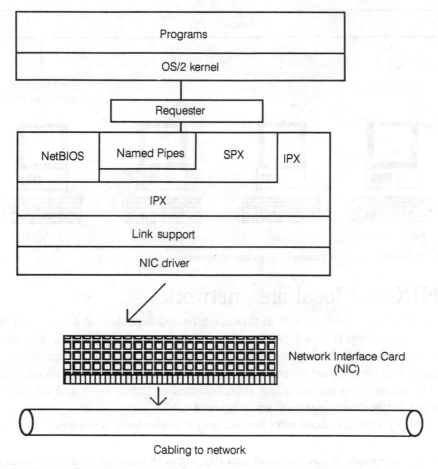

2-16 The NetWare Requester.

the Macintosh, and portable NetWare designed to be ported to several different operating systems.

Novell has announced that it will support Network File Systems (NFS), a critical part of UNIX, and also support IBM's Server Message Block (SMB) protocol. Figure 2-17 illustrates why NetWare is the closest thing we have to a "standard" network operating system because it crosses so many boundaries. The DEC VMS/VAX product in particular deserves some attention. It is possible to use a DEC minicomputer as a file server and see NetWare files on it in DOS format. Once established as a network server, the minicomputer is virtually transparent to the end user who treats it exactly the same as a PC-based server. You do have to be comfortable with VMS to install the software on the minicomputer, but this product does illustrate that we have moved a bit closer toward seamless, transparent communication between minicomputer and microcomputer running the same type of network software.

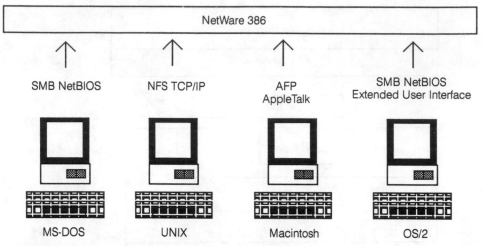

2-17 NetWare runs under several different operating systems.

UNIX and local area networks

A few years ago the best way to provoke a heated argument at a computer trade show was to suggest that UNIX would soon overtake MS-DOS and become the operating system of choice for corporate America. Microsoft managed to maintain its market share because most businesses were far more concerned about keeping their business software including such favorites as Lotus 1-2-3 and dBASE than with the network management advantages of UNIX.

UNIX, after all, does offer several major advantages as a network operating system. It is a true multiuser, multitasking operating system specifically designed for large networks. It has excellent security, network management, and communications capabilities and, just as important, it has a track record of reliability that extends over a decade. If only there were a way to merge Microsoft's network operating system for the 1990s (LAN Manager) and UNIX.

LAN Manager/X

Hewlett-Packard and Microsoft have jointly developed LAN Manager/X, a network operating system that enables LAN Manager to run under the UNIX System V operating system. The first release is designed to run on Intel 80386-based file servers running UNIX, but Microsoft has since provided versions that companies have ported to minicomputers running UNIX. Hewlett-Packard is able to run its version of LAN Manager/X on its own HP-9000. LAN Manager/X is able to utilize UNIX's multi-tasking ability to create a UNIX file server that can provide file, print, and other network services for workstations running MS-DOS, OS/2, and UNIX.

Because LAN Manager/X uses the same Named Pipes and mailslots processes as the OS/2 version, programs running on a workstation running MS-DOS or OS/2 can communicate with programs on the UNIX server; in effect, they are all speaking the same language. The LAN Manager/X software is smart enough to smooth over the differences between the two operating systems. It converts MS-DOS and OS/2 file names to file names that are acceptable under UNIX and vice versa. One major limitation, though, is that Microsoft has developed LAN Manager/X so that it can run only as a server and not as a client; hence, UNIX programs cannot call applications running on LAN Manager servers. Do not lose too much sleep worrying about this restriction, though, because the ability of minicomputers running UNIX to handle several dozen users and numerous tasks without degradation makes them attractive choices as network file servers for LAN Manager/X.

AT&T's StarGroup illustrates UNIX power

AT&T licensed Microsoft's LAN Manager/X and enhanced it substantially so that it reveals the real power of UNIX as a network file server. In fact, to make it more efficient, AT&T chose to rewrite the program as an application running under UNIX on AT&T's Intel 80386-based StarGroup Server. AT&T's enhanced version includes a full-screen administration of networked DOS workstations. Another enhancement includes the ability to administer a UNIX server from a DOS workstation or an OS/2 workstation.

AT&T's StarGroup version includes a client-server program called Simul-Task. This program permits users to run multiple DOS sessions from a 386-based workstation while running UNIX System V/386. This means that even though a user is working on a UNIX computer, it is possible to access DOS network applications and UNIX applications simultaneously. A user could be working in a DOS-based application such as a database while a UNIX communications program works simultaneously. Skeptics just might have written off UNIX a bit too soon.

Summary

MS-DOS is an operating system developed for the IBM PC and its Intel 8088 microprocessor. Its limitations include an ability to address only 640K of RAM and 32 megabytes of secondary storage. OS/2 is a multitasking operating system that has a protective mode that permits several programs to run without disturbing each other's operations. OS/2 features virtual memory that means that the operating system is able to use both internal and secondary storage memory to run large programs. OS/2 also features several types of interprocess communications including semaphores, pipes, and Named Pipes.

Of major importance for the future is LAN Manager, the network management portion of OS/2. It features a server component (the Server) and a workstation component (the Redirector). LAN Manager permits a client/server relationship, which will mean much more sophisticated distributed processing in the future on LANs, particularly in the area of database management.

A UNIX version of LAN Manager called LAN Manager/X developed by Hewlett-Packard and Microsoft means that computers running UNIX are able to act as file servers and provide network services to workstations running MS-DOS or OS/2. AT&T has completely written its licensed version so that LAN Manager runs as an application under UNIX with even greater functionality.

3
CHAPTER

Unlocking network protocol mysteries

In this chapter, you will examine

- Network protocol—what it is and how it works.
- The Open Systems Interconnect (OSI) model as well as Government OSI Profile (GOSIP).
- The significance of Transmission Control Protocol/Internet Protocol (TCP/IP).
- How companies will migrate from TCP/IP to OSI.
- Xerox Network System (XNS) protocol.

Introduction

Take a deep breath before starting this chapter and keep telling yourself how good this material is for you. After ten years' experience working with LANs, I have concluded that while protocols might not be the secret of life, they do provide the key to understanding internet connectivity.

In the novel *Shogun*, an Englishman in sixteenth century Japan is led through a maze of paths surrounding a castle. At each gate his companions present a pass that is carefully examined before they are allowed to continue. The Englishman cannot read or understand the passes written in Japanese, but he knows that if anything is wrong with any of the passes he will not be able to complete his journey.

In a similar way, data on a network is packaged in just the right order along with accompanying control information. The data and control information is placed in the equivalent of an envelope that must be addressed correctly. If everything is not done completely according to the rules (or *protocol* in data communications terminology), the data will not reach its destination.

The focus in this book is on the situation where the data needs to travel not just to another workstation on the same network but to a workstation on another completely different network. Here is where protocol really becomes crucial. The data and control information that can travel easily around its own workstation's network with its current packaging and envelope must carry additional information (in effect, another pass or envelope) to enter and travel on another network with its different set of rules (or protocol).

Many networks built around minicomputers have adopted the Transmission Control Protocol/Internet Protocol (TCP/IP) protocol while many microcomputer networks turned originally in the direction of Xerox Network Systems (XNS) protocol and later toward IBM's NetBIOS interface. More recently, the Open Systems Interconnect (OSI) model with its suite of protocols that are international standards.

This chapter examines these different protocols and looks for their packaging data and control information. It also looks at the differences between the current dominant internetwork protocol (TCP/IP) and the OSI model that will eventually replace it. You can count on referring to this chapter later when you examine the bridges, routers, and gateways that link different networks together by dealing with these protocol issues.

The importance of protocols

While an operating system manages a computer's resources and a network operating system manages an entire network's hardware and software resources, there can be no network communication without protocol. *Protocol* is the set of rules that govern how packets containing data and control information will be assembled at a source workstation for their transmission across the network and then disassembled when they reach the destination workstation. Assume that you just received a message from a network user on another planet. This message contains a series of characters and numbers with no spaces or apparent punctuation.

You can decode an English sentence because you know the rules or protocol that English follows. You know that sentences begin with a capital letter and end with a period. You know that individual words are separated by spaces. You also know that proper nouns are capitalized and that verbs often end in "ed."

Without knowing the protocol that a message is following, you would have no idea which part of the message contained information for you and which part contained the inside address.

Protocol permits network communication by specifying which bits represent a greeting, which bits represent error checking, and even which bits indicate the size of the data portion of the packet. Without this information, a receiving workstation would have no idea how to decipher the message.

A basic data communications model

In order to discuss different protocols, you need a basis of comparison, a set of terms to describe the common elements in any network communications. Some basic data communications terminology has evolved over the years and has become an integral part in defining the standards. An *Application Process* (AP) is software such as an inventory program or an accounts receivable program. It resides on a device described as *Data Terminal Equipment* (DTE) which could be a computer or terminal. If the application process needs information from a second computer, it needs to establish communications with another DTE.

To establish communications with a second DTE, the computer utilizes *Data Circuit-terminating Equipment* (DCE) such as a modem to provide an interface for the DTE to the communications network which can take the form of a cable or a digital or analog phone line. The information is transmitted over this communications network to a second DCE which converts the information into a form that the application process running on the second DTE can understand. Figure 3-1 illustrates the elements found in a basic data communications model.

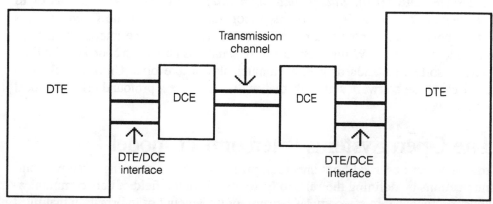

3-1 The elements of a data communications model.

Protocols in a data communications model

The key to standardizing the interfaces found in this data communications model is the development of protocols, which can be defined more fully here as sets of very specific rules on how the data communications devices will exchange information. Protocols cover such issues as how data will be transmitted (what pin or wire will carry what kind of signal), what kind of error checking will take place, and how data should be assembled with accompanying control information into packets for transmission and then disassembled successfully at the receiving end.

Protocols cover virtually all phases of communications including the synchronization of the receiving and sending computers' clocks, the method of coding the binary data into corresponding voltages, and even instructions on how information can be routed across several different networks with different addressing schemes without losing its integrity.

Moving toward standards

A number of United States and international organizations have been working for several years to develop a set of standards for data communications equipment in general and local area networks in particular. The benefits of standardization include the reduction in equipment costs, the enhanced ability to link different devices, and the ability to mix and match hardware and software products from different vendors.

How standards are created

A set of protocols defining a particular data communications model or interface must undergo several different steps before it can become an international standard.

In the case of the International Standards Organization (ISO), the long road begins as a WP (*Working Paper*); it then becomes a DP (*Draft Proposal*). The next stage, DIS (*Draft International Standard*) is followed by the status of IS (*International Standard*). In the discussion that follows on the Open Systems Interconnect model, note that much work still remains in the international standard adoption arena. While most hardware standards have been adopted with little fanfare, software standards have been much slower to evolve. Unfortunately, it is precisely these software standards that really will have a profound effect on local area networks.

The Open Systems Interconnect model

You have just observed how important protocols are for ensuring effective communications by defining the rules to be followed. In the field of data communications, protocols are very complex because of the amount of information that must be agreed upon for an interface to be effective. Because technology is constantly changing, often the interface defined after several years of discussion and negotiation among committee members with different viewpoints fails to include a new, vastly improved technique.

Layered protocols

Most standards organizations use a layered approach toward developing protocols with each layer concerning itself with some very specific functions and services. Because these standards must cover a variety of different possible hardware and software configurations, often several different layers of protocols are required to define a particularly complex communications interface. The advantage of this approach is that changes can be incorporated in one layer without having to redevelop the entire model. Because each layer is developed by a different subcommittee, it tends to overlap some of the functions and services of other layers. The result is that with all the major advantages of layered protocols comes the one major disadvantage, a significant amount of overhead. It takes more bits to cover all the functions and services defined in each layer than it would if two computers were communicating using a manufacturer's own proprietary operating system where there are fewer options and defaults that must be represented.

The rationale for the OSI model

The International Organization for Standardization (ISO) in conjunction with the *Consultative Committee on International Telegraphy and Telephony* (CCITT) developed a layered set of protocols known as the *Open Systems Interconnect* (OSI) model to facilitate communications between computer networks. One of the major goals of the OSI model is that in the not too distant future, it will be relatively easy for computers using OSI compliant hardware and software to exchange information regardless of the fact that they were manufactured by different vendors. End users will be freed of the compatibility worries that still characterize companies with multivendor equipment.

Figure 3-2 illustrates how the layered protocols composing the OSI model facilitate the transfer of information from one computer to another computer. Notice that each layer with the exception of the physical layer adds a header containing control information for its corresponding counterpart on the other computer. The Data Link layer even adds a trailer with additional control information. The control information found in the headers and trailer contains such key negotiable data as the form the information will take (will it contain floating point numbers?), the address the sending and receiving workstations, the mode of transmission (full duplex, half-duplex, etc.), the method of coding the information (EBCDIC, ASCII, etc.), and the type of error checking that will take place. After this information is received by the second computer as a bit stream, it is

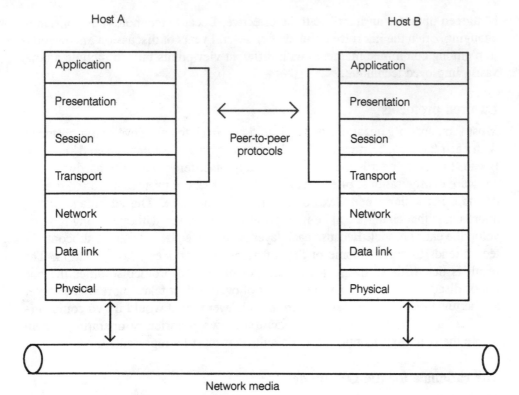

3-2 The OSI model.

reassembled into frames and the control information is stripped off by each corresponding layer as the frame moves up through the layered protocols until only the original data remains for the application program.

A layer in the OSI model

It might be helpful to view the individual layers of the OSI model as groups of programs designed to perform specific functions. One layer, for example, might be responsible for providing data conversion from ASCII to EBCDIC and have the necessary programs required for performing this task. The programs might contain individual modules, which are known in the OSI model as *entities*. Each layer provides services for the layer above it while requesting services from the layer immediately below it.

The upper layers request services in a rather general fashion; they might want some data routed from network A to network B. The actual mechanics of how the data needs to be addressed to ensure that it is routed correctly are left to the lower level layers providing the services. The communication between layers involves different types of transactions known as primitives.

Primitives

These *primitives* involving transactions can take several forms including requests, indications, responses, and conforms. A layer serving as a service user can invoke a function by requesting an action such as data encryption. The layer serving the role of service provider will issue a confirmation indicating that the function has been completed ("yes, the data has been encrypted"). Sometimes the request is for action to be taken by a layer on a second computer. This request is received the layer on the second computer as an indication primitive. This layer replies by issuing a response primitive which informs the layer on the first computer that the function requested has been completed. It might be helpful to think of these primitives as control information that takes the form of certain bit patterns in the frames that are transmitted during the data communications process. The way the OSI model facilitates communications between data networks using this system of primitives to relay control information is directly applicable to how workstations communicate on local area networks.

The Application layer of the OSI model

Under the OSI model, an application program needing to accomplish a specific task such as updating a database on computer B sends specific data in the form of datagram to the *Application layer*. One of the prime responsibilities of this layer is to determine how the application program's request should be treated, or, in other words, what form this request should take. If the application program requests remote job entry, for example, this might require several programs to collect the information, organize it, process it, and then send it to the appropriate destination. Electronic mail is also a major function for the Application layer. Chapter 12 examines some of the X.400 OSI protocols for electronic mail and X.500 protocols for a global directory in conjunction with the chapter's description of how electronic mail is moving toward global communications and breaking down the barriers between heterogeneous networks.

Application service elements in the Application layer   The Application layer also contains several *Application Common Service Elements* (ACSE) and *Specific Application Service Elements* (SASE). The ACSE services are available to application processes on all systems. They include such services as quality of service parameters. A workstation on a local area network in Los Angeles, for example, might need to communicate over a wide area network via modem with a mainframe computer in Boston. Because of the possibility that the quality of the phone line might prove unsatisfactory, the application process running on the LAN might request a quality of service that includes an acknowledgement that all information was received and understood. This quality of service would correspond to a request at the post office that your package's delivery be acknowledged with a return receipt.

The *Specific Application Service Elements* (SASE) provide services for specific applications such as file transfer and terminal emulation. If an application program required a file transfer, for example, one key Application layer protocol that would be involved is *File Transfer, Access, and Management* (FTAM).

Imagine, if you will, the implications for the future when local area networks as well as mainframe computers run OSI compatible software. FTAM functions as a virtual filestore with its own directory service, so programs will be able to access databases unaware of the file's actual location. Because FTAM supports a variety of different types of file structures (including sequential, ordered hierarchical, and general hierarchical), information will be able to flow from one database located on a distant Burroughs computer, update a second database running on a local area network in Los Angeles, and finally be updated by a third database residing on an IBM mainframe in Phoenix.

Another major SASE found in the Application layer is Virtual Terminal service. *Virtual Terminal* (VT) is a sophisticated service that frees a computer from having to send the appropriate signals to address all terminals residing on a second computer. The first computer can use a set of virtual terminal parameters and leave specific terminal configuration concerns to the second computer which has already been configured to address the signaling requirements of its own terminals.

Other SASEs in various stages of development include transaction processing, electronic data interchange (EDI), and job transfer and manipulation (JTM). The development of an OSI standard for EDI, in particular, could be very significant for LAN users. Workstations on a LAN could create purchase orders, for example, and then transmit the information electronically directly to the manufacturer or distributor where the data would automatically go into an invoice. Inventory would be checked and decremented automatically and arrangements made to ship the goods all without a significant amount of paperwork or delay.

Network management functions under the Application layer   Network management has become an issue as data networks have become more complex. As voice and data become integrated parts of data communications and local area networks link more and more with wide area networks and mainframe computers, the need for an effective method of managing and controlling this information is increasing. IBM has offered its NetView and NetView/PC as the solution while AT&T has countered with its UNMA hardware and software package.

The problem up to now is that there have been several proprietary solutions, but no effective international standard for network management. Under the Application layer of the OSI model there have been several management information protocol specifications working their way toward the position of international standard. Chapter 12 discusses the movement toward international standards for network management.

The Presentation layer

The Presentation layer concerns itself with how information is to be physically displayed or presented. Data might need to be processed as floating point numbers while certain database fields might require both characters and numbers. Some fields might even require graphics.

The Presentation layer facilitates communication by ensuring that Application processes wishing to exchange information can resolve any syntax differences that might exist. The two processes must share a common representation or language for communication to take place.

The Presentation layer's real value to the other OSI layers is its creation of Abstract Syntax Notation (ASN.1), which is its way of describing a file's data structures. ASN.1 is used by the Application layer for all its file transfers and virtual terminal information. It is also essential that the encryption function, a major concern for managing large networks, can be done at the Presentation layer. The development of an OSI standard at this level will have a significant impact on facilitating machine-to-machine communications.

The Session layer

The Session layer can be described as the administrative assistant with a good eye for detail who is responsible for arranging all the details for an important upcoming meeting between two executives. In reality, the session layer's activities facilitate the session resulting in an interchange of information between two application processes, but the analogy holds together rather well.

The Session layer is concerned about such basic issues as the mode of transmission and synchronizing points. In other words, the issue is whether transmission between the two application processes be *half-duplex* (the processes alternating sending and replying) or *full-duplex* transmission (both processes sending and receiving at the same time). In half-duplex transmission, the Session layer provides the side that speaks first with a data token. When it is time for the other side to respond, it receives the data token. Only the side with this data token is permitted by the Session layer to speak. Similarly, synchronizing points represent points during the "conversation" that the Session layer checks to ensure that actual communication is taking place. If you have ever observed two Japanese businessmen carrying on a conversation, you will certainly remember that both people were constantly nodding their heads and saying "Hi" (yes in Japanese). This did not mean that the two businessmen agreed with each other, simply that they were indicating that they were hearing and understanding what the other person was saying.

Another concern of the Session layer is how to re-establish communications if they are disrupted during a session. In other words, at one point can a session be re-established? A synchronization point between pages of a text, for example, would be a logical approach since re-establishment of a session would not require beginning again and repeating all text already received correctly. In a similar vein, this layer is also responsible for the details associated with an orderly (known as a "graceful") release of the connection when a session ends. There are also procedures for what is known as an "abrupt" release of a connection, a situation where one side ends communications and refuses to receive additional data from that moment on.

The Session layer does not automatically accept every connection. It might issue a Refuse Connection primitive if, for example, it determines that it would result in too much network congestion or because the Application process requested is unavailable.

The Transport layer

The Transport layer is of great importance to computer network users because it provides the quality of service required by the Network layer. An analogy that might help clarify the Transport layer's responsibilities is to think of it as a collection of special services available for additional cost at your local post office. In other words, for an additional fee, you can receive a return receipt indicating that a letter was delivered to the person you specified. Similarly, you might require expedited service such as specifying that a package needs to reach Boston by the next day. While the U.S. Postal Service collects fees for these high quality, added services, the price paid by a computer user running OSI compatible hardware and software is the overhead of additional bits required to provide information on the status of these possible services.

In effect, the Transport layer offers three different types of network service. Its type A service provides network connections with acceptable residual error rates and acceptable rates of signalled failures. Type B offers an acceptable residual error rate and an unacceptable rate of signalled failures, while type C provides network connections with residual error rates that are not acceptable to the Session layer.

Why have classes of service that provide unacceptable error rates? The answer is that many network connections utilize additional protocols that provide the error detection and recovery required, and the overhead required for this service under the Transport layer is not necessary.

On the other hand, the Transport layer does offer programmers the opportunity to write programs for the Application layer for a wide variety of networks without concerning themselves with whether or not transmission on these networks is reliable or unreliable. In fact, some people distinguish the different layers of the OSI model by calling the top three layers as Transport layer users and the bottom 4 layers as Transport layer providers.

The five classes of Transport protocol services are:

Class	Title	Type
0	Simple	A
1	Basic error recovery	B
2	Multiplexing	A
3	Error recovery & multiplexing	B
4	Error detection & recovery	C

Class 0, known as Telex, is the simplest quality of service. It assumes that the Network layer (below the Transport layer) provides flow control. It releases its connection upon release by the Network layer of its connection. Class 1 service was developed by the CCITT for its X.25 packet switched network standard. It does provide expedited data transfers but still relies on the Network layer for flow control. Class 2 represents an enhanced class 0. The basic assumption made here is still that the network is highly reliable. The quality of service offered here includes the ability to multiplex multiple Transport connections from a single network connection. Class 2 ensures that multiplexed packets of data arriving out of order can be reassembled properly.

Class 3 provides the services offered by both 1 and 2 as well as the ability to resynchronize so that a connection can be re-established if an error is detected. Finally, Class 4 assumes that the Network layer service is inherently unreliable. It offers its own error detection and recovery procedures.

The Network layer

The Network layer is where network routing takes place. As such, it is a key to understanding how gateways to IBM mainframe and other computer systems function. While upper-level OSI protocols request that a packet be transmitted from one computer system to another, it is the Network layer that concerns itself with the actual mechanics of the journey.

The Network layer also forms the basis of the CCITT's X.25 standard for wide area networks. Chapter 9 examines the actual structure of an X.25 packet, including how the control information is packaged in several different fields.

The Network layer performs a number of key services for the Transport layer immediately above it in the OSI model. It notifies the Transport layer when it detects unrecoverable errors and helps this layer maintain quality of service and avoid network congestion by stopping the transfer of packets whenever it becomes necessary.

Because physical connections might change from time to time during the time two networks are communicating, it is the Network layer that maintains virtual circuits and ensures that packets arriving out of sequence are reassembled correctly. In effect, it utilizes routing tables that help it determine which path a particular packet should take. Often a message composed of multiple packets will take different pathways. The Network layer provides such essential "shipping" information for these packets as the total number of packets composing a message and the sequence number of each packet.

One very unfortunate complication in network communications is that different networks have different sized address fields, different sized packets, and even different time intervals that they permit a packet to circulate before they *time out*— when the packet is considered lost, and a duplicate packet is requested. The Network layer must provide enough control information within the packets to address these issues and ensure successful delivery and reassembly.

As I mentioned earlier, the functions of the Transport layer and the Network layer have a good deal of duplication between them, particularly in flow control and error checking. The primary reason for this duplication is that the two different types of connections, connection-oriented and connectionless, make far different assumptions regarding network reliability.

A *connection-oriented network* functions very much like the telephone system. Once a connection is established, communication continues point-to-point without the two parties feeling compelled to conclude each statement with their name, the name of the party they called, and that party's address. The assumption made is that the communication is reliable and that the other party is receiving the message as it is being sent.

Given the assumption of a reliable, connection-oriented network, the destination address is only required when the connection is being established; individual packets do not have to carry this address in a separate field. The Network layer assumes responsibility for error checking in a connection-oriented network as well as for flow control. It also concerns itself with the actual sequencing of the packets.

Connectionless service, on the other hand, relies more on the Transport layer for error checking and flow control. Destination addresses are required on each packet and packet sequencing is not guaranteed. The basic assumption made concerning this service is that a premium should be placed on speed and that end-users should have their own error checking and flow control software rather than rely on an OSI standard built into the OSI model.

As is usually the case whenever committee members argue a complex issue, a compromise was reached that really did not totally satisfy anyone. The compromise is that the capabilities for both connection-oriented and connectionless service are both built into the OSI model's Network layer and Transport layer. End users can select appropriate default values for these two layers' control fields and use the approach they prefer. The only negative side to this compromise is that the significant amount of redundancy built into these two layers means a significant amount of bit overhead. When information using this OSI format is sent over long distance lines, it translates into increased costs since the transmission takes longer.

The Data Link layer

The Data Link layer can be likened to the warehouse and receiving/shipping dock of a large manufacturing company. It must take the packets it receives from the Network layer and prepare them for transmission (shipping) by placing them in the appropriately sized packages (frames). When information is flowing up the layers of the OSI model, the Data Link layer must be able to take the raw bits coming from the Physical layer and make sense of them. It must establish where a transmission block starts and where it ends as well as detect whether there are transmission errors. If it does detect errors, this layer is responsible for initiating action to recover from lost data, garbled data, and even duplicate data. Several data links can exist simultaneously and function independently between computer systems. The Data Link layer is also responsible for ensuring that these transmissions are not overlapping and that data does not become garbled.

The Data Link layer initializes a link with its corresponding layer on another computer with which it will communicate. It has to ensure that both machines's clocks are synchronized and that they both are using the same encoding and decoding schemes.

Because flow control and error checking are also the responsibilities of the Data Link layer, it monitors the frames it receives and maintains statistical records. Upon the completion of a user's transfer of information, the Data Link layer assumes responsibility for determining that all data was received correctly before terminating the link.

Error checking under the Data Link layer Related to *Automatic Repeat Request* (ARQ) techniques used by the Data Link layer to perform error checking are at least three different methods, depending upon the Data Link protocol it happens to be running. *Stop-and-wait ARQ* is a method in which a computer transmits a frame of information and then waits to receive an acknowledgement (ACK) control code indicating that the frame was received correctly. If an error is detected, a negative acknowledgement (NAK) is transmitted by the receiving station, and the sending station responds by repeating its transmission.

The *Go-back-N Continuous ARQ* approach enables a station to receive several frames (depending upon the protocol used) before replying with either an ACK or an NAK pinpointing which frame contained an error. If a station sent seven continuous seven frames and an error was detected in frame number four, then the sending station would reply to the NAK by retransmitting frames 4 through 7.

The *Selective-repeat Continuous ARQ* method provides an enhancement to the Go-back-N Continuous ARQ approach. A receiving station maintains a buffer to store all frames received in a sequence and then replies that a particular frame, say number 4, contained an error. The receiving station keeps the other frames in a buffer and sends an NAK. The sending station retransmits only the frame containing an error (number 4 in this example). The receiving station then reassembles the frames into their proper sequence (1 through 7) and processes the information.

The key protocols associated with the Data Link layer   The Data Link layer contains a number of protocols that have been defined by the IEEE's 802 Committee. In order to understand this key OSI model layer, you should examine some of the work by this committee.

The IEEE and network standards

The Institute of Electrical and Electronics Engineers (IEEE) is an international professional society whose activities are organized around a series of boards including a Standards Board. The Standards Board, accredited by the American National Standards Institute (ANSI), submits the standards it develops to ANSI for approval as national standards. Take a few moments to examine what some of these standards are and how they define various tasks networks perform.

The IEEE 802 committee

The IEEE established an 802 committee in 1980 to develop a set of standards for local area networks. Its goal was to develop standard interfaces which would make it cost-effective for manufacturers to develop products for new type of technology. The IEEE and ISO work closely together, so that IEEE standards are incorporated into the OSI model. The 802 committee currently is divided into several subcommittees:

802.1	Higher Layers and Management (HILI)
802.2	Logical Link Control
802.3	CSMA/CD Networks
802.4	Token Bus Networks
802.5	Token Ring Networks
802.6	Metropolitan Area Networks
802.7	Broadband Technical Advisory Group
802.8	Fiber Optic Technical Advisory Group
802.9	Integrated Data and Voice Networks

802.1 and 802.2 standards

This section covers some of the issues related to the 802.1 and 802.2 subcommittees because their work is basic to any understanding of how a local area network functions. Because the committees developing the OSI model and the IEEE committees worked together closely, you see that these IEEE 802 standards use the same terminology. The OSI material you just read will make it easier for you to understand these LAN standards. The IEEE 802 standards shown in this section will provide a foundation for later discussions of how bridges and gateways function.

The 802.1 high-level interface for LANs

The IEEE 802.1 committee is responsible for developing standards for bridges. The committee has adopted a Spanning Tree standard, which is the method that DEC has used for its Ethernet bridges. Another subcommittee (802.1D) is looking at the possibility of adding IBM's approach to bridging (Source Routing) as a standard. Chapter 7 looks at these various approaches to bridging.

While an army might travel on its stomach, an international standards organization travels on the seat of its pants with committees breaking into subcommittees. One 802.1 subcommittee (802.1A) is responsible for providing a network management architecture consistent with the OSI model. Still another subcommittee (802.1B) is developing network management protocols. Network management protocols are covered in chapter 12, where I compare and contrast them with current network management approaches.

The 802.2 Logical Link Control and Medium Access Control sublayers

The IEEE 802.2 subcommittee had to define a number of LAN functions. The layer above the Physical layer corresponding to the OSI model's Data Link layer was to be responsible for such key functions as assembling data into a frame with address and error-detection fields and, at the receiving end of a communications link, disassembling the frame, recognizing the address and detecting any transmission errors. The subcommittee divided the second layer into two sublayers, called the Logical Link Control (LLC) and Medium Access Control (MAC), based on specific functions performed. The LLC is independent of a specific access method while the MAC is protocol specific. The result of this split makes it much easier for network designers to provide more flexible local area networks.

The IEEE 802.2 standard does provide for both connectionless and connection-oriented services. Connectionless service is the norm in a local area network because of the high rate of speed and reliability. Type 1 LANs under this standard do not use the Logical Link Control layer to provide for error checking, flow control, or error recovery. Instead, they use the appropriate protocols found under the Transport layer of their network operating system software.

A Type 2 connection-oriented service is also offered under the LLC standard. This service does provide acknowledgements (ACKs) for error checking as well as flow control and error recovery.

The Logical Link Control sublayer   The primary purpose of the LLC sublayer is to enable network users to exchange data across the transmission channel controlled by the MAU. Connection-oriented LLC service contains primitives to control the establishment of a connection, the transfer of data, and the termination of a connection. Connectionless service, on the other hand, does not provide any error checking or acknowledgement that data arrived safely; usually it relies on Transport layer services for this task.

An LLC frame as illustrated in Fig. 3-3 includes both a source and a destination address as well as control information. The commands exchanged by the corresponding LLCs on the two computers that establish communications with each have a control field one byte in length. These eight bits can provide commands for connection, disconnection, acknowledgement, and rejection of frames. With a connection-oriented service, the LLCs send sequence numbers so that frames can be reassembled in the proper order. Each LLC maintains a send counter and a receive counter to keep track of frames sent and received and check for errors.

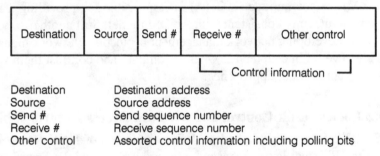

Destination	Source	Send #	Receive #	Other control

Destination   Destination address
Source   Source address
Send #   Send sequence number
Receive #   Receive sequence number
Other control   Assorted control information including polling bits

3-3   The LLC frame.

Figure 3-4 illustrates how the LLC sublayers are involved in any communication between workstations under the IEEE 802 scheme. An application process on Computer A wishes to communicate with an application process running on Computer B. When this information reaches the Network layer on Computer A, it is

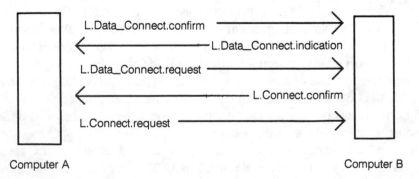

3-4   Looking more closely at how the LLC sublayers communicate.

converted into an L_CONNECT.request which is given to the LLC sublayer. The LLC sublayer passes on this request to Computer B. Assuming that the connection is acceptable, the Network layer on Computer B issues an L_CONNECT.confirm which ultimately reaches the Network layer on Computer A.

Once communication is established, the two computers can exchange data using L-DATA_CONNECT. request, indication, and confirm primitives. When they are finished communicating, they can use the appropriate requests, indications, and confirm primitives associated with L_DISCONNECT.

The Medium Access Control sublayer The Medium Access Control (MAC) sublayer defines how different stations can access the transmission medium. The LLC frames are non-hardware specific. It is the MAC that must ensure that it provides information in the appropriate form for a bus, token bus, or token ring network.

The OSI model Data Link layer functions of addressing (both source and destination), error detection, and framing also take place at this level.

The Physical layer

The Physical layer of the OSI model is the least controversial because it contains international hardware standards that have become commonplace. In fact, one real issue concerning this layer is how the ISO will handle emerging new hardware standards. As transmission methods become faster and new interfaces develop with additional error checking functions, will these standards be added to the OSI model or will the Physical layer remain static? At this point, the jury is still out, and it is impossible to predict the ISO's response.

The Physical layer spells out in great detail what kinds of pluggable connectors are acceptable. It lists, for example, 25-pin connectors for RS-232-C interfaces, 34-pin connectors for CCITT V.35 wide band modems, and 15-pin connectors for public data network interfaces found in CCITT Recommendations X.20, X.21, X.22, etc. It also spells out what electrical characteristics are acceptable including RS-232-C, RS-449, RS-410, and CCITT V.35.

The Physical layer is able to handle both the asynchronous (serial) transmission utilized by many PCs and by some low-cost LANs and the synchronous transmission utilized by some mainframe computers and minicomputers.

The Physical layer in LANs

Because the ISO and the IEEE subcommittees have worked together so closely for the past few years, it is not surprising that many LAN standards utilize the definitions provided at the Physical layer by the OSI model.

Various IEEE subcommittees have developed detailed descriptions regarding the actual physical equipment that transmits network information as electrical signals including specifics on the types of cabling, plugs and connectors to be used using the OSI model's Physical layer as its basis for description. The OSI model's Physical layer defines such key network components as the type of baseband coaxial cable required to achieve 10 megabit/second transmission speed. The layer incorporated an IEEE 802.3 definition for a thinner type of baseband coaxial cable for an approach known as Cheapernet. The IEEE 802.3 definition of a 10 megabit/second twisted pair baseband standard will also be added to this Physical layer.

Under the Physical layer's area of responsibility, you can also find definitions for the type of fiber-optic cabling and twisted pair cabling required for a wide range of LANs. Some networks such as IBM's Token Ring Network work with unshielded twisted pair while other types of networks might require shielded twisted pair. The subcommittee also has defined the various types of coaxial cabling required for a variety of broadband local area networks.

The Physical layer defined by the OSI model subcommittee also must specify the type of encoding scheme a computer must use to represent binary values for transmission over a communication channel. Ethernet as well as many other local area networks, utilize *Manchester encoding*. Using this approach, all network workstations are able to recognize that a negative voltage for the first half of the bit time followed by a positive voltage for the second half of the bit time represents the value 1 while a positive voltage followed by a transition to a negative voltage represents the value 0; therefore, a transition from negative to positive or from positive to negative occurs during every bit time.

You have seen that the Physical layer assumes responsibility for the type of physical media used, the type of transmission, and the encoding method and data rate associated with different types of local area networks. It is also responsible for establishing the physical connection between the two communications devices, generating the actual signal, and then making sure that the two devices are synchronized. The timing of the two units' clocks must be the same so that transmitted information can be decoded and understood. Figure 3-5 summarizes the key protocols we have been discussing associated with the lower four OSI layers. It is these layers that provide the connections that link heterogeneous LANs together. Notice particularly the redundancy built into the OSI model when it comes to connection-oriented and connectionless modes.

The Government OSI Profile (GOSIP)

August 15, 1990, is a significant date in computer history, especially if your favorite subject is protocol. As of this date, the U.S. government has made the *Government OSI Profile* (GOSIP) a mandatory requirement for networking procurements. GOSIP is a subset of the OSI model protocols as reflected in Fig. 3-6.

Transport layer	Transport Service Definition Connection-oriented Transport Protocol		
Network layer	Connectionless-mode network service		
Data Link layer	Logical Link Control Unknowledged connectionless service Connection-oriented service Acknowledged connectionless service		
Physical layer	CSMA/CD Baseband coax Broadband coax Unshielded twisted pair (1 mbs) 10BaseT (10 mbs)	Token-Bus Broadband coax Carrierband coax	Token Ring Shielded twisted pair Optical fiber

3-5 Protocols associated with the four lower layers of the OSI model.

Application layer	File Transfer Access & Management (FTAM) association control service element
Presentation layer	Message Handling Systems (MHS) X.400 Connection-oriented presentation protocol
Session layer	Connection-oriented session protocol
Transport layer	Connection-oriented transport protocol Class 4
Network layer	Connectionless network protocol X.25 Packet layer protocol
Data link layer	X.25 Packet layer protocol HDLC LLC
Physical layer	IEEE 802.3 Baseband/Broadband/10BaseT IEEE 802.4 Broadband IEEE 802.5 Shielded twisted pair

3-6 GOSIP protocols.

GOSIP is implemented in at least three different versions. The first version permits government computers to use the Application layer's electronic mail service (Message Handling Services X.400) and its file management service (File Transfer, Access & Management or FTAM), in addition to the IEEE Logical Link Control protocols for the popular bus, token bus, and token ring networks. Notice that GOSIP includes the X.25 Packet Layer protocol, which means that both wide area networks and local area networks will be able to communicate together. Notice also that both connection-oriented (the Transport layer) and connectionless (the Network layer) services are provided.

The second version of GOSIP is expected to add a protocol known as Office Document Architecture (ODA) above the Application layer. This protocol will enable software to manipulate the paragraphs, sections, chapters and pictures that comprise a document and treat each of these document components as a distinct object.

GOSIP's third version is expected to add X.500 global directory service, the importance of which you will see in chapter 12 when you look at electronic mail on a network. Other protocols on the drawing board for GOSIP include FDDI (a network discussed in chapter 5) and Electronic Data Interchange (EDI), a way to exchange documents and the contents therein electronically. Chapter 12 also looks at EDI.

NetBIOS networks and OSI

Remember the discussion of the NetBIOS and Microsoft's MS-NET in chapter 2? What about all the network applications found in local area networks today that are designed to make NetBIOS calls? Will it be necessary to replace all these programs in order to communicate with computers running OSI software? The MAP/ TOP Users Group (two standards discussed in chapter 4) have developed a specification known informally as "NetBIOS over OSI" and formally as "The NetBIOS Interface to ISO Transport Services and Name-Service Protocol."

The title is very imposing. This specification is really a recommended procedure for migrating to OSI. The specification provides a partial stack of OSI protocols so that software developers can write programs that link NetBIOS based programs and OSI applications more easily. This specification software provides the translation necessary for calls made to the NetBIOS and calls made to the OSI model's transport and network layer protocols.

One problem with this set of specifications is that it's not an official international standard. It is simply an interim solution until a company is ready to implement all OSI software.

OS/2 and the OSI model

Because the Medium Access Control (MAC) level is hardware specific, it is this OSI sublayer that programmers must address if they want network software to run with specific network interface cards and media. Microsoft and 3Com jointly developed the *Network Driver Interface Specifications* (NDIS) found in OS/2. This set of specifications provides an interface with a new set of interface specifications that frees higher level protocols running under OS/2 from any concern at all over the hardware on a network. Any network adapter card will work under NDIS assuming it contains NDIS-compliant drivers. This interface ensures that, for example, 3Com LAN software running under OS/2 can run on token ring networks as well as Ethernet networks. This new set of specifications frees higher level protocols such as those found in the Transport layer from any hardware specificity. Using this approach, protocols are written to the Medium Access Control layer interface specifications. This approach enables local area networks running under OS/2 to mix and match different hardware and different transport protocols.

IBM's OS/2 Extended Edition and OSI

IBM has announced that it will bring out an OS/2 Extended Edition version of its OSI/Communications Subsystem. The OSI/Communications Subsystem currently runs on IBM's mainframe computers. Until then, IBM's OSI/Communications Subsystem programming interface feature for Version 3, Release 3 of its Advanced Communications Facility/Virtual Telecommunications Access Method SNA software will have to do. Do not ask me to repeat this mouthful, but essentially it means that one IBM mainframe can act as a gateway to OSI networks. IBM's has indicated that it will migrate this communications subsystem to other IBM systems including its AS/400 minicomputers.

IBM has good reason for this approach. Customers who have "true blue" or all-IBM networks can continue to run IBM's own proprietary network protocols. Proprietary protocols tend to run more efficiently with less overhead because they are designed for specific hardware resources and because they do not have to carry the overhead associated with the redundancy built into the OSI model.

TCP/IP as today's internet protocol standard

Almost every computer industry expert predicts that the OSI suite of protocols will become the standard for internetwork connectivity *in the near future*, but what about today? The current de facto standard for internet connectivity is Transport Control Protocol/Internet Protocol, which is better known as TCP/IP.

TCP/IP was developed almost two decades ago at the request of the Department of Defense Advanced Research Projects Agency (ARPA) and is incorporated in the government network known as the Defense Data Network (DDN), which includes ARPANET and MILNET. It also serves the internet, a network of networks linking over 800 networks and 120,000 host computers. This chapter examines TCP/IP's various protocols, its advantages and disadvantages, and then looks at the issues associated with a company migrating from TCP/IP to compliance with OSI standards.

TCP/IP is a set of layered protocols just like the OSI model. As Fig. 3-7 illustrates, TCP and IP correspond roughly to the OSI's Transport and Network layers. Because TCP/IP is concerned primarily with transport and network services, it is not limited to specific hardware platforms. It is able to run over X.25, the Data Link protocol that comprises the bottom three layers of the OSI model and is commonly used for packet switching networks described in chapter 9.

Application Presentation Session	Simple Mail Transfer Program (SMTP) File Transfer Program (FTP) Telenet (terminal program)
Transport	TCP UDP
Network	IP ARP
Data Link	Ethernet

3-7 TCP/IP protocols and the OSI model.

TCP/IP began to grow in the private sector in 1982 when the UNIX 4.2 BSD operating system incorporated TCP/IP into its kernel (the very heart of the operating system). This married TCP/IP and UNIX, which made TCP/IP's protocols free and readily available to all UNIX networks. A second major event in 1982 for TCP/IP was the incorporation of the Address Resolution Protocol (ARP). ARP is very significant because it maps Ethernet to TCP/IP Internet addresses. Imagine the significance of these two events for the business community. A company running UNIX on its minicomputer networks and Ethernet on its LANs had a viable way of connecting the two worlds seamlessly.

More recently Sun Systems has also taken advantage of TCP/IP. It uses its own Network File System (NFS) protocol on its Sun workstations that dominate the workstation market. It uses TCP/IP in conjunction with NFS to provide internet communications. In fact, it is hard to find hardware or operating systems that do not have a TCP/IP implementation. Versions run on IBM Token Ring LANs as well as on Ethernet LANs, on Macintosh computers, and on DEC's VMS operating system.

Network services under TCP/IP

Notice in Fig. 3-7 that TCP/IP also provides network services through its Telnet, FTP, and SMTP applications. Its *Telnet* offers virtual terminal service. This means that TCP/IP provides a network standard terminal to which other terminals can be mapped. In effect, hosts can exchange information using a generic terminal mode, and then each host is responsible for mapping the generic terminal to the terminals at its location. The advantage of such an approach is that a network in Washington really does not need to know or care about what kind of terminals are running on the computer network in Los Angeles.

While the majority of terminals using Telnet select the full-duplex ASCII character code set, an EBCDIC mode is available for communicating with IBM mainframes and their terminals.

The File Transfer Protocol (FTP) is the TCP/IP service for file transfers. It enables two heterogeneous networks to exchange files in binary, ASCII, or EBCDIC format and permits unattended transfers, the most common mode of file transfer from remote sites. To effect a file transfer, a user would provide FTP commands indicating the TYPE of files (ASCII, EBCDIC, or image), the STRUCTURE of the file (important if files have a page structure), and MODE (sending data as a stream or sequence of bytes is one option while the block mode and compression mode comprise the two other choices).

The Simple Mail Transfer Protocol (SMTP) is the TCP/IP service for electronic mail. It is flexible enough to handle distribution lists as well as mail forwarding for computers not connected to the Internet using TCP/IP.

The OSI suite of protocols offer more advanced versions of these services (see chapter 12 for a look at network management). These TCP/IP services are so appealing for several reasons, though. They are virtually free. Equally important, they are found on tens of thousands of network nodes and work efficiently, if not spectacularly. They still represent the easiest "quick and dirty" way to provide file transfer, terminal emulation, and electronic mail services for linked heterogeneous networks.

Transmission Control Protocol (TCP)

The best way to see how TCP/IP works is to follow some data being sent from one computer network to another network using this suite of protocols. Transmission Control Protocol (TCP) corresponds roughly to the OSI's Transport layer, but TCP also contains some Session layer functions. TCP is responsible for establishing a session between two user processes on the network. It also is responsible for error recovery. It is primarily responsible for encapsulating information into a datagram structure, transmitting the datagrams, and keeping track of their progress. It handles the retransmission of lost datagrams and ensures reliability. Finally, on the destination computer receiving a message, TCP extracts the message from the datagram structure and forwards it on to the destination application program.

TCP will add a header containing its control information to any data coming from an application program to create a datagram. The Internet Protocol (IP) will add its own header containing its own instructions to the datagram. Finally, the local network will add its own local network control information in the form of its own header to the datagram. Figure 3-8 illustrates how a datagram includes three distinctly different headers, each of which contains different control information.

Ethernet header	IP header	TCP header	Data

3-8 A TCP/IP datagram with its three headers.

The Transmission Control Protocol (TCP) takes data it receives from an application program and encapsulates it into a datagram that includes its own header containing its control information. Figure 3-9 illustrates this datagram structure. The source and destination port fields represent the station calling the TCP and the station being called. The Sequence Number keeps track of the order of the datagrams to be received so that the data is received in the correct order. The Acknowledgement Number field indicates the next byte sequence that is expected.

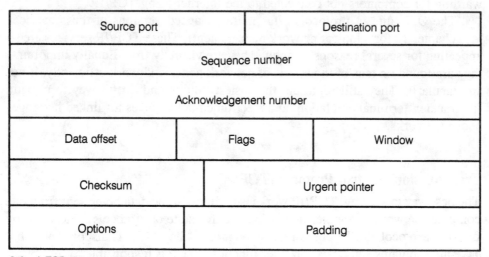

3-9 A TCP datagram structure.

The Data Offset field tells us the number of 32-bit words in the TCP header. Do not confuse the information in the header with the data field. The Flag section gets more technical than I want to at this point, but among the functions represented here are an indication of how urgent this particular datagram is as well as notice of a session's setting up or closing down.

The Window field indicates the number of octets of information the sender is willing to accept or receive. The Checksum field is a 16-bit number that indicates whether the datagram is received intact. The Urgent Pointer contains the number of octets from the beginning of the TCP segment to the first octet following any urgent data. The Options field can contain a variety of information, including the maximum TCP datagram size. Finally, the TCP header includes some zeroes to pad the datagram to the next multiple of 32 bits.

User Datagram Protocol (UDP)

Sometimes TCP is overkill. There are occasions when there is no need for the reliable transport services provided by this protocol. The TCP/IP suite of protocols also includes User Datagram Protocol (UDP), a protocol designed for applications which do not need the firepower of several datagrams sequenced together. You might want to think of TCP as Federal Express with its elaborate computerized tracking of packages and its promise of reliability. UDP is more like regular mail delivered by the U.S. Post Office. It is inexpensive in the sense that it does not require a lot of overhead, extra bits for all TCP's fields. It does not split large packages into smaller packages, and it does not keep track of what arrives safely and what needs to be resent.

The UDP header is shorter than TCP's, but it still includes a source and a destination address. It has a checksum field to check for errors, and that is about it. This protocol is used by other protocols that need to lookup something short such as a name from a name table.

The Internet Protocol (IP)

The Internet Protocol serves as the router for the datagrams. This protocol concerns itself with such issues as fragmentation of datagrams and internet addressing. Because different networks vary in the size of their packets, datagrams might have to be fragmented so they do not exceed maximum packet size. The IP provides the control information necessary to reassemble these fragmented datagrams.

A second major task of the Internet Protocol is internet and global addressing. Three different types of addressing schemes are available depending upon the size of the network to which the datagram will be routed. The best way to understand the IP is to examine its datagram structure.

Figure 3-10 illustrates an IP header. The Version field indicates which version of IP is being used and, therefore, the Internet header's format. The Internet header length field is its length in 32 bit words. The Type of Service field indicates the quality of service desired. The parameters for this field provide information on the datagram's precedence (importance), its intervals (will there be a steady stream of these datagrams at regular intervals in the future?), the level of reliability desired (are mistakes critical?), the importance of speed of delivery of this datagram, and an indication of the relative importance of speed versus reliability in the event of a conflict between the two.

Version	Internet header length	Type of service	Total length
Identification		Flags	Fragment offset
Time to live		Protocol	Header checksum
Source address			
Destination address			
Options		Padding	

3-10 An IP header.

The Quality of Service field is followed by the Total Length field, which is similar to the same field found in the TCP header. It represents the total length of the datagram including its IP header. The Identification field contains a unique number for identifying this particular datagram, while the Flags and Fragment Offset fields include information on whether a datagram is fragmented, whether more fragments are still coming, and the number of octets from the beginning of the datagram for specific fragment in 64 bit units.

The Time to Live (TTL) field record how long the datagram should be permitted to exist in the network. This number is decremented each time the datagram is processed along its journey through the network, and it is discarded when the number reaches zero. The maximum number permitted is 255 seconds; the point of having a TTL field is to preserve the resources of the network and avoid time delays due to a large number of undelivered datagrams.

The Protocol field following the TTL field indicates which protocol follows the IP. If there is a TCP header, its number would be found in this field. The functions of the Header Checksum, Source Address, and Destination Address are self-explanatory, and they serve the same purposes as their counterparts in the TCP header, which you have seen already in the previous section. Finally, the Options field can contain information on such tasks as routing specifications.

The aging champion TCP/IP vs. the challenger OSI

You have seen the current leader in internet connectivity (TCP/IP) as well as the OSI model that most experts predict will become the future leader. As a systems integrator, what do you do if your company needs to link disparate networks today? You have a UNIX-based minicomputer network in Los Angeles, a VAX

Ethernet network in Chicago, and a NetWare network running in Boston. Right now you can run TCP/IP protocols on all these networks. This means that you can have internet corporate electronic mail (SMTP) as well as file transfers between sites (FTP).

There are limitations to TCP/IP. Its mail program is very basic and lacks the bells and whistles of the OSI model's X.400 mail service. Its file transfer program also is much more limited than the OSI model's FTAM.

More significantly, it is ironic that TCP/IP is finally becoming an actual standard and not simply a de facto standard. A task force of the American National Standards Institute (ANSI) called the X3S3.3 Committee is moving toward official standardhood for this venerable suite of protocols. It is almost like honoring an actor with an Academy Award even though the actor's best work was several years ago. TCP/IP will not grow and evolve. As pointed out in the GOSIP section, emerging OSI standards will provide support for Electronic Data Interchange as well as sophisticated network management functions. A company that knows it will need these features in the future, will need OSI protocols.

Strategies for moving toward OSI

OK. Your company bit the bullet and implemented TCP/IP a couple of years ago because you could not wait for OSI to develop fully and for software publishers to start releasing OSI software. Your job is on the line now because your boss keeps reading about the OSI model and how antiquated TCP/IP is. What kinds of plans can you develop to show him or her that you have considered the need ultimately to move to OSI and have come up with viable alternatives to simply scrapping what you have and starting over?

The gateway approach

One solution to linking TCP/IP and OSI is to use a *gateway*. A gateway is much too sluggish for real time network applications, but it can prove adequate for mail service as well as other store-and-forward applications. Gateways are not good for large file transfers or other activities that result in traffic jams and backups. Many companies might opt for this approach because their primary network communications for the foreseeable future will be over TCP/IP with just occasional communications needed with OSI networks.

Several companies have been working on creating TCP/IP to OSI gateways, including Retix, Wollongong, and Touch. Currently you can purchase FTAM to FTP and X.400 to SMTP Application layer gateways.

The dual protocol stacks approach

A similar approach to bridge the TCP/IP to OSI gap is the *dual protocol stack*. Using this approach, each machine on a network has an OSI protocol stack and a

TCP/IP protocol stack. In effect, you have two completely different networks running over the same cabling. This approach offered by several software companies, including Wollongong and Touch, is illustrated in Fig. 3-11.

TCP/IP computer	Computer with Dual Protocol Stack		OSI computer
TCP/IP application	TCP/IP application	OSI application	OSI application
TCP/IP transport	TCP/IP transport	OSI transport	OSI transport
Physical layers	Physical layers		Physical layers

Network

3-11 A dual protocol stack.

Companies have chosen this approach because it is "quick and dirty" to implement and simplify technology. Drawbacks include the extra memory and processing power used. The State of Minnesota is an example where this approach is being implemented.

A third way to bridge the gap between TCP/IP and OSI is to use a Transport-service bridge. This type of bridge, already offered by the Wollongong Group and Retix, allows you to run OSI applications over TCP/IP networks by acting like a router. It routes the OSI protocol data units by packaging them so they emulate TCP/IP. The RFC1006 standard is part of the OSI model's suite of protocols and is defined under the International Standards Organization Development Environment (ISODE).

A major advantage of using the Transport-service bridge is that a dual protocol stack is only required for the first three layers. Networks can take advantage of their existing TCP/IP network links while adding OSI's upper layers and their functionality. The price you pay for this approach is a loss in the reliability that the Transport layer normally provides. Because you are routing data by repackaging it to emulate a different protocol and not actually translating from one protocol to another, you wind up with a TCP checksum at one end and an OSI TP4 checksum at the other end. Because the two checksums are not compatible, it is impossible to use this normal error checking tool.

Xerox Network Systems (XNS) suite of protocols

A decade ago, when micros were just starting to emerge as serious business machines, two roads diverged in the network woods. The government and universities, both of which were havens for mainframes and minicomputers, embraced TCP/IP's suite of protocols. The LAN industry leaders at that time (3Com, Novell, and Ungermann-Bass) all embraced a suite of protocols called *Xerox Network Systems* (XNS). In more recent times, Banyan Systems has used XNS protocols as part of its VINES network operating system.

LAN manufacturers opted for XNS rather than TCP/IP for a number of reasons. The major reason was that XNS was designed specifically for the needs of a LAN. It cut overhead (compared to TCP/IP) by reducing the amount of error checking required by upper-level protocols. The greater reliability of LANs compared to internet communications meant that they could get away with this tradeoff.

Xerox never did develop conformance tests for its XNS. Because the LAN industry developed during a time when every manufacturer was striving for the best proprietary hardware and software system, the lack of a standard XNS did not seem to be much of a problem at that time. After all, Novell, 3Com and Ungermann-Bass were selling essentially closed systems at the time. No one reasonably expected to link together LANs running different protocol suites.

It is worth spending a few moments with XNS, though, because several of its protocols are still used (albeit significantly modified in the case of NetWare). XNS uses a layered approach for grouping its protocols according to function that became the basis of the OSI model. Figure 3-12 illustrates how XNS compares to the OSI model.

OSI model	XNS
Application	Clearinghouse Gap
Presentation	Courier
Session	Courier
Transport	SPP RIP PEP
Network	IDP
Data link	Ethernet RS-232 RS-449
Physical	Ethernet RS-232 RS-449

3-12 XNS and the OSI model.

Each of XNS's layers provides services to the next higher level. Its top layer (layer 4) corresponds to the OSI model's Application layer. It contains application protocols implemented for specific platforms. The Clearinghouse service, for example, is an application-level directory service that links the names and aliases of users to the corresponding network and data link addresses. An Authentication service in this level allows specific users to access specific resources while barring others; unfortunately, given the different implementations of XNS, these protocols lack the universality of the OSI model's X.400 and X.500 protocols (see chapter 12 to examine these emerging standards in great detail). The Courier layer provides services similar to OSI's Session and Presentation layers.

Because XNS was developed specifically for LANs, its major emphasis is on the Network and Transport layers. At the Network layer, XNS uses an Internet Datagram Protocol (IDP) that specifies a maximum packet size of 576 bytes; various proprietary XNS versions use an IDP that specifies a different-sized packet, which illustrates the difficulties in linking these network "cousins" together. For its NetWare product, for example, Novell has taken IDP and modified it to create its Internet Packet Exchange (lPX) protocol, which is no longer compatible with IDP.

The very heart of XNS is its suite of Transport layer protocols for routing packets across the network. Because routing packets is the primary job of a LAN, take a look at how XNS (and 3Com's LANs that use it) handles routing. I also touch on some ways that Novell has taken XNS and modified its protocols to enhance performance. Chapter 8 returns to this topic when you look at several other types of routing approaches and devices that function specifically as routers to link together networks using different protocols.

A look at XNS in action

XNS's key transport protocols include Routing Information Protocol (RIP), Sequenced Packet Protocol (SPP), and Packet Exchange Protocol (PEP). The closest analogy I can give you to describe how XNS routs a datagram from one network to another is the way a tourist finds a specific address in Tokyo.

Because of the haphazard addressing scheme found in Tokyo where buildings are given addresses based on when they were built rather than their physical location on a block, the normal way to locate a specific building is to go from police station to police station and inquire. Each police box handles a specific neighborhood. The officer then provides you with specific directions to the next police box that is closer to your target. Finally, you arrive at the police box for the appropriate neighborhood where you receive directions to the actual building.

Now let me show you the similarities in the way that XNS and its RIP protocol handles the transport of a datagram from one network to another. The source node where the packet originates checks a table to determine the internet address of the destination node. It might also broadcast a request across the network requesting this information ("Does anyone know where Bill Taylor lives?").

If the destination address is on the same network, the process is very simple. IDP adds its header to the packet containing the data and address and passes the information down to layer 0 (equivalent to OSI's Data Link layer) for delivery.

Assume, though, that you are sending a packet from one network to another. IDP takes the packet and places its network router's address on it. This router workstation keeps detailed address tables using RIP protocol. The router looks at these tables and determines the best route for the packet. It then places the address of the next router on that route (removing its own address in the process) and sends the packet along its way.

This process continues as many "hops" as necessary until the router on the network containing the destination node receives the packet. It forwards this packet directly to the appropriate destination workstation.

XNS routers "listen" to network traffic and update their routing tables every thirty seconds. If a router cannot get information to a specific LAN, all other routers try and ultimately might fail before there is general agreement that a LAN is not capable of responding. RIP stipulates that each router broadcast its address information to all LANs including the LANs from which it received the information.

Vendors such as Novell have modified their versions of RIP to make the protocol more efficient. NetWare broadcasts its routing information every sixty rather than thirty seconds which reduces some traffic. It also has increased the RIP packet size to include room for time-to-net information to keep packets from being discarded when they fail to complete their journey in the time that RIP normally allocates.

What happens under XNS if packets arrive out of sequence? The Sequenced Packet Protocol (SPP) ensures reliability above the simple datagram delivery of IDP by synchronizing sending and delivery using a full-duplex communication method. Because packets are numbered, packets that are lost or damaged can be requested and then retransmitted. NetWare has taken SPP and modified it to create its Sequential Packet Exchange (SPX) protocol.

3Com's Demand Protocol Architecture (DPA)

Different vendors offering LAN Manager have addressed multiple protocols in different ways. An example of LAN protocol management worth noting is 3Com's product known as *Demand Protocol Architecture* (DPA) that works in conjunction with their OS/2- based 3+ Open network operating system. DPA reduces network operating system memory needs by moving network transport protocols in and out of memory as needed. 3+ Open can use this approach to handle a number of different protocols including NetWare's IPX/SPX, TCP/IP, AppleTalk Filing Protocol (see chapter 6), NetBIOS (IBM's NetBIOS Extended User Interface or NetBEUI, DataLink Control (DLC), Xerox Network Systems (XNS), and 3Com's own NetBIOS Protocol (NBP). Earlier in this chapter, I indicated that protocol was a difficult subject, but probably was the key to understanding how LANs work. For better understanding, examine how 3Com's DPA handles what is becoming a very common situation—a network that must deal with several different protocols.

Figure 3-13 illustrates the status quo situation for a 3Com 3+ Open workstation under Demand Protocol Architecture (DPA). 3+ Open LAN Manager 1.1 supports NBP as its primary protocol for maximizing performance. It supports Xerox Network Systems (XNS) as its secondary protocol. DPA uses the client-server arrangement described in chapter 2. NetBIOS Protocol (NBP) serves as the primary client-server protocol for workgroup operations communicating between workstations and the network server.

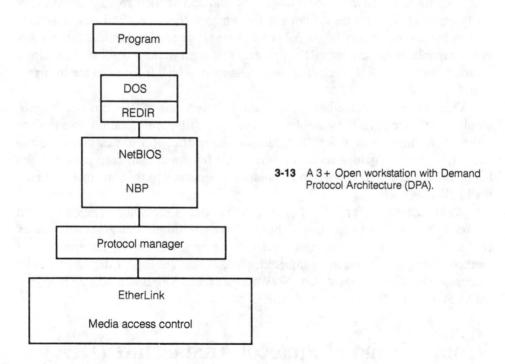

3-13 A 3+ Open workstation with Demand Protocol Architecture (DPA).

Workstations can load secondary, industry-standard protocols on demand when they are running protocol-specific applications. A Resident Protocol Manager (RPM) links and unlinks these secondary protocols. In Fig. 3-14, the workstation loads TCP/IP to perform a file transfer using FTP with a TCP/IP network.

Now, assume that the workstation needs to communicate with a NetWare server and use a program that resides there. As Fig. 3-15 reveals, the workstation would unload whatever secondary protocol it was running, and then load the NetWare IPX protocol and NET3 network shell software.

The NetWare shell intercepts an application call to DOS and recognizes that it is directed to a NetWare server. The IPX protocol is used to transport the request to 3+Open's Resident Protocol Manager (RPM). The Protocol Manager provides the communication between the network and hardware using its Network Device

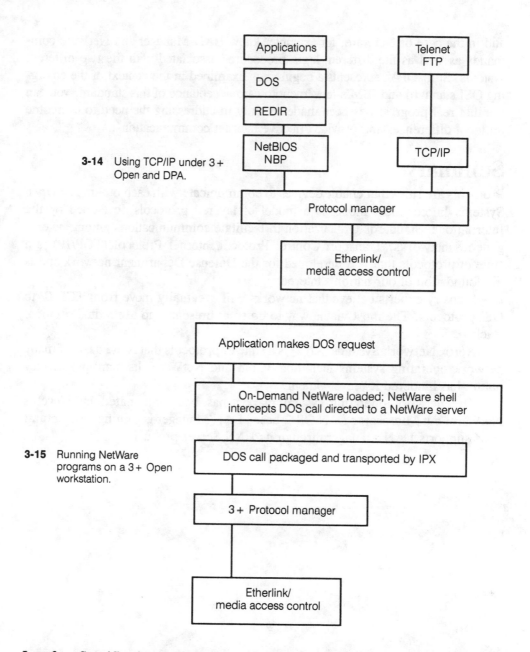

3-14 Using TCP/IP under 3 + Open and DPA.

Applications
DOS
REDIR
NetBIOS NBP
Telenet FTP
TCP/IP
Protocol manager
Etherlink/ media access control

3-15 Running NetWare programs on a 3 + Open workstation.

Application makes DOS request

On-Demand NetWare loaded; NetWare shell intercepts DOS call directed to a NetWare server

DOS call packaged and transported by IPX

3 + Protocol manager

Etherlink/ media access control

Interface Specification (NDIS) to ensure that the appropriate hardware driver is loaded when requested. Data flows to the Media Access Control layer (MAC) and then over physical cabling to the appropriate destination.

DPA does not solve all the problems associated with bridging the gap between different protocols, and it does not yet provide the seamless, transparent operation designed to shield end users from a need to understand protocols as well as different network operating systems. Administrators still must manage two distinct systems and in the case of NetWare, for example, know LAN Manager and NetWare commands as well as the different login procedures associated with the two different systems. Still, DPA represents a beginning. Examined in the context of the emerging OSI standard and IBM's movement toward acceptance of this standard, you can see that real progress has been made recently in addressing the need to overcome protocol differences and provide effective internet communications.

Summary

Protocols are rules that enable devices to communicate with each other. The Open Systems Interconnect model is a model of layered protocols developed by the International Standards Organization to facilitate communications among heterogeneous networks. Transport Control Protocol/Internet Protocol (TCP/IP) is a suite of protocols that was developed for the Defense Department network and is the foundation of our nation's internet.

Industry experts believe that networks will eventually move from TCP/IP to OSI protocols. The most viable way to do so at present is to use a dual protocol stack.

Xerox Network Systems (XNS) is a suite of protocols that is the basis of many network operating systems including 3Com and NetWare. Its semi-proprietary nature has hindered its development.

The network operating system market has been dominated by Novell's NetWare, but Microsoft's LAN OS/2-based LAN Manager is gaining momentum. IBM supports LAN Manager through its LAN Server product.

4
CHAPTER

Ethernet
and token bus

In this chapter, you will examine

- How Ethernet versions 1 and 2 evolved.
- How the IEEE 802.3 standard differs from Ethernet.
- Configurations for thick and thin Ethernet topologies as well as the new 10BaseT twisted pair 802.3 standard.
- How media access differs in 802.3 CSMA/CD from the token bus method used in 802.4 networks.
- What protocols are associated with the MAP standard for manufacturing and the TOP standard for engineering, accounting, and marketing functions that support a manufacturing site.

Ethernet

May 22, 1973, does not quite have the ring of July 4, 1776, but it is a significant day in network history. On that date, Robert Metcalfe wrote a memo at Xerox's Palo Alto Research Center and used the word *Ethernet* while explaining the principles behind this new type of local area network. That same year Xerox began producing Ethernet network interface cards for its Xerox Alto PC.

Intel provided the chips necessary for the network hardware, Xerox provided the software, and Digital Equipment Corporation was prepared to run this new network on its minicomputers. In September 1980, these three companies released a set of specifications for Ethernet that is now referred to as "Ethernet version 1." A second version of Ethernet ("Ethernet version 2") was released November 1982. Because both versions still are found in the field, it is important to know that significant differences exist between them. The line-idle state was changed from 0.7 volts idle in version 1 to zero volts idle in version 2. The interface coupling specifications of these two versions also differ. A controller designed for one version will not work with a transceiver designed for the other version.

Traditional Ethernet is associated with the version 1 specifications, which defined the network's physical medium (thick coaxial cabling), the network access control method (carrier-sense, multiple-access with collision detection (CSMA/CD), and the speed (10 megabits/second transmission). The set of specifications also described the size and contents of an Ethernet packet (72 bytes to 1526 bytes) as well as the method of encoding data (Manchester encoding). Shortly after this release of Ethernet specifications, the IEEE 802 committee began deliberations on the development of a set of international, non-proprietary standards for LANs. Given the industry prominence of the three major founders of Ethernet, it should come as no surprise that one standard, IEEE 802.3, is so close to Ethernet (version 2) that it often is described as the "Ethernet standard" even though there are differences that I discuss in this chapter.

Carrier Sense Multiple Access with Collision Detection (CSMA/CD)

The IEEE 802.3 committee developed a protocol virtually identical to Ethernet's for describing how multiple workstations can access a network when they need to transmit information. *Carrier Sense Multiple Access with Collision Detection* (CSMA/CD) dictates that a workstation wanting to use a network must first listen to the network to see if it is busy. If it does not detect any signals, it begins transmitting its message. This workstation continues to listen for possible network collisions while sending its message.

If a collision is detected, the sending workstation backs off and transmits a special *jam* signal to let network users know that a collision has taken place. The receiving station normally discards the contents of the partial message it has received, and all network workstations wait a certain randomly selected amount of time before any station begins transmitting again. Each network interface card has a different amount of time programmed for waiting. This time increases if a collision occurs the very next time the same message is transmitted.

Collisions are inevitable with an Ethernet or 802.3 network because of the very nature of CSMA/CD. There is a time interval between the time a workstation listens to see if any other workstation is using the network and the time it actually begins transmitting. It is entirely possible that a workstation further down the network has begun sending but that the signal has not yet reached this workstation. Because the IEEE 802.3 standard describes the same bus network topology used by Ethernet, on both networks each workstation broadcasts its message in both directions on the network. Figure 4-1 illustrates this method of transmission.

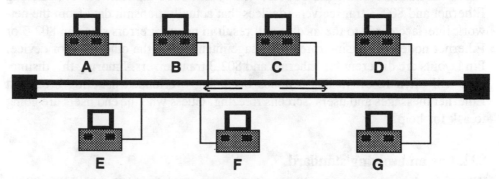

Workstation "F" sends a message to workstation A.
Notice that the message is transmitted in both directions.

4-1 An Ethernet or IEEE 802.3 network.

This Ethernet type standard describes a *contention* network, a type of network in which more than one workstation must contend or compete for use of the network. While collisions are inevitable given the network's architecture, the designers assume that the 10 megabit/second transmission speed ensures that even with repeated collisions, users will not experience any noticeable delay. When the number of collisions does cause noticeable delays in response time, it becomes a network management issue, a topic that is discussed in chapter 12.

The 802.3 and Ethernet frame format differences

Figure 4-2 displays the 802.3 frame format. The Preamble consists of 56 bits of alternating 1s and 0s which provides a method for two networks to synchronize. The Start Frame Delimiter (10101011) signifies the beginning of a frame of information. The Destination and Source fields come from the LLC frame. The Length field indicates the length of the information field that follows it. Data can range from 46 to 1500 octets in length. The Information field is followed by a Pad field that ensures that the frame meets the minimum 802.3 length standards. Finally, a Frame Check Sequence field provides information for error checking.

Preamble	Destination address	Source address	Length	Data	Frame check sequence

4-2 The 802.3 frame format.

The major difference between the 802.3 frame and the traditional Ethernet frame is that Ethernet does not have a two-byte length field because the length is fixed. Instead, it has a two-byte Protocol Type field that indicates which higher-layer protocol is used in the data field. Remember the discussion of protocol in chapter 3? You are likely to see some familiar names in this field. A value of hex 0800, for example, indicates TCP/IP, while a hex 0600 indicates XNS. Matching Ethernet and 802.3 transceivers (devices that actually transmit data from the network interface cards to the media) will result in network errors since an 802.3 or Ethernet node will misinterpret a message intended for the other type of device. Pin layouts are different for Ethernet and 802.3 transceivers. Ignoring this distinction will often result in 802.3 nodes becoming overloaded handling broadcast Ethernet messages and users' screens freezing. Guess who the end users are going to ask for help?

802.3 as an evolving standard

While standard Ethernet specifies only 50-ohm coaxial cabling, the IEEE 802.3 standard currently supports several different types of transmission including baseband and broadband coaxial cable and twisted pair wire. The cabling chosen varies according to the recommended maximum distance. A version known as StarLAN offered by a number of vendors including AT&T provides one megabit/second transmission speed over 500 meters (1Base5). Thick coaxial cable (50-ohm) has a 500 meter limit, so we refer to this 802.3 standard as 10Base5, meaning 10 megabits/second baseband coaxial cabling with a 500 meter limit. Thin coaxial cable can carry a signal 185 meters (*10Base2* or *Cheapernet*) while unshielded twisted pair (10BaseT) is recommended up to 100 meters.

The older StarLAN 802.3 specification for a 1 megabit/second network with a 500 meter maximum length is known as 1Base5. We briefly examined 10BaseT in chapter 1, but we'll return to this topic shortly. Because the IEEE 802 subcommittees continue to meet as new technology develops, the standards continue to evolve. Since the 802 standards utilize a layered set of protocols very similar to the OSI model, it is possible to add to the MAC layer without having to change anything in the LLC layer.

A closer look at an Ethernet network

Before you look at some variations, examine the components comprising the traditional Ethernet or 802.3 LAN; just as the Colt 45 became known as the gun that won the West, Ethernet is the LAN that made local area networks respectable to corporate managers. They could install it and depend on it without worrying about being fired for buying fringe technology.

An Ethernet workstation contains an Ethernet-specific network interface card (NIC) which has its own intelligence. This NIC is responsible for handling collision management and encoding and decoding signals. With thin coaxial cabling a transceiver is part of this NIC as illustrated in Fig. 4-3, while transceivers are external on thick coax networks. The terminators complete the segment's electrical circuit.

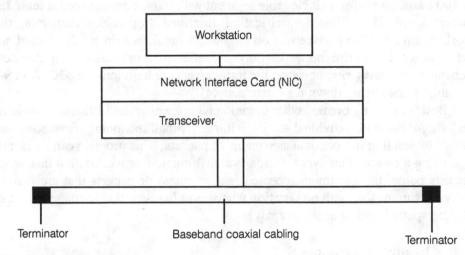

4-3 Ethernet architecture.

A single segment can hold a maximum of 100 workstations, and multiple segments can be linked by repeaters. Up to 1024 workstations can exist on a single Ethernet network with a maximum of two repeaters in the path between any two stations.

The transceiver actually generates the electrical signals to the coaxial cabling and maintains their quality. Conversely, transceivers also have responsibility for receiving network signals. They are responsible for detecting packet collisions. When a transceiver on the transmit side detects a collision, its NIC link management function turns on a collision detect signal. The transmit side of link management in turn transmits a bit sequence known as a *jam*. This jam signal causes transmitting workstations to terminate their transmission and their NICs randomly schedule their retransmission. Meanwhile NICs on receiving workstations have been examining damaged packets, noting their fragmentary size, and discarding these *runts*.

Ethernet transceivers internally generate a signal known as a *signal quality error* (SQE) which is often referred to as a "heartbeat." This heartbeat is read by the NIC to ensure that the transceiver is working properly, sort of like having your spouse say "uh-huh" every couple of minutes so you know he or she is alive and listening to your story. Unfortunately, the heartbeats for 802.3 and Ethernet transceivers use different timing. Some manufacturers provide transceivers that can be manually set for one standard or another.

Because Ethernet broadcasts in all directions, it has cable length limitations as discussed earlier in this chapter. Original Ethernet with its thick coaxial cabling permitted one 500 meter segment with a maximum of three segments joined together by repeaters that rebroadcast the packets on the network.

Other limitations for 10Base5 due to signaling limitations include a maximum of 100 transceivers for a single cable segment with transceivers spaced at least 2.5 meters apart. The 10Base5 specification described drop cables connecting the workstation's NIC to transceivers on the bus. A break in a drop cable would not bring down the entire network, only the affected workstation. On the new "cheapernet" networks, however, the transceivers are built into the NIC. A break in cabling does bring down the entire network.

Besides cabling breaks, other common equipment-related Ethernet problems include *jabber* and individual station failures. A malfunctioning transceiver can jabber by sending out continuous streams of packets. This problem can be identified using a protocol analyzer. Similarly a malfunctioning workstation that sends packets below the minimum accepted length (runts) or packets that are continually maximum size with no variation whatsoever (causing traffic congestion) can also be spotted with a protocol analyzer.

A bus by any other name...

As you saw earlier in this chapter, Ethernet and 802.3 are bus networks. The bus is a data highway that is laid in straight sections known as segments. Segments can be linked together, and repeaters can be used to extend a network's size.

The StarLAN topology and that of the new 10BaseT is a distributed star. Physically, as seen in Fig. 4-4, such networks have workstation cabling radiating from concentrators in a star-like arrangement. Logically, though, they still operate as bus networks.

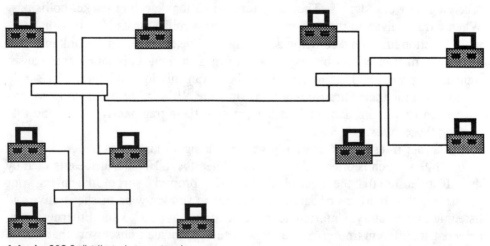

4-4 An 802.3 distributed star network.

Sometimes known as *passive stars*, these networks enjoy the benefits of a star-like architecture because it is possible to maintain better network management and control. *Bypass circuitry* means that if one workstation fails, it can be bypassed by other workstations in that star by the concentrator or multiport transceiver from which the workstations' cables radiate.

10BaseT

While you briefly looked at the new IEEE 802.3 10BaseT standard for Ethernet running on unshielded twisted pair wire, this is a good spot to summarize the major specifications that make this product so appealing to systems integrators. Synoptics Communications was the first company to release an Ethernet product running 10 Mbs over unshielded twisted pair in 1987. It was followed by several other companies including David Systems, Hewlett-Packard, 3Com, and DEC. Unfortunately, each company had its own proprietary set of specifications that were incompatible with other companies' offerings. Large companies were reluctant to invest heavily in a small company's proprietary technology, because it very well might lead to a dead end should the small company fail. The 802.3 committee ameliorated these fears with its 10BaseT standard.

10BaseT has a 100 meter maximum segment length, a link integrity test specification discussed in chapter 1, and the ability to disconnect a segment if there is a failure without bringing down the entire network.

A 10BaseT description of the Media Access Unit (MAU) indicates several new features not found in other 802.3 specifications. It has a jabber function that disables the MAU if it transmits after an allowable maximum time period. After being "gagged" for a period of time, the MAU will enable itself and try talking to the network once again. A workstation signal quality error (SQE) test discussed in chapter 1 monitors the health of each MAU and ensures that workstations are able to participate as receivers and sends of network packets. Repeaters under 10BaseT are able to disconnect a malfunctioning MAU without disconnecting all other workstations from using the network. When the failure is corrected, the specified port that has been taken out of service is reconnected to the network.

Still another useful 10BaseT feature is "intelligent squelch." This means that 10BaseT is able to function in an environment with a wide range of conflicting signals including voice traffic, the new Integrated Services Digital Network (ISDN) traffic, and asynchronous data traffic. Like a mother who is able to pick out her baby's cry even in a crowded room full of crying babies, intelligent squelch filters out other signals so that the Ethernet signals can be detected.

Another problem that 10BaseT was forced to address is the distortion that results to a signal as it travels over the twisted pair wire. This problem long prevented high speed Ethernet traffic over this medium. A pre-equalization technique is used in which the signal is distorted before it travels to compensate for the distortion that will take place during transmission. The signal reaches its destination in very much the same form as it began before its initial distortion.

The major advantages of 10BaseT is that so much unshielded twisted pair wire is already installed and that installation is easier and connections more reliable than the coaxial cable version of Ethernet. One large aerospace company recently linked 500 workstations on 10BaseT; it reported less downtime and easier installation than coaxial connections.

Having extolled all the virtues of 10BaseT, it is time for a friendly word of warning for the systems integrator who becomes a bit too optimistic about this "easy-to-work-with" medium. Buildings that appear to have lots of extra un shielded twisted pair can have poor assignment records so that it is almost impossible to trace back all pair. Pairs tied together somewhere inside the building might have bridge taps. Some loops might hang in air, roads that lead nowhere. Conduits might be blocked, and pairs broken or poorly spliced together. Some systems integrators who are on the "bleeding edge" of this new technology have reported having to pull new twisted pair where often it initially did not seem necessary.

Ethernet on optic-fiber cable

It is possible to use optic-fiber cabling on an 802.3 network. The major advantages of this approach are the immunity to any kind of electrical interference and the distance you can cover. The fiber-optic links can be up to 4.5 Km in length. Codenoll, one of the leading vendors in this market, points to its installation of the world's largest fiber-optic network, the 1.5 million square foot, 44-story network with over 3000 stations on 92 miles of fiber at Southwestern Bell's headquarters in St. Louis, Missouri.

Each network workstation must have an NIC designed for 802.3 transmission over an optic-fiber network. Codenoll offers an external transceiver alternative. In any event, the transmitters in these products convert electrical signals to pulses of light while the receivers convert the lightwave signals back into electrical signals.

An optical bus star coupler sends optical signals to each station on a network. They are the equivalent of the concentrator or hubs you saw on the 10BaseT standard. Repeaters extend distances; they also permit *cascading stars* by connecting together different optic star couplers. Using Codenoll's products as an example, these couplers are available in coax-to-fiber, fiber-to-fiber, and coax-to-coax models. The actual fiber cables come with connectors pre-attached and replace coaxial cable and twisted pair wiring. Codenoll uses 3Com's MultiConnect multiport Ethernet repeaters which we looked at in chapter 1. Figure 4-5 illustrates an optic-fiber Ethernet network.

Using optic-fiber backbones to link Ethernet networks

One popular use of optic fiber is as a backbone from which radiate concentrators and their networked workstations. Figure 4-6 illustrates how Novell in 1988 used

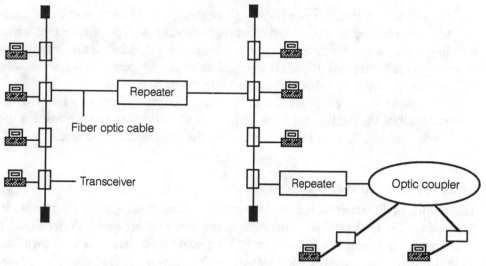

4-5 An optic fiber Ethernet network.

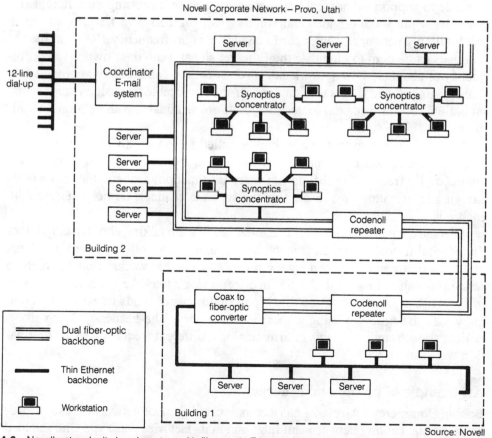

Novell Corporate Network – Provo, Utah

4-6 Novell networks its headquarters with fiber optic Ethernet backbones. *InfoWorld, June 27, 1988.*

this concept to link together two buildings. Building 1 at Novell's corporate head-quarters was running a version of Arcnet (see chapter 6 for specific details) while Building 2 was wired for Ethernet over twisted pair wire. Because this installation occurred well before any 10BaseT standard had been adopted, Novell went with the leading twisted pair Ethernet vendor at the time, Synoptics.

Notice that the Arcnet network in Building 1 contains a coax to Fiber-Optic converter. Once the packets are in optic form, a fiber-optic repeater transmits the packets to Building 2 where they travel along the fiber-optic backbone.

Ethernet on broadband coaxial cable

The ability of Ethernet to run on broadband coaxial cabling is fairly recent. In September 1985, the IEEE standards board met and approved *10Broad36*, a broadband coaxial cable version of an 802.3 network that transmits at 10 megabit/second broadband coaxial cable standard with a maximum cable length of 3600 meters. What makes 10Broad36 so appealing to many companies is that it is now possible to support other local area networks such as token-ring on different frequencies while sending video and voice signals on their own frequencies. Each workstation's network adapter card contains a radio frequency (RF) transceiver that uses its modem to modulate the Ethernet signals onto their own network frequency or channel. This network can cover a distance consisting of approximately 4 miles. Broadband LANs use standard off-the-shelf cable television components, including a 75-ohm coaxial cable. Endpoints are terminated with a 75-ohm terminator.

Broadband networks use a technique called frequency division multiplexing to send information over channels, each of which has a designated frequency. Guardbands, frequencies that do not carry information, separate the frequencies carrying information and ensure that the separate channels do not interfere with each other.

Because we are talking about frequencies, we are talking about analog rather than digital transmission. Broadband networks use modems to convert data back and forth between digital and analog form. Assume that workstation 44 wants to send information to workstation 66. In effect, using a tree-like structure illustrated in Fig. 4-7, workstation 44 on this broadband network sends its packet to a unit known as the *headend* using a specified frequency. The headend, acting like a radio station, retransmits this information on a different frequency to the destination workstation 66.

An example of broadband Ethernet

Boeing Commercial Airplanes has a complex multivendor network. It uses broadband coaxial cabling between buildings and in its factories and Type One shielded

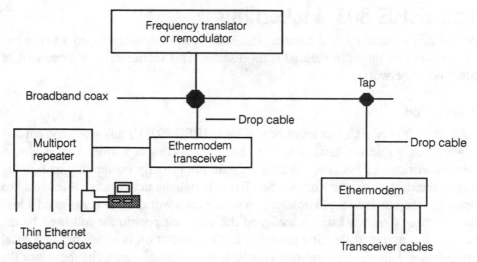

4-7 A broadband Ethernet network.

twisted pair wiring within buildings to connect workstations using Synoptics' LattisNet version of Ethernet. The broadband cabling is divided into several forward and reverse 6 MHz channels with guard bands separating them.

Networked Apple Macintosh computers are linked to the broadband Ethernet network over a Kinetics gateway, which has a link into the Synoptics LattisNet concentrator. An Ethernet drop cable runs from the Fastpath gateway to a LattisNet transceiver and then to a spare port on the LattisNet concentrator. I will defer specific details about how the Macintosh computers are networked to chapter 6, which will cover this topic in depth.

Chapter 11 examines gateways to the mainframe world, but note that gateways can link the Ethernet network to IBM mainframes as well as DEC computers. TCP/IP plays an important role in this network. It provides a common denominator, a common set of higher level protocols for the DEC VAX, IBM hosts, Macintosh computers, and PCs running on Ethernet to share.

Why use Ethernet or 802.3

Contrary to what you might hear from IBM, the entire world is not rushing to adopt its Token Ring Network. Ethernet has several advantages. As the most mature network technology, it has the broadest vendor support and the largest installed base, which translates for the systems integrator into significant cost savings. Its media flexibility means that it is possible to mix and match different media (coax, twisted pair, fiber optic, etc.) as needed, which lowers costs still further. The new 10BaseT standard ensures that Ethernet will be around for quite awhile longer because its value/price ratio is so favorable.

The IEEE 802.4 token bus

Not all bus networks are the same. The 802.4 committee developed a token bus arrangement based on broadband transmission. This section takes a close look at this type of network.

Description

IEEE 802.4 specifies a bus network similar to IEEE 802.3's bus topology, but one in which only one workstation tries to use the network at a time. This is a *non-contention* network because workstations are not actually contending or fighting among themselves for network access. Even though the network is cabled in a bus topology, the bus forms a logical ring in which each workstation is assigned a logical position. The workstation assigned the very last position is followed by the workstation assigned the first position. Each workstation is aware of the logical workstation following it and proceeding it. Interestingly enough, these are the only two addresses a workstation really knows. When you think of it, it is much the same approach used by espionage rings that are organized into groups of three. By knowing which workstation hands it the token and by also knowing which workstation receives the token from it, a workstation is able to identify a network breakdown (where is my token?).

The concept of a token is worth taking a moment to explain. Imagine, if you will, a campfire around which several Indians are sitting. A chief rises and raises a carved piece of wood that stands as a symbol of his authority, his right to speak. All the other speakers fall silent as he begins. When he finishes, he simply passes his symbol of authority to the next brave who then rises to speak. A control packet with a certain bit pattern known as a *token* operates in much the same way. Only the workstation controlling the token has permission to speak, and all other workstations must wait their turn to control this packet.

A workstation with the token has it for a specified period of time during which it may transmit one or more frames of information and poll other stations for their responses. A workstation that has very important network functions can be assigned additional time frames in a table that allocates this. There are actually four different priorities of access with the highest level (level 6) receiving the maximum amount of network bandwidth for its highest priority transmissions. Data can be classified into levels 6, 4, 2, and 0 priorities. After a workstation has broadcast its level 6 data and no other workstation has level 6 data to broadcast, the workstation may broadcast its level 4 data. The same principle holds for broadcasting level 2 data or even level 0 data. Each workstation controlling the token also has a responsibility to permit new workstations to join the logical ring. During its time period with the token, a workstation issues a solicit-successor frame. A *solicit-successor frame* is an invitation for a workstation to join the network at a location between itself and the next node in the logical ring. If there is no response to this invitation, the token controlling workstation passes the packet to the next workstation in its logical ring. If a workstation does request entrance, then the token is passed to it so that it can set all its parameters and linkages before the next workstation in the logical ring gets its chance.

As Fig. 4-8 illustrates, a workstation with the token broadcasts its message over the entire network. Only the workstation with a destination address matching that of the packet will copy the packet to its NIC and process it. If a workstation is inoperative, it will time out and the token will be passed to the next workstation. While Fig. 4-8 shows the token moving from higher addressed workstations to lower addressed workstations, they need not be adjacent to each other because you are looking at a logical bus and not a physical bus.

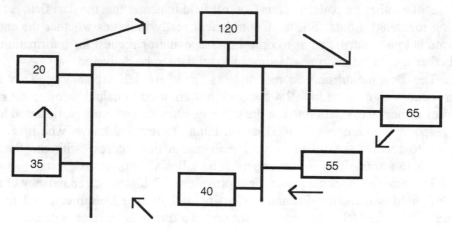

4-8 A token bus network.

IEEE 802.4 also specifies that its packets travel along a broadband medium consisting of 75 ohm CATV coaxial cable. This means that several different channels can be transmitting different types of information on different frequencies simultaneously. Broadband also offers a couple of other major advantages over the baseband cabling associated with Ethernet and the IEEE 802.3 standard. Taps can be placed anywhere on a broadband network while Ethernet's baseband standard usually requires a minimum distance of 2¹/₂ meters between nodes. In addition to broadband's less sensitivity to noise, it can stretch much further than baseband. With repeaters a broadband network can extend up to 25 miles. Depending upon the number of channels used, data rates between 1 Mbit/second and 10 Mbit/second are possible.

The 802.4 frame

Figure 4-9 illustrates the 802.4 frame; it is actually a bit more complicated than it looks. At first glance, it looks very similar to an 802.3 frame. The Preamble is a

Preamble	Start frame delimiter	Frame control	Destination address	Source address	Data	Frame check sequence	End frame delimiter

4-9 A token bus frame.

bit pattern that enables workstations to synchronize their signals. The Start Delimiter indicates the start of a frame. The Control field can indicate a number of different formats. It can function as a token, for example. A different bit pattern means that the frame is functioning as a "Who follows" frame. This is a request to other workstations to try to match the Source Address and reply which workstation should next receive the token.

Still another bit pattern in this Control field indicates that the data field is carrying meaningful data. So, the Control field really indicates whether the entire frame is to be interpreted as a control message and/or request for information or whether it is to be interpreted as meaningful data to be delivered.

The Destination and Source Address fields are self-explanatory. They are particularly significant in 802.4 because they are used to help determine the successor or next workstation to use the token in situations where a workstation fails to respond. Remember, the workstation failing to respond knows who it is supposed to receive the token from. It can match that address with the Source Address in a frame that is carrying a "Who follows?" control request.

The Frame Check Sequence field provides a 32-bit cyclic redundancy check on all fields except the Preamble, Starting and Ending Delimiters, and itself. Finally, the End Delimiter indicates the end of a frame. If an error is detected by a receiving workstation, it will set an error bit in this field to one that indicates that the source workstation needs to retransmit the frame.

Some advantages of a Token Bus network

One advantage of a Token Bus network is that each workstation is guaranteed a chance to access the network no matter how many workstations or how much traffic. When a station passes the token, it starts a timer that runs until the station is ready to pass the token again; in other words, the timer measures a complete rotation around the ring of the token. The workstation now looks to see if it has anything else to transmit using a system that prioritizes messages to ensure that the highest prioritized messages always are transmitted first.

Eventually a workstation's token time will exceed a maximum set by the network administrator. The workstation will then pass the token to the workstation it has listed as the next destination for token. Another advantage to Token Bus is its broadband media, which makes it less vulnerable to electrical interference and thus a better choice for factory communications.

Finally, the priority system on a Token Bus network ensures that highest priority messages will always be transmitted. A workstation must transmit its highest priority items (THT) before it is permitted to transmit its next level of priority (TR4).

Protocols to manage the factory and office

Several years ago, General Motors realized that it was facing an automation nightmare unless it took immediate action. Its factory floors were filled with different types of computerized tools including several kinds of robots; unfortunately, these various devices were unable to communicate with each other and unable to send information to other parts of the plant. The company began developing *Manufacturing Automation Protocol* (MAP), a suite of protocols based on the OSI model that would facilitate network communications with special provisions for a manufacturing environment.

Because a factory floor is vast, often well beyond the scope of baseband coaxial cabling, and because of the amount of potential electrical interference, a broadband token bus network seemed the logical LAN choice. GM worked closely with a powerful MAP users group to develop the protocols needed.

At approximately the same time that General Motors was wrestling with its automation nightmare, Boeing Computer Services set out to develop a suite of protocols to cover the office environment and address its very different needs. *Technical and Office Protocol* (TOP) was developed specifically for office services such as engineering, marketing, accounting, and administration that supported a manufacturing environment such as that found at Boeing. TOP is also a subset of the OSI model's set of protocols, but an 802.3 bus network was selected as its topology.

While 802.3 and 802.4 have different frames and different network access methods as discussed earlier in this chapter, they share the same Logical Link Control data link protocol. Because they share the same LLC, it is possible to build bridges connecting MAP and TOP with each other as well as with 802.5 networks. Both Ethernet versions 1 and 2 have a different LLC, which would have created a serious incompatibility issue.

Figures 4-10 and 4-11 reveal the protocols associated with MAP and TOP versions 3.0. Notice that both sets of protocols are identical from layers 2 through 7. The major difference, beside the 802.3 versus 802.4 split, was in the Application layer protocols. Because MAP and TOP have very different user needs, it is precisely in this layer that you would expect to see differences.

Because MAP was developed specifically to meet the needs of manufacturing, its Application layer contains Manufacturing Message Standard (MMS), an

Application Layer	Manufacturing Message Specifications File Transfer Access & Management (FTAM) X.500 Global Directory Network Management Agent Associated Services and Control Elements
Presentation Layer	Presentation
Session Layer	Basic Combined Subset
Transport Layer	Transport Class 4
Network Layer	Internet Protocol
Data Link Layer	802.2 Logical Link Control 802.4 Media Access Control
Physical Layer	10 Mbs 5 Mbs Broadband Carrier Band

4-10 MAP's set of protocols and the OSI model.

Application	X.400 X.500 FTAM Association Control Service Element
Presentation	OSI Presentation Protocol
Session	OSI Session Protocol
Transport	OSI Transport Protocol Class 4
Network	OSI Connectionless Network Protocol
Data Link	LLC Type 1
Physical	IEEE 802.3 IEEE 802.5

4-11 TOP's set of protocols.

OSI Application layer protocol designed for formatting and transmitting commands between controlling programs and machines. MAP 3.0's version includes the ability to support robots and other real-time control applications.

MAP contains the Association Control Service Element (ACSE) and Remote Operations Service Element (ROSE); these protocols enable MAP to start jobs on remote systems and bind them into communications with the parent application.

MAP Network management protocols gather information on the usage of the network media by network devices and ensure the correct operation of the network as well as provide reports.

TOP, on the other hand, places more emphasis on office automation needs. It uses the OSI X.400 standard for electronic mail, the emerging X.500 standard for global directories, and the VT protocol for terminal emulation. TOP also contains protocols for graphic data interchange and distributed transaction processing. MAP/TOP protocols are compatible with the Government OSI Profile (GOSIP).

The Corporation for Open Systems (COS) has a special program that certifies products that meet its standards for compatibility with OSI's protocol stack. It offers an integrated tool set that tests products for MAP/TOP 3.0 compliance.

While General Motors helped nurse MAP and Boeing developed TOP, both corporations have turned over leadership of these standards to a joint MAP/TOP Users group. Recently leadership has passed to a permanent independent organization called the Information Technology Requirements Council (IRTC).

MAP and TOP in action

A good example of MAP in action is General Motors' assembly plant in East Pontiac, Michigan. Robots provide 98% of all welds while a vision system measures 40 dimensions on each truck. Thirty-two miles of cabling support 2000 devices that can transmit data over a MAP network at 10 Mbs. What makes this plant so important in supporting the MAP cause is that in addition to the hundreds of different types of robots and process control machinery, the plant has a wide range of different vendor computer systems including IBM hosts and DEC VAXes. What makes communication possible and efficient is that all machinery share the same suite of MAP protocols.

The 1988 Enterprise Event and the freezing of MAP/TOP standards

In June 1988, a convention known as the Enterprise Networking Event took place at the Baltimore Convention Center. Vendors demonstrated real products running under MAP/TOP. The theme of this event was the Enterprise-wide network, a network that includes both the factory and the office. General Motors' demonstration featured two robots that worked in unison to assemble an enterprise product according to visitors' specifications. The booth also featured electronic mail applications and use of the MAP/TOP Network Manager and Directory Server protocols.

The point of this convention was to demonstrate products from multiple vendors that worked together because of their MAP/TOP compatibility. Boeing's booth featured eleven different vendors. Visitors entered personal information into a visitor tracking system that demonstrated order entry and bar code reading. The bar code was read and compared against the visitor's personal files to verify registration.

The Boeing booth also exhibited several aspects of the procurement process including creating a request to be sent to suppliers, selecting the suppliers, preparing and delivering the request electronically, receiving and evaluating the responses electronically, sending the order, and then finally receiving the order acknowledgement from the supplier. Figure 4-12 illustrates how this network was organized. The backbone ran TOP protocols over IEEE 802.3 baseband coaxial cabling. Notice that the OSI FTAM and VT protocols that TOP has incorporated for file management and terminal emulation were used.

Presently MAP implementations are growing much faster than TOP installations. Many vendors and potential customers were very disturbed when MAP was upgraded from version 2.1 to 3.0 because of the number of changes that were not upward compatible. Why spend money developing a product or implementing MAP protocols when the standard seems so unstable? The MAP/TOP group responded to this criticism at the Enterprise Event by announcing that MAP will not be changed for six years. This meant that companies count on a stable period extending to 1994. Many industry experts feel this announcement will spur additional MAP adoptions.

MAP and TOP in the future

If a recent meeting of the North American MAP/TOP Users Group is any indication, specifications for both these products will be broadened in the near future to include several OSI as well as other protocols. There appears to be a good deal of

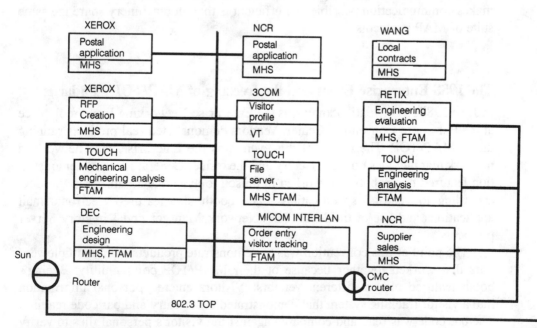

4-12 TOP's set of protocols.

support for an 802.4 fiber-optic version as well as a Fiber Distributed Data Interface (FDDI) and Integrated Services Digital Network (ISDN) versions.

DEC's loud pronouncements that 802.3 should be included under MAP has sparked controversy for the past couple of years. Because DEC is a major player in the factory automation market, it is not surprising that they have pushed so hard for this addition. Hewlett-Packard recently announced a MAP product that supports 802.3.

While General Motors has dropped its leadership role and let the users group administer MAP/TOP, a spokesman has announced the company would oppose 802.3's addition to MAP.

Summary

Ethernet was the first non-proprietary local area network, and it still commands the largest number of users. The IEEE 802.3 standard for a CSMA/CD contention bus network is similar to Ethernet, with some significant differences. 10BaseT is a new 802.3 standard for unshielded twisted pair transmission at 10 Mbs. 10Broad36 represents the broadband coaxial cable version of the 802.3 standard.

The 802.4 standard for a Token Bus network describes a non-contention network which is a physical bus but a logical ring. Manufacturing Automation Protocol (MAP) is based on 802.4. Technical and Office Protocol (TOP) is a suite of protocols closely based on the OSI model and 802.3 that provides network services for such departments as accounting, marketing and engineering as they support manufacturing and its MAP protocols.

5
CHAPTER

Token Ring network and FDDI

This chapter explores the role of

- 802.5 network components including NICs and Multistation Access Units (MAUs).
- Active Station Monitors on 802.5 networks.
- 16 Mbs 802.5 networks and contrast them with 4 Mbs versions.
- FDDI's components and learn the different types of network configurations possible.
- FDDI as a backbone to connect other networks.

Introduction

When IBM released its Token Ring Network, it immediately became the leading competitor to Ethernet and 802.3 networks. The IEEE 802.5 committee has developed standards for token ring networks and their key components. This chapter examines how a token ring network works and the kinds of network management services available. Understanding the 802.5 network operations is critical to understanding the internetwork operability issues explored later in this book when you look at bridges and routers.

Closely linked to 802.5 is a new fiber-optic standard for a network capable of transmitting information at 100 Mbs. This chapter examines the Fiber Distributed Data Interface standard and shows how it differs from 802.5 networks and how it can serve as an effective backbone to link other networks. I also look at the internetwork operability issues associated with FDDI bridges. In any event, remember what your mother or spouse has been saying the past few years: Fiber could be very important for your health—or at least the health of your networks.

The IEEE 802.5 Token Ring description

The IEEE 802 committee developed a standard which became known as IEEE 802.5 for a non-contention local area network, a network that is a logical ring but a physical star. Cables to individual workstations radiate from wire concentrators known as Multistation Access Units. Workstations transmit information in a packet known as a *frame*. IEEE 802.5 committee published its set of specifications in a Blue Book and has been adding to this standard on a regular basis. The original specification described a 4 Mbs transmission speed. IBM and several other vendors now offer a 16 Mbs version, which is covered later in this chapter.

The Open Token Foundation and 802.5 interoperability

If you have ever worked with LANs, you are aware that IEEE 802 specifications by themselves do not guarantee interoperability since they represent guidelines. IBM, for example, has published programs that meet 802.5 specifications but contain calls directly to their own NIC firmware; the result is that the programs do not work with other vendor 802.5 products. Several vendors would like to see a movement toward greater cooperation between the IEEE and 802.5 network equipment manufacturers and increased interoperability among 802.5 products.

In 1988 a group called the *Open Token Foundation* (OTF) was formed to increase 802.5 network interoperability. The OTF has staged a demonstration at NetWorld in Dallas in 1989 where more than 20 companies demonstrated their products' 802.5 interoperability.

Take this interoperability issue a step further. For two network nodes to communicate with each other, they must run the same higher level protocols so that they can "understand" each other. The same two network nodes can coexist even with different higher level protocols and hardware as long as they share the same 802.5 Medium Access Control (MAC) layer. It is this layer that enables the nodes to recognize which frames are to be processed or dropped and to interpret network addresses correctly. The IEEE 802.5 committee has been involved in coexistence issues while the OTF is concerned with both coexistence and communications issues. Table 5-1 indicates how differences in token ring elements affects the ability to coexist or communicate.

Table 5-1 Coexistence and Communication. Data Communications

These token ring elements:	Need to be the same between nodes for:	
	Coexistence	Communication
Physical layer signaling	Yes	Yes
MAC layer and frames	Yes	Yes
Address and network management	Yes	Yes
Source routing header filtering	Yes	Yes
LLC layer SAP address filtering	Yes	Yes
LLC types (I, II, or III)	No	Yes
Upper layer protocol (TCP/IP NetBios)	No	Yes
Card/PC hardware interface	No	No
System processor (80XXX, 68XXX)	No	No
PC machine type	No	No

The use of a token on 802.5 networks

When you examined the IEEE 802.4 token bus standard in chapter 4, you saw a token consisting of a predetermined bit pattern can only be used by one workstation or network node at a time. The transmitting workstation physically alters this token's bit pattern, which announces to all other workstations that this token is being used. This method resembles the way a taxi cab driver alerts potential customers that his cab is in use by setting an "in use" flag on top of the cab. The token, now transformed into a frame of information containing the message to be sent is transmitted around the ring until it reaches its destination workstation.

Messages sent along a token ring network are received by each network workstation which in turn checks to see if it is the frame's correct destination. If it is not, the workstation acting as a network repeater retransmits the frame to the next network workstation. Finally, the destination workstation receives the message and copies it to its internal memory before retransmitting the frame back to the sending workstation. The frame makes its way around the ring back to the sending workstation, which observes that the message was successfully copied and then resets the token so that it is available for another station to use.

This passing of a token might remind you of a children's game in which children sitting around a circle transmit a message by rebroadcasting the information by whispering it from one child to another until the child who started the cycle hears the information. What happens if a child falls asleep and cannot transmit the message? Obviously, the message would fail to come full circle. Later in this chapter you will see how a multistation access unit or wire concentrator alleviates this problem by bypassing inactive workstations so that the continuity of the ring is not broken.

Basic components of a Token Ring network

This section looks at the key components of a token ring network including its network interface card, its multistation access unit, and its cabling. It is important to recognize that IBM's Token Ring Network (IBM loves to use capitals as well as abbreviations) differs in some ways from other 802.5 networks. That does not necessarily mean IBM's approach is better, but it does mean that you have to be careful not to mix and match NICs with different chip sets or different 802.5 cabling schemes.

Network Interface Cards (NICs)

Workstations must have Token Ring network interface cards (NICs). These cards contain the Medium Access Layer protocols that are at the heart of the 802.5 standard. Not all 802.5 NICs are the same; while all 802.5 standard NICs support IBM's Source Routing scheme, which is discussed in chapter 8, IBM's NICs actually handle the Source Routing with their firmware and do not require additional software to perform this task.

IBM and Texas Instruments jointly developed an 802.5 chip set to ensure that third-party manufacturers of LAN equipment would provide compatible products. Ironically, virtually all 802.5 NIC manufacturers use this chip set except Ungermann Bass and IBM. Even though dozens of vendors offer 802.5 NICs, there are significant differences. One major difference is in the way these cards handle memory.

The three major approaches toward handling memory are *Shared Memory*, *Direct Memory Access* (DMA), and *Bus Mastering*. With Shared memory, a portion of the host's memory is mapped to the NIC's memory. The host can read information directly from its own memory, thus providing very fast access. The NIC will have jumper or switch settings to assign the buffers on the card to a system memory address. The CPU reads the RAM information on the card just as if the information was found in high memory RAM on the motherboard. There is a drawback, however. How much host memory does the manufacturer allocate? Too little memory allocation will result in the need for additional communications and transmissions that will slow down operations. Also, some information could be lost during this process. Too much memory allocation could cause conflicts with other key operations. The normal address range used by the chip set for this function could create conflicts with other functions that use this range of memory including system video memory and the Extended Memory Specifications (EMS) paging area.

Direct Memory Access (DMA) offers an alternative memory approach. A DMA controller residing on the NIC's motherboard assumes responsibility for determining the source and destination addresses of the data to be moved along the data bus. It requests and receives permission to use the data bus and then performs the necessary read and write operations. Unfortunately, on PCs the DMA speed remains what it was on the original Intel 8088 machines, 4.77 MHz. This approach is not as fast or efficient as Shared Memory. It is reasonably efficient when used for large data transfers, but very inefficient because of overhead when used for small data transfers. As a systems integrator, your ability to determine what kinds of data transfers will take place routinely will help you decide whether this DMA approach is acceptable for the network you configure.

The third memory approach, Bus Mastering, is the most efficient way to use memory, but you need the Micro Channel Architecture (MCA) based PS/2 workstations or the Extended Industry Standard Architecture (EISA) 16-bit bus clones and appropriate NICs use it. The NIC in effect is the "Master of the Bus" because it controls the bus and not a DMA controller sitting on a motherboard. The NIC writes information directly to the host's memory without the need for request permission. Also, the NIC only needs to perform a write operation and not the read operation required with the DMA approach. If the network you are configuring has a lot of small data transfers, this approach might be significantly faster for you than the DMA approach.

Just as NICs use different memory schemes, they also offer different sized buffers. It is particularly important that you select a card with a very large buffer for your file server so it can handle its heavy I/O load.

Other significant features that differentiate 802.5 NICs include the software included on them and the quality of their driver software. Remember the discussion of Demand Protocol Architecture (DPA) in chapter 3? DPA was 3Com's approach to minimizing RAM cram by using special software to load protocols as needed. Similarly, some 802.5 NICs include protocols as well as other software so that workstations need not try to cram them into RAM. IBM's Token Ring NICs include the Logical Link Control (LLC) 802.5 software.

Take software included on an NIC a step further. TI's 802.5 chip set includes basic driver software, but some companies have rewritten these drivers for their NICs using assembly language routines that speed up the throughput between the operating system and the hardware.

I have friends who never thought they'd live to see IBM salespeople suggesting a rival product, but up until LAN Server became a viable product, "Big Blue" salespeople were seen recommending NetWare to their large corporate accounts. By Novell's own account, over fifty percent of IBM Token Ring Networks run NetWare. In any event IBM has opened up its networks to make it easier for systems integrators to mix and match some products. When it released the PC LAN program, the NetBIOS Extended User Interface (NetBEUI) was required as an interface to NetBIOS, IBM's de facto network interface standard and its equivalent to the OSI model's Session layer. IBM's own Token Ring NICs used the

TOKREUI adapter handler to interface with the NetBEUI. More recently, IBM introduced its LAN Support Program which replaces NetBEUI and permits install-able device drivers. This means that a systems integrator now has more flexibility. It is possible, for example, to use 3Com's Token Link NICs with 3Com's 3Com-REUI adapter handler as an interface to NetBIOS. The network could then run a wide range of network operating systems such as NetWare or VINES. The Net-BIOS link could be handled by this 3Com device driver.

Cabling and multistation access units

The cabling connecting the network can range from type 3 unshielded telephone wire to include optical fiber and IBM data grade cabling. The promised 4 mega-bit/second transmission speed might not be achieved using the unshielded tele-phone wire if there is any interference. Another limitation of using inexpensive telephone wire is that it will support a maximum of only 72 workstations com-pared to the 260 workstations that can be supported on one ring with data grade coaxial cabling.

While a Token Ring network is a logical ring, it is a physical star with work-stations radiating from *Multistation Access Units* (MAUs). These MAUs contain bypass circuitry so that if a workstation is not plugged in or logged off the net-work, a relay bypasses the workstation's MAU port so that continuity of the ring is not broken. Figure 5-1 illustrates how these MAUs function.

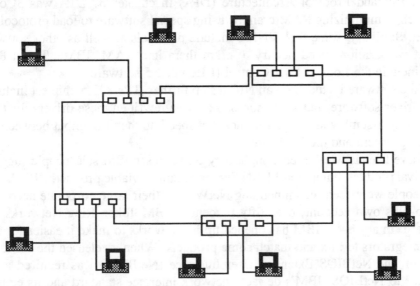

5-1 Multistation access units in a Token Ring network.

Usually MAUs are placed in a centralized wiring closet. The cable connecting the MAU to a workstation is known as a *lobe*. The maximum distance of these lobes varies according to the type of cabling used with the 4Mbs version of Token Ring network supporting a maximum length of 330 feet for twisted pair telephone wire and 984 feet for data grade media.

Figure 5-2 illustrates a group of MAUs in a centralized wiring closet. Connections at the wiring closet are made at punchdown blocks or through patch panels. Connections at the workstations are made using standard telephone wall jacks.

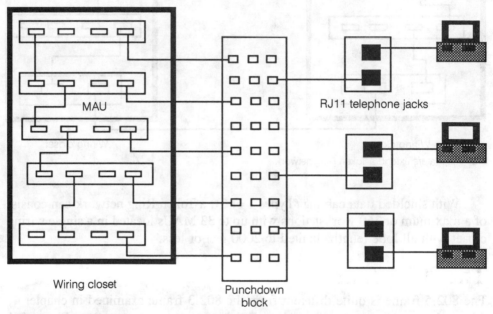

5-2 MAUs in a wiring closet connected to workstations using a punch-down block.

MAUs and repeaters

For larger installations it might be impossible or simply undesirable to place all MAUs in one central wiring closet. Copper repeaters can extend the distance between MAUs by up to approximately 2500 feet. Figure 5-3 illustrates how these repeaters are linked to MAUs.

Some rules of thumb are associated with token ring networks. Generally, you want to minimize the number of wiring closets needed. With twisted pair telephone wire, you can have a maximum of 72 workstations using up to 9 MAUs located in a single wiring closet as long as all lobe lengths are limited to 1000 feet or less. If you go beyond this length, you will need to use repeaters or bridges (see chapter 7).

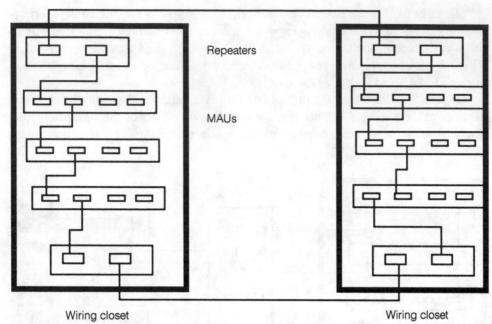

Repeaters

MAUs

Wiring closet   Wiring closet

5-3 Repeaters extend a Token Ring network.

With shielded data cabling (Types 1 or 2), a Token Ring network can consist of a maximum of 260 workstations with up to 33 MAUs located in a single wiring closet with all lobe lengths limited to 2000 feet or less.

The 802.5 frame

The 802.5 frame is quite different from the 802.3 frame examined in chapter 4; this explains why you simply cannot plug the two networks together. Figure 5-4 illustrates the 802.5 frame.

Starting delimiter	Control	Destination address	Source address	Information	FCS	EFS	Ending delimiter	Frame status

5-4 The 802.5 frame.

The Starting Delimiter signifies the beginning of a frame; its unique pattern (JK0JK000) prevents it from being mistaken for data. J and K here represent non-data symbols. The Access Control field is where you find the priority and reservation bits as well as the monitor bit. A workstation can use any one of eight different priority levels to indicate that it needs to reserve use of a future token. Other workstations will compare their priority levels with this number and defer if they see a higher priority in this field. The monitor field refers to token management, a topic considered shortly.

The Frame Control field is used to indicate whether the frame contains Logical Link Control (LLC) data or a Medium Access Control (MAC) control parameters. The Destination Address and Source Address fields are self-explanatory. The Source and Destination address fields are designed to convey a number of different kinds of information. The first bit is set to 1, then the message is a group broadcast for everyone on the network. An initial zero bit, on the other hand, indicates that this is a message addressed to a specific workstation. The second bit in the address field indicates whether the address is global (0) or local (1). *Local* refers to another node on the same network. Each workstation has a unique 48-bit address obtained by the manufacturer from IEEE and burned into the PC Adapter ROM chip. Locally administered addresses are assigned by the local network administrator; these addresses override the universally administered addresses found on the ROM chip. The address fields have been designed to accommodate the addresses of workstations that exist on other rings; in fact, the first two bytes of these two fields are designated for a workstation's ring number. The addressing can become quite complex because the 802.5 committee has proposed an address structure that includes space for indicating multiple rings, bridges, etc., very much like a letter to a college student might require several lines of address to indicate the specific college, street address, dormitory, post office box, etc.

The Frame Check Sequence field is used for error checking, while the End of Frame Sequence and Ending Delimiter are fields associated with specifying the end of a frame. The Frame Status field indicates whether the frame is Good or With-Error. If the frame is With-Error, the field specifies one of several reasons including an FCS that does not match, a frame too large for the buffer space, or a frame too small (*runt*) to be valid.

The Frame Status field is used by the workstation originating the information frame to determine if the workstation designated to receive the message actually recognized its own address. The originating workstation sets the Addressed Recognized bit to 0 (zero) while any other station on the ring sets it to 1 if it recognizes the address as its own. The originating workstation also sets the Frame Copied bit to 0. When the receiving workstation copies the frame into a read buffer, it sets this bit to a 1. When the frame returns to the originating workstation, it checks this key Frame Status field to see if the frame was recognized and copied correctly.

The token on an 802.5 network

A token is nothing more than a specific bit pattern that the workstations can recognize. Figure 5-5 illustrates the token on an 802.5 network. A workstation needing to use the network will grab the token when it arrives and change one bit to transform it from a token into what is known as a Start of Frame Sequence (SFS).

Start delimiter	Access control PPPTMRRR	End delimiter

5-5 An 802.5 token's format.

P   Priority mode
T   Token bit
M   Monitor count
R   Priority reservation

Workstations that need to use the token on an 802.5 network can indicate any one of eight different levels of priority while placing a reservation for it. A network workstation releases its token after each transmission because it is not permitted to broadcast continuously regardless of its high priority. The monitor bit is broadcast as a zero in all frames and tokens except the monitor itself in order to ensure that no frame monopolizes the ring and no token has a priority greater than zero. Every workstation thus has equal access to the network. When a workstation is ready to continue a message's path through the network by rebroadcasting its bit pattern, it examines the reservation bits (RRR). If it has a message of its own that it wants to send and its priority is higher than the present sender, it raises the value of this three-bit field to its own level assuring that its message is the highest one waiting to be transmitted. Further down the network a second workstation with even a higher priority might change this bit pattern to reflect its own priority level and thus "bump" the previous workstation from its reservation for the next available token. The priority established in the PPP Priority field reflect the workstation's priority to use the network. If a workstation observes that its priority is higher than the one already reflected in the RRR Reservation field, it raises this value to its own level and thus reserves the next token for its own use. The address of the bumped workstation goes into a memory location that serves as a queuing area for displaced workstations seeking access to the network but forced to wait their turns.

The role of the Active Monitor

Token Ring Network uses an *Active Monitor* to ensure smooth network operations and handle error conditions. The first workstation to join a ring becomes the Monitor, sort of like being President of a country consisting of one citizen. As the Monitor, this workstation generates an Active Monitor Present frame periodically that tells other workstations that there is a Monitor alive and functioning. Other workstations issue Standby Monitor frames periodically to indicate that they are ready to assume this role if the Monitor fails and it becomes necessary.

What happens if the Monitor does fail? Each workstation keeps track of time. When one realizes that it is long past time for the Active Monitor Present frame, it generates a Claim Token frame. Other workstations begin to realize the same thing now, and they too begin to generate these Claim Token frames. Which workstation is going to win the job of Active Monitor?

Now something very interesting happens, sort of like the way dogs determine which one is going to rule the neighborhood. Each workstation receives Claim Token frames issued by other workstations. It compares its Source Address with the Source Address of the Claim Token frame it receives. If it has a lower Source Address, the workstation drops out of this contest and begins issuing Standby Monitor frames. If it has a higher Source Address, then it ignores this other contender's frames and continues generating its own Claim Token frames.

The Frame Check Sequence field is responsible for error checking for the Frame Check, Destination Address, Source Address, and Information fields. Bit seven of this field is the error-detected bit. The workstation originating a frame sets this bit to zero while the first station to detect a transmission error sets it to one. The first station to detect this error flag counts the error and prevents other stations from also logging this error. This method helps to localize where an error has taken place. The workstation serving as the Monitor scans the network for transient and permanent errors. Transient errors are logged by various workstations on the network as "soft error conditions." These errors generally can be corrected by retransmitting the frame. Permanent errors, on the other hand, can disrupt network operations. If a frame comes back with the indication that a destination workstation has not recognized its own address and copied the frame, the Monitor workstation can use the bypass circuitry built into the multistation access units to bypass the defective station and maintain the network's integrity.

Error checking or "Someone To Watch Over Me"

The Active Monitor examines the frames circulating on the network and removes any of them that are defective, issues a new token, and ensures that the network runs smoothly. It also helps identify and remove defective network nodes. Figure 5-6 illustrates a Token Ring network with four workstations (1–4). Workstation 1 starts to receive fault messages indicating that a problem exists somewhere between it and its Nearest Active Upstream Neighbor (NAUN). Workstation 1 begins issuing Media Access Control (MAC) layer beacon frames that contain its own address as the source address with its NAUN (workstation 4) as the frame's destination address. When workstation 4 receives a total of eight beacon frames, it removes itself from the ring and begins self-testing. It is able to test its own NIC hardware, lob cabling and interface to the MAU. If workstation 4 does not find any errors, it will re-enter the ring. Note that when a workstation is powered on, the NIC initiates a self-test that checks its memory and circuitry. If an error is found, the workstation will not enter the ring until it is corrected.

Meanwhile Workstation 1 is still receiving error messages. It knows workstation 4 is not the guilty party? Horror of horrors, could it be the cause of these

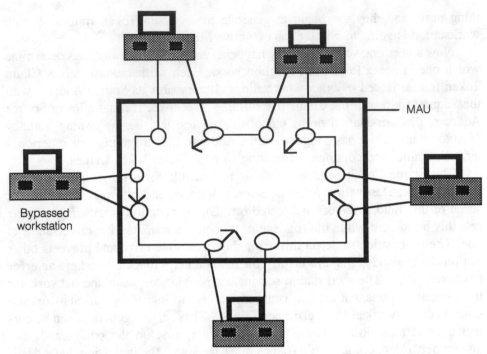

5-6 A Token Ring network with a defective node.

error messages? Workstation 1 takes itself out of service and begins self-testing. If it does not find anything wrong, it will return to the ring. Because Workstation 1 was the Active Monitor, the remaining workstations will contend for this job using the method described in the previous section.

The functions of the Monitor workstation are provided by the IBM Token-Ring Network Manager Program. It provides continuous monitoring of the network for errors as well as the corrective actions discussed here. It also logs network error and status information for report generation. It is this program that provides the mechanism for the creation of addresses for each workstation as well as the establishment of passwords.

Common problems on Token Ring networks

When you examined Ethernet, you saw that there were a number of common network problems including cable breaks and "jabber" conditions. Many systems integrators will swear that even with all its self-diagnostics, Token Ring is far more difficult to maintain than Ethernet. 802.5 networks also have their cable breaks, and it is also possible for the relays that take a workstation out of service on an MAU to stick so that the integrity of the ring is broken. Sometimes NICs will garble or abbreviate frames. There are many reasons why this can happen including electrical interference, low batteries, NICs going bad, and loose connectors. Chapter 12 examines some effective tools for diagnosing these problems when you look at network management issues.

Sometimes on Token Ring networks, a token is accidentally duplicated or lost. Two workstations might believe they hold the token and then attempt to transmit a frame simultaneously. This situation is handled very nicely by the network. Workstations examine the Source Address field of a returning frame and make sure that this address matches their own address. If the two addresses do not match, the station aborts its own transmission and does not issue a new token.

IBM's 16 Mbs Token Ring Network

Today, several vendors including IBM offer 16 Mbs versions of their 802.5 networks. IBM offers a 16 Mbs version of its Token Ring network requiring its own special adapter cards which come with 64K of on-board RAM. This extra memory allows larger frame sizes and more concurrent sessions when the adapter is used in a server. The larger frame sizes permit high volume RAM-to-RAM transmissions such as images.

This high-speed version of a token ring network comes at a price, though, because it requires IBM Type 1, 2, or 9 shielded cabling and cannot use the inexpensive unshielded twisted pair wire. Wire closets can be up to two kilometers apart when connected with fiber-optic cable. Although IBM claims that it cannot use unshielded media for 16 Mbs transmission speeds because of electrical interference, other companies such as Proteon (ProNET-10) offer speedy alternatives using this media. At the moment, many experts feel that the primary function of such speed is to serve as a *backbone network*, a kind of super router that connects several different networks together.

The importance of fiber optics with 16 Mbs Token Ring

Because the companies likely to install 16 Mbs Token Ring are likely to be the companies with very large networks, fiber optics will play an important role in such networks' design. Many vendors offer optical fiber converters to Token Ring. These converters permit optical links between wiring closets with 62.5/125 or 100/140 multimode optical fiber cabling.

These relatively new fiber-optic systems often provide network management software as well as two distinct signal paths. One path is in the primary direction of the network while the other path is in the backup direction. Normally the primary path will carry the network traffic while the backup path carries ring maintenance signals. The optical converters are intelligent enough to remove themselves from the ring if they sense that they are malfunctioning and then later to reinsert themselves if they no longer identify a problem. Early Token Release on the 16 Mbs Token Ring A workstation on a 16 Mbs Token Ring Network is permitted to transmit a token immediately after sending a frame of data instead of waiting for its frame to return. Figure 5-7 illustrates two different tokens traveling simultaneously on a 16 Mbs Token Ring network. IBM has claimed that the use of multiple tokens traveling on the same network can boost efficiency to more than 95 percent on frames larger than 128 bytes.

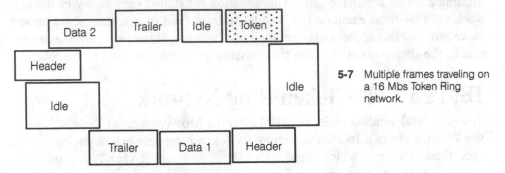

5-7 Multiple frames traveling on a 16 Mbs Token Ring network.

A Token Ring network in action

A good example of how Token Ring Networks can be used in a campus environment is IBM's own facility at Research Triangle Park in North Carolina. As Fig. 5-8 illustrates, IBM has chosen to use backup Token Rings for all LANs with more than 200 users. This redundancy feature illustrates how a company must balance the expense associated with redundancy with the cost of a network being out of service. In IBM's situation, the company decided that 200 users or more down at any one time was painful enough to warrant the cost of redundancy. There are at least 39 production mainframe computers and 15 test mainframe computers at Research Triangle that are linked to the Token Ring Network. Chapter 11 examines how IBM's Advanced Program-to-Program Communications (APPC) programming interface enables mainframe programs to talk directly with LAN programs assuming programmers have done their jobs properly.

This Research Triangle Park facility features IBM Cabling System Type 1 and fiber cabling for interoffice communications while connections between wiring closets are IBM Cabling System Type 2.

Fiber Distributed Data Interface (FDDI)

As you have seen when examining IBM's Token-Ring Network and its ability to link large multiple ring networks, IEEE 802.5 Token Ring networks are designed for heavy data traffic yet the speed of these networks (4 Mbs or 16 Mbs) falls well below what a network with heavy traffic really requires. Even using optic fiber cabling which is capable of much faster transmission does not help; the IEEE 802.5 standards were not designed to take advantage of optic fiber's incredible transmission speed.

Developed by the American National Standards Institute (ANSI) committee X3T.9, the *Fiber Distributed Data Interface* (FDDI) standard is a counter rotating

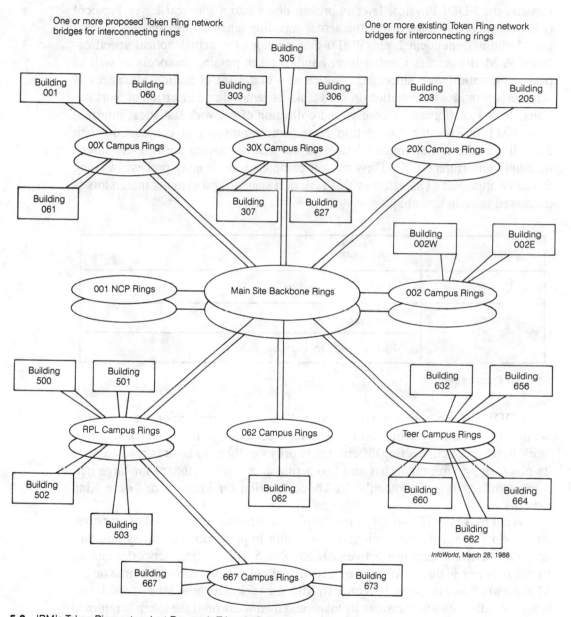

Research Triangle Park Token Ring Local Area Network

One or more proposed Token Ring network
bridges for interconnecting rings

One or more existing Token Ring network
bridges for interconnecting rings

Building 001
Building 060
Building 305
Building 303
Building 306
Building 203
Building 205

00X Campus Rings
30X Campus Rings
20X Campus Rings

Building 061
Building 307
Building 627

Building 002W
Building 002E

001 NCP Rings
Main Site Backbone Rings
002 Campus Rings

Building 500
Building 501
Building 632
Building 656

RPL Campus Rings
062 Campus Rings
Teer Campus Rings

Building 502
Building 062
Building 660
Building 664

Building 503
Building 662

InfoWorld, March 28, 1988

Building 667
667 Campus Rings
Building 673

5-8   IBM's Token Ring network at Research Triangle Park.

token ring capable of covering a very large area (200 km) while transmitting data at 100 megabit/second speed, a standard that ensures compatibility with IEEE 802.5 token ring networks by maintaining the same frame fields found in that standard.

The FDDI model is reasonably consistent with OSI model. As Fig. 5-9 reveals, the FDDI Physical layer is broken down into a Physical Layer Protocol (PHY) that concerns itself with the actual encoding schemes for data and a Physical Medium Dependent layer (PMD) that provides the actual optical specifications. A Media Access Control layer handles token passing protocols as well as packet formation and addressing. Notice also that a set of Station Management standards provides information on such tasks as removal and insertion of workstations, fault isolation and recovery, and collection of network statistical information. SMT utilizes the Connection Management protocol in conjunction with PHY line states to determine whether or not nodes entering the ring are linked together; unfortunately SMT has not yet completed the lengthy process of being formally approved. The effect of this lack of a standard on systems integrators is discussed later in this chapter.

OSI layer	FDDI layer
Data link	MAC
Physical	PHX (physical layer)
	PMD (physical medium dependent)

5-9 The structure of FDDI.

FDDI was used initially primarily for "back-end" applications such as connecting mainframe systems and mass storage devices and for the backbone network function of connecting different networks together. Today it is ready to take its place along with token bus and token ring as a viable standard for large networks while still performing the backbone function for Ethernet or Token Ring networks.

What makes FDDI so appealing despite its expense are its speed of transmission and its dual ring approach that offers built-in protection against system failure. One major difference between IEEE 802.5 Token Ring networks and an FDDI network is that a Token Ring network circulates one token at a time on a 4 Mbs network and perhaps 2−3 on a 16 Mbs network. On the 4 Mbs network version, a sending station transmits its token and then waits until the token is returned to it by the receiving station with an acknowledgement that the message has been received before passing the token to the next workstation on the ring. In an FDDI network the workstation sending a message passes on the token immediately after transmitting the message frame and *before* receiving an acknowledgment that the message has been received. The result of this procedure is that several message frames can be circulating around the ring at any given time. Another difference between FDDI and Token Ring which enhances network speed is the use of a restricted token; it is possible to keep other workstations off the network while a time critical task is performed. A Timed Token Protocol also used in IEEE 802.4 networks ensures that low-priority messages will not clog up a network during peak hours. Timed Token Protocol uses both synchronous and asynchronous transmission. Workstations utilize a certain amount of transmission bandwidth defined for use as synchronous service while the remaining bandwidth is used by workstations that transmit signals asynchronously when the token service arrives earlier than expected. They continue to do so until the expected time of token arrival when they switch to synchronous transmission.

In addition to greater speed of transmission, FDDI networks enjoy a built-in redundancy that protects against system failure. The FDDI standard specifies a dual ring, one primary ring to carry information while a secondary ring carries control signals. Figure 5-10 shows a typical FDDI network. Notice that should a break in cabling result between stations A and B it would be possible for them to continue to communicate through station C which is acting as a wiring concentrator. Note that it is possible to send data over both sets of cabling traveling in opposite directions so that if there is not a break in the cabling a transmission speed of 200 megabits/second is possible.

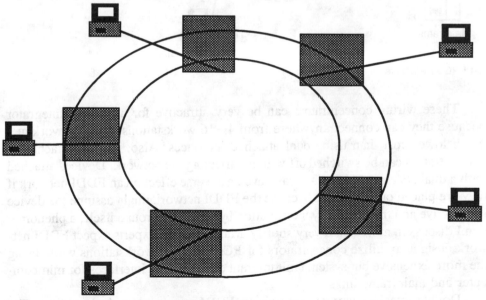

5-10 A typical FDDI network using dual cabling.

The basic components of an FDDI network

The FDDI standard defines the network components required including a *Single Attachment Station* (SAS), a *Dual Attachment Station* (DAS), and wiring concentrators. Single attachment stations are attached to wiring concentrators using a star topology as illustrated in Fig. 5-11. Notice that the concentrators can include mainframes, minicomputers, and high-performance workstations. A cable break with a single attached workstation will not bring down the network because the concentrator is able to bypass this workstation and continue transmitting and receiving information.

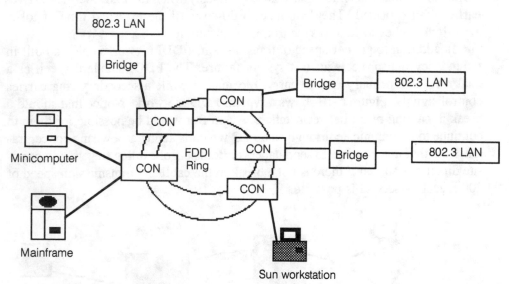

5-11   Concentrators on an FDDI network.

These wiring concentrators can be very attractive for a systems integrator because they can connect anywhere from 4 – 16 workstations to the network at a much lower cost than using dual attached interfaces. Also, devices attached to concentrators can be switched off without affecting the network. Devices attached with a dual attachment interface can have an adverse effect on an FDDI network if they are placed out of service because the FDDI network might assume the device is defective and try to remedy the situation by wrapping around itself, a phenomenon I discuss in more detail very shortly. Many industry experts expect FDDI network designs to utilize concentrators for PCs and other workstations while using the more expensive but system fault tolerant dual attached interfaces for minicomputer and mainframe links.

Double attached workstations on an FDDI network use dual cabling. The dual attached interface provides system fault tolerance through its redundancy. In Fig. 5-12, you see an FDDI double attached network with a token traveling in one

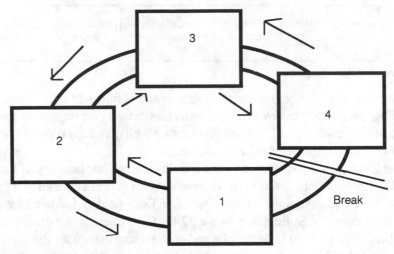

5-12 Wrapping after a cable break on an FDDI network.

direction. A break in the cabling causes the network to perform a function called *wrapping* in which it activates the second ring to bypass and isolate the failed station. The network will continue to operate but performance will decrease. Some vendors offer an optical bypass cable on their double attached interfaces so that the connection between the right side of the network and left side of the network can be maintained even with a cable break.

FDDI permits a maximum of 1000 connections with a maximum fiber optic path length of 200 Km. The cabling specified in the FDDI standard is 62.5/125 micron multimode optic fiber with light generated from long-wavelength LEDs transmitting at 1300 nm. Each station on an FDDI network functions as an active repeater, which helps explain why FDDI networks can be so large without signal degradation.

As I touched upon earlier in this chapter, another reason why FDDI networks are so fast is their use of a restricted token mode. Normally FDDI networks use synchronous transmission to transmit large blocks of information. Restricted token mode reserves all asynchronous bandwidth for a dialogue between two workstations that wish to use this type of transmission. All other workstations continue to broadcast in synchronous mode while this dialogue is taking place.

The FDDI frame

The FDDI frame illustrated in Fig. 5-13 can have a maximum size of 4500 bytes, which makes it ideal for large file transfers. The Preamble field synchronizes the frame with each station's clock using a signal that consists of 16 1-bits. Unlike an 802.5 network where the Monitor Station sets its master clock and then all other stations use its transmission signal to set their own clocks, FDDI uses a distributed clocking approach where each station's NIC sets its own clock. The Starting

Preamble	Starting delimiter	Frame control	Destination address	Source address	Data	Frame check status	Ending delimiter	Frame status

5-13 The FDDI frame format.

Delimiter signifies the beginning of the frame and is followed by a Frame Control field. This field indicates whether the transmission is synchronous or asynchronous, what size address will be used (16-bit or 48-bit), and the type of frame to be found (an LLC frame or MAC control frame).

The Destination and Source Address fields are self-explanatory. If the first bit in the Destination field is set, then we have a group address indicating a broadcast message to all workstations on the ring. The Data field is followed by a Frame Check Sequence (FCS) field that uses a 32-bit CRC to check for errors. The Ending Delimiter (ED) field indicates the end of the frame except for the Frame Status (FS) field which is used for a station to indicate it has detected an error.

Using multiple tokens on an FDDI network

Figure 5-14 illustrates the FDDI token. A station wishing to transmit seizes a token, absorbs it, and then adds its information to form a frame. This station begins transmitting and continues to do so until it runs out of information to send or its token-holding timer expires.

Preamble	Starting delimiter	Frame control	Ending delimiter

5-14 The FDDI token.

The frames transmitted are repeated by other workstations around the ring. The Destination workstation identifies its address on the frame and copies the information, checks for errors, and then sets a bit in the FS field if it detects an error before transmitting the frame. When the frame is returned to Source workstation, it retransmits it if there was an error detected or it purges the frame.

The moment a workstation releases a token, other workstations can seize it and begin transmitting frames. Workstations do not need to wait for the return of the frame they sent before releasing the token.

Integrating FDDI networks with existing LANs

Primarily because the Station Management (SMT) layer of FDDI has not been approved yet by the IEEE, the burden of integrating FDDI networks with existing LANs falls on the systems integrator. This link requires some kind of router or bridge, and at the moment there are vendors offering completely different types of solutions.

The major approaches to linking FDDI nets with existing LANs are data encapsulating bridges, translating bridges, spanning-tree bridges, and source-routing bridges. The data encapsulation method used by companies such as Fibronics, Inc., bundles data into FDDI format using proprietary algorithms. It takes a packet from a LAN and encapsulates it within an FDDI packet for its trip around an FDDI ring. The encapsulating bridge at the receiving end strips the encapsulation from the packet and sends it along its way. The encapsulating and de-encapsulating processes utilize proprietary algorithms that make this approach vendor-specific and incompatible with other vendors' encapsulating bridges as well as other types of bridges.

The translating bridges approach offered by companies such as FiberCom, Inc., readdress data using a protocol-independent method that is open rather than proprietary. A translating bridge will take a packet from a LAN such as Ethernet and translate the packet into FDDI packet protocol. At the destination end, a second bridge will translate the FDDI protocol back into the original LAN protocol.

The other two types of FDDI bridges also use the translating bridge approach. Chapter 7, which discusses Spanning-Tree and Source-Routing bridges in great detail, is devoted to bridges. At this time, defer discussion of these two types except to note that Spanning Tree is utilized by Ethernet LANs and is defined by the IEEE 802.1 standard. The Spanning Tree approach is known as a transparent approach because the bridge is transparent to a workstation when it transmits a frame with a destination address and no routing information. The bridges read these destination addresses and copy those frames that they will pass across to the other side. The Source Routing approach that is used by 802.5 networks has long been advocated by IBM. It requires workstations to maintain tables of network addresses. The workstation must plan out the route it wants its frame to travel. Recently IBM backed a proposal by both the 802.1 and 802.5 groups to the 802.1D committee that will enable Source Routing and Spanning Trees to interoperate. It probably will be at least another year before you see this new standard formally adopted. One problem faced by FDDI developers is that whatever approach they use to bridge FDDI to existing networks, they must be able to handle the multiple protocols found on larger networks. While FDDI does support a number of protocols including TCP/IP and IPX, the FDDI devices having framing formats must be fine-tuned to handle each protocol.

As a systems integrator needing solutions now, you can do something when designing FDDI networks to ensure interoperability in the future. Some vendors are willing to guarantee that they will replace their current FDDI bridges that use proprietary methods with SMT compatible equipment when the standard is formally approved. You might want to look for this guarantee as a way of ensuring that you will not lock your client into a proprietary path that might be a dead end.

XTP and FDDI

With IBM's backing, a new high speed LAN protocol called eXpress Transfer Protocol (XTP) has been formally proposed to ANSI. Corresponding to the network and transport layers of the OSI model, this protocol is intended for use with FDDI and higher speed networks to overcome throughput limitations of software-based protocols.

Presently, high-speed networks like FDDI only realize a fraction of their potential speed. FDDI using TCP/IP might only achieve speeds of 15 Mbs because of the amount of time consuming buffering required. XTP will provide low data transmission delay and high throughput with minimal overhead.

FDDI-II might be better than Rambo II

Most movie sequels disappoint, but a new version of FDDI might provide solutions for network designers who want to use FDDI in an environment where voice, data, and video are integrated. It divides the available bandwidth into a maximum of 16 separate and equal full-duplex channels using a time-division multiplexing approach.

FDDI-II will help systems integrators link intelligent PBXs as well as process control facilities. FDDI-II stations will be compatible with FDDI stations, but will run at the slower speeds in mixed environments. FDDI-II is not yet finalized, but it is coming soon perhaps to one of your neighborhood networks.

An example of FDDI in action

Imagine having to design a way to link several networks spread out over a 250-acre campus. That's the problem that faced Microsoft at its Redmond corporate headquarters. Microsoft has developed a corporate policy on how it cables its networks and subnetworks. Its buildings are all prewired for Ethernet subnetworks.

Microsoft's E-mail demands exceed 1.6 million messages each month, this coupled with all the large files programmers handle routinely creates quite a load on any network backbone. Microsoft originally had linked its various networks using standard LAN bridges. When it established its FDDI backbone, it kept its original LAN bridges for system fault tolerance.

Figure 5-15 illustrates the role of Microsoft's FDDI backbone. To give you some idea of the level of traffic on this network, Microsoft must link more than 9000 PCs and more than 3000 Macintosh computers. The PCs are linked to the backbone through Ethernet cards and an Ethernet-to-FDDI bridge. The Macintosh computers are linked to the backbone asynchronously via a LocalTalk connection to Farallon Starcontrollers, which are then connected to Ethernet using Kinetics Fastpath gateways. The Ethernet network includes the Ethernet-to-FDDI bridge already mentioned. Microsoft might replace some of these cards with Ethernet cards in the Macintosh computers.

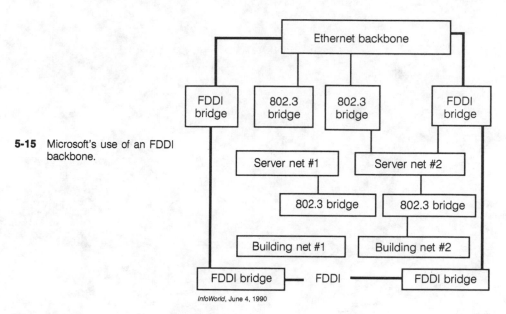

5-15 Microsoft's use of an FDDI backbone.

InfoWorld, June 4, 1990

Summary

The 802.5 standard describes a local area network using a token ring, non-contention approach. Currently both 4 Mbs and 16 Mbs versions are available, but a systems integrator must be careful in network design because of cabling distance restrictions. The 802.5 standard is broad and general enough that many vendors have experienced interoperability problems. The Open Token Foundation is an attempt at cooperation among 802.5 vendors.

The Fiber Distributed Data Interface (FDDI) is a 100 Mbs transmission speed fiber-optic network modeled on the 802.5 standard that does have some significant differences. It uses a completely different error correcting scheme that features a double ring and a wrapping technique. Network timing is handled by each workstation rather than by 802.5's Monitor station. Rather than the token reservation system used by 802.5 networks, FDDI uses a timed token system. Finally, FDDI is strictly a fiber network and does not permit the use of twisted pair or coaxial cabling.

6

CHAPTER

The nonstandard Apple networks and Arcnet standards

In this chapter, you will examine

- AppleTalk's suite of protocols.
- How Macintosh workstations can run on Ethernet and Token Ring networks under AppleTalk.
- Advantages and disadvantages of using NetWare, 3+, and TOPS on a Macintosh network.
- How Macintosh and DOS-based workstations can communicate under AppleTalk.
- How Arcnet operates.
- Why Arcnet is so popular.

Introduction

The public has embraced AppleTalk and Arcnet LANs, yet neither network technology is an official standard. A network manager or systems integrator must be aware of how these two technologies differ from IEEE 802 standard LANs in order to understand how these LANs can be incorporated in an enterprise-wide network. This chapter examines how AppleTalk and Arcnet work and why they are so popular.

The Macintosh environment

The Macintosh operating system contains many advanced features not available to PC users until recently with OS/2. Macintosh advocates will argue that this operating system is still far superior. It can address up to 16 megabytes of RAM, and with System 7.0 it will provide true 32-bit addressing rather than the current industry's 24-bit addressing.

Systems integrators are excited about System software 7.0. This version of the Macintosh operating system offers a number of features that can enhance network communications. Virtual memory can mean up to 128Mb of memory on some Macintosh models. This operating system will use virtual memory to swap out the most recently used part of its memory for storage on the hard disk. The memory manager will swap it back for other material when this information is requested.

Another connectivity feature associated with System 7.0 is its *Interapplication Communications Architecture* (IAC). This structure permits one application to send data or commands to other applications located on the same machine or on a different machine on the network.

IAC consists of three key components. A program-to-program communication module inside System 7.0 will handle routing as well as store-and-forward functions from one task to another. An editions manager automatically updates information changed in one application in other applications. IAC also includes AppleEvents, a module that enables developers to have one program send commands to another program. Finally, System 7.0 includes *Data Access Manager* (DAM). Applications communicate with DAM, which in turn communicates with appropriate databases. Apple believes that developers will want to write drivers for DAM that will facilitate internetwork database queries. An application program could use DAM to query databases on VAX, IBM, and Apple computer networks. As long as the database programs had DAM drivers, this process would take place and be transparent to end users.

Still another connectivity feature provided by System 7.0 is distributed file sharing software known as Macintosh *FileShare*. This Apple Filing Protocol (AFP) compatible software enables users to make all or part of a hard disk available to other networked users. What Apple did, in effect, was to build into System 7.0 some of its own AppleShare file server software so that every workstation has the ability to serve as a file server for other workstations.

The building blocks of AppleTalk networks

Because the terminology used in the Macintosh world is so different from that found in the PC world, it is useful to begin our look at Macintosh networks by defining the basic building blocks. An AppleTalk local area network includes a Macintosh workstation, a hardware network interface and cabling, appropriate protocol software, and a network operating system.

While IBM PCs and compatibles equipped with AppleTalk network interface cards can operate on an AppleTalk network, I focus initially on an all Macintosh network.

The Macintosh workstation

The Macintosh comes with a built-in hardware interface to the AppleTalk network. If you want to use Macintosh computers on an Ethernet or Token Ring LAN, you will have to add the appropriate network interface card. This AppleTalk interface is also found on Apple's LaserWriter printers.

LocalTalk

Here's where the terminology might get a bit confusing. The Macintosh's hardware interface contains the low-level software responsible for transmission and media access control to Apple's *LocalTalk* cabling system, which uses shielded twisted pair wire. In other words, the Macintosh's LocalTalk interface is capable of packaging bits into packets and then transmitting them following the network bus's rules for media access at a speed of 230.4 Kbs.

Cabling

Apple's shielded twisted pair cabling uses RS-422 signaling for transmission and reception over LocalTalk and requires repeaters for distances greater than 1000 feet. Two repeaters can extend the network to a maximum of 3000 feet. One limitation of the LocalTalk shielded twisted pair cabling is that its bandwidth is limited, and likely to become saturated if a network grows much beyond 25 users. One solution is to use cabling with greater bandwidth such as the coaxial cabling associated with Ethernet. This chapter looks at Macintosh Ethernet networks later. A second solution is to utilize AppleTalk's ability to create a series of subnetworks and bridge them together. This chapter looks at creating AppleTalk bridges later when you examine AppleTalk's protocols.

PhoneNet

Many systems integrators select Farallon Computing's PhoneNet cabling scheme for their AppleTalk networks because of its ability to use existing telephone cabling which consists of unshielded twisted pair wire. What is equally attractive to the systems integrator is PhoneNet's ability to be configured a number of different ways. A *passive star* topology as illustrated in Fig. 6-1 consists of wires branching out of a central block. Telephones normally are wired in this manner with each office receiving its own branch. This passive star arrangement only requires a single pair of unused wires. They have an effective length of up to 4000 feet and can support up to six branches.

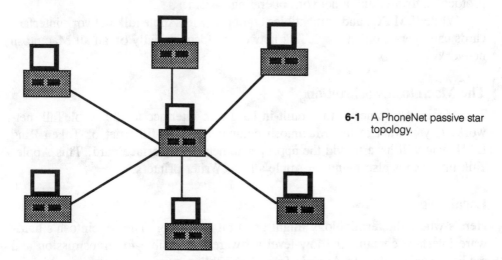

6-1 A PhoneNet passive star topology.

An *active star* topology utilizes a device known as a star controller. This intelligent device has 12 ports that can support 12 physical networks, each up to 3000 feet of cable. As I mentioned in chapter 1, this star topology facilitates network management. Farallon offers software that provides error detection, configuration control, and other network management functions. Figure 6-2 illustrates this active star topology.

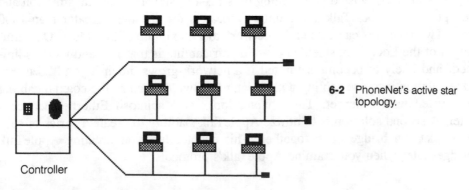

Controller

6-2 PhoneNet's active star topology.

A third topology offered by PhoneNet is the daisy chain. Using this approach, each workstation is daisy chained to another workstation as illustrated in Fig. 6-3. This type of architecture is ideal for a very small network, perhaps an office with just a few workstations and a printer. This topology has a 2000 foot maximum length.

6-3 A daisy chain topology.

A backbone topology consists of PhoneNet telephone wall wiring serving as a data highway. Workstations and other devices connect to the backbone through wall boxes. This topology can extend up to 4000 feet and is designed for heavy traffic. While standard PhoneNet runs at the AppleTalk network speed of 230.4 Kbs, an Ethernet version is available that runs at 10 Mbs over telephone wire.

CSMA/CA

LocalTalk uses a multidrop bus, the same scheme used by Ethernet (see chapter 4). It uses a media access method that is similar to Ethernet's CSMA/CD but slightly different. Carrier Sense Multiple Access With Collision Avoidance (CSMA/CA) is an approach in which a workstation that wants to transmit information first senses any activity on the network. If a collision occurs, all workstations avoid additional possible collisions by waiting for the network to be idle a specified amount of time plus an additional amount of random time that varies from station to station.

Unlike CSMA/CD where hardware detects a collision, CSMA/CA works on the premise that a collision *might* have occurred. It relies on "handshakes" between sending and receiving workstations. When a workstation does not receive an appropriate handshake or control packet reply to its request to send information, it infers that a collision has occurred and begins the process of requesting the right to transmit all over again. To examine this process in more detail, look specifically at the LocalTalk protocol responsible for this data link access method.

LocalTalk's Link Access Protocol (LLAP)

LocalTalk has its own link access protocol known as the LocalTalk Link Access Protocol (LLAP). Figure 6-4 illustrates the LLAP packet. A Preamble indicating the start of a frame is followed by Destination and Source Node Identifiers. These

Preamble	Destination node ID	Source Node ID	Type	Length	Data	FCS	Flag	Abort

6-4 The LLAP frame.

8-bit addresses can range from 1 to 127 for user nodes and 128 to 254 for server nodes under AppleTalk first version which is known as Phase 1. The number 255 is reserved for a broadcast Node ID. When a workstation starts up, it randomly assigns itself an ID and then test to see if another node already is using it by sending out an inquiry control packet.

The LLAP type field indicates whether a packet is carrying control information or actual data. The data length field indicates the amount of data the packet carries; an LLAP packet can carry between 2 and 600 bytes of data. A Frame Check Sequence field is used for error checking and is followed by a trailer flag (01111110) field and an Abort field that indicate the end of a frame. LLAP uses a technique known as *bit stuffing* to ensure that no other field contains more than five consecutive 1- bits. It will insert a 0-bit after five consecutive 1-bits to ensure the Flag field's uniqueness. A receiving workstation's LLAP will reinsert the appropriate 1-bit so that the data can be read correctly.

How workstations transmit using LLAP

When a workstation using LLAP wants to transmit, it checks the network until it has been idle for at least 400 microseconds. It then waits an additional random period. The source workstation then sends a request-to-send packet to the destination workstation, which replies with a clear-to-send packet. The source workstation then transmits its data packet. If a source node does not receive a clear-to-send control packet, it assumes that there has been a collision and once again waits until the network has been idle for at least 400 microseconds.

Broadcast transmissions work somewhat differently. A source workstation waits at least 400 microseconds and then an additional period of time before sending out a request-to-send control packet with a broadcast address. It then checks the network for a maximum period of 200 microseconds before broadcasting its transmission. The source workstation will attempt up to 32 retransmissions before reporting failure.

AppleTalk

AppleTalk refers to the entire suite of protocols that comprise Apple's own layered network architecture.

AppleTalk Phase 1

AppleTalk Phase 1 imposed the limitation under LocalTalk of no more than 32 nodes in a single network including workstations, servers, and peripherals including the LaserWriter. It was possible, however, for several AppleTalk networks, each one limited to a maximum of 32 nodes, to be bridged together.

Apple uses the term *internet* to define two or more local area network linked together with a router or gateway. When a router combines network segments into an internet (Fig. 6-5), the networks remain independent of each other. The networks connected together by routers are known under Apple's terminology as *zones*. A zone consists of logical grouping of networks on an internet; it is very important to realize that a zone need not be identical with the original LAN's physical configuration. In other words, nodes that share functionality (accounting, word processing, etc.) might be grouped together in a zone by a network manager even though they are located on different LANs on the same physical site comprising the internet. Often a backbone network (also seen in Fig. 6-5) is used

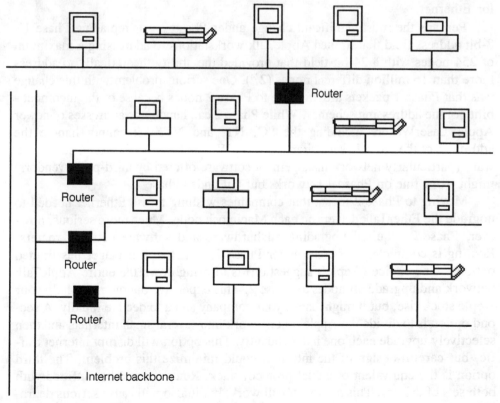

6-5 An AppleTalk internet.

to reduce traffic congestion between networks on an internet. The name of the game is to reduce the number of routers necessary to transmit information from one node to another node.

In addition to its own LocalTalk, Apple's AppleTalk Phase 1 provided drivers for Ethernet (EtherTalk). This meant that it was possible to design a Macintosh network using coaxial cabling and Ethernet NICs to achieve 10 Mbs transmission speed. The 8-bit field AppleTalk assigned for node addressing meant that even under Ethernet there was a limitation of 254 network nodes which included workstations, printers, modems, etc. For some corporations, this restriction simply was not acceptable.

AppleTalk Phase 2

AppleTalk Phase 2 added improved internet routing for up to 1024 interconnected AppleTalk networks. It provided extended resource grouping to support up to 256 zones per network. Even more appealing to the systems integrator concerned with connectivity, it provided drivers for Token Ring (TokenTalk) and enhanced drivers for Ethernet.

Perhaps the most significant change under Phase 2 was replacing Phase 1's 8-bit address field that limited AppleTalk workstations to addressing a maximum of 254 nodes with a 24-bit field that provided the ability theoretically to address more than 16 million different nodes (2^{24}). One serious problem with this change was that Phase 1 packets are invisible to Phase 2 nodes because of the incompatibility of the addressing schemes. While Phase 2 can handle the addresses of newer Apple LaserWriters including the SC, NT, and NTX, it cannot handle the addresses of the older LaserWriter and LaserWriter Plus models. Also, some software (particularly network management software offered by third-party vendors) might work fine on Phase 1 networks but fail under Phase 2.

Moving to Phase 2 meant that companies wishing to use Ethernet needed to upgrade the EtherTalk drivers on each Macintosh node. Much more serious, however, Phase 2 required upgrading all hardware and software network routers. Routing is completely different under Phase 2. A network manager has limited options. One choice (Apple's suggestion) is to bring down the entire AppleTalk network and upgrade all nodes to Phase 2. This expensive option might help your Apple stock rise, but it might cause your company stock to decline rapidly. A second option is to divide the AppleTalk network into several small internets and then selectively upgrade each one independently. This option will disrupt internet traffic, but careful design of the internets could minimize this problem. The third option is the equivalent of a dual protocol stack. Routers could be outfitted with both sets of drivers. This approach will work, but it also will cause serious degradation in network efficiency because of the overhead imposed.

AppleTalk protocols and the OSI model

As I mentioned earlier in this chapter, AppleTalk is a network architecture consisting of a suite of layered protocols. Figure 6-6 illustrates how it compares to the OSI model.

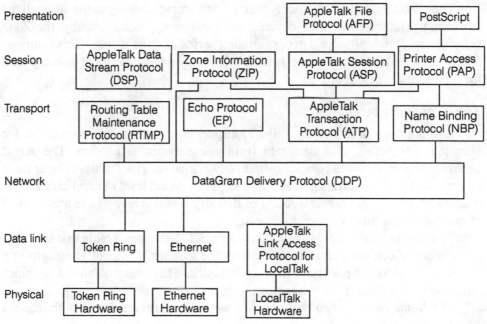

6-6 AppleTalk protocol and the OSI model.

The Presentation layer

In the Presentation layer, the AppleTalk Filing Protocol (AFP) provides the basis for the entire network's file structure; it also provides a key network interface for file server software. AFP provides any translation required for native AppleTalk file system calls to be understood by a file server.

The PostScript protocol is also found at the Presentation layer; it ensures that the network can communicate with PostScript printers.

The Session layer

AppleTalk protocols found in this layer are concerned primarily with the Session layer's responsibility for establishing a communications session. The *Session Protocol* handles the correct sequencing of datagrams when they arrive out of order. It also takes responsibility for ensuring that datagrams are the correct size and that there are break points during conversation sessions. As I pointed out in chapter 3 when you examined the OSI model, break points are used to re-establish disrupted sessions without having to start over again from the very beginning.

The *Data Stream Protocol* establishes the actual communications session. It can provide full duplex service, detect and eliminate duplicate datagrams, and request retransmission when needed to ensure error-free service.

The *Printer Access Protocol* handles streaming tape systems as well as streaming printer sessions for devices that use this approach. Finally, the *Zone Information Protocol* maps a network into a series of zone names. This information is used by both bridges and routers when they determine their delivery path for a particular message.

The Transport layer

As I also pointed out in chapter 3, the Transport layer is primarily responsible for planning the routing of a datagram from one network to another. The actual details of this routing are handled by the Network layer. The Transport layer must determine the types of transport services required. What level of error checking is necessary? Should acknowledgement of delivery be required? These are the type of questions that this layer must address.

The *Routing Table Maintenance Protocol* (RTMP) keeps a table that indicates the number of bridges that must be crossed (the number of "hops") to transport a datagram from one network to another network. This protocol also determines alternate routes should the primary route fail.

The *Name Binding Protocol* matches workstation server names with internet addresses. Users need not concern themselves with the appropriate internet address because this protocol makes the process transparent. The *AppleTalk Transaction Protocol* is an extremely critical component of OSI compatible Transport layers because it provides the acknowledgement of a datagram's error-free delivery that some network applications require.

Finally, the *Echo Protocol* enables the destination workstation to echo the contents of a datagram to the source network workstation. This service lets the network know that a workstation is functioning and also provides a measure of the round trip delays encountered on the network.

The Network layer

As we pointed out when examining the Transport layer's functions, the Network layer performs the nitty-gritty details required for the transport of datagrams from one network to another. The *Datagram Delivery Protocol* is able to address specific logical ports on different networks and to establish the route a datagram will take. This protocol is able to use the Transport layer's Name Binding Protocol to translate a server's name into an internet address and then use the Routing Table Maintenance Protocol to establish a network path for the datagram.

The Data Link layer

As I pointed out in my earlier discussion of AppleTalk Phase 2, AppleTalk has link access protocols for Token Ring (TokenTalk) and Ethernet (EtherTalk) as well as its own LocalTalk hardware. The drivers AppleTalk provide are able to handle the different addressing schemes, different sized packets, and different media access methods required by these different types of networks. Figure 6-7 illustrates how an EtherTalk packet differs from the LocalTalk packet discussed earlier in this chapter. Notice it contains the Ethernet-specific fields required for communications on an Ethernet network.

Ethernet destination	Ethernet source	Type	AppleTalk destination	AppleTalk source	AppleTalk type	Length	Pad

6-7 An EtherTalk packet.

Assume that a user sitting at a Macintosh workstation decides to send a file over an Ethernet network with AppleTalk protocols. The File Manager in the Macintosh operating system (System) requests the file from another module within the Macintosh operating system, the SCSI Manager. The SCSI Manager issues the commands required for the hard disk to locate the file and copy the data into RAM.

The Macintosh's central processor takes this file and packages it into Apple-Talk packets, which are sent to the EtherTalk Link Access Protocol (LAP). The Macintosh NuBus Manager (also part of the Macintosh operating system) sends these EtherTalk packets over the NuBus to the Macintosh's Ethernet NIC. This circuit card translates the EtherTalk packets into electrical signals and uses a CSMA/CD media access method to transmit these Ethernet signals at 10 Mbs.

The Physical layer

The Physical layer on an AppleTalk network defines the hardware required to communicate with Token Ring, Ethernet, and LocalTalk networks. AppleTalk Phase 2 supports a Token Ring card called the TokenTalk NB (for NuBus). This 32-bit Macintosh II network adapter has its own 68000 processor and memory as well as its own support software. This software enables the Macintosh to use all the higher level AppleTalk software including AppleTalk Filing Protocol on a Token Ring network. This support software also has an SMB (Server Message Block) file transfer program that enables Macintosh workstations on a Token Ring network to exchange files with PCs on the network. The program transfers a PC file into the Macintosh, but does not support sharing the PC file while it is on the PC. AppleTalk cannot let a Macintosh application run on an SMB server because this server does not have the intelligence to understand AppleTalk file structure.

One limitation at the present time that might be corrected soon is that despite its current hefty price ($1250), TokenTalk NB only supports Token Ring's 4 Mbs transmission speed and not the 16 Mbs standard.

AppleShare

AppleShare is Apple's own network file server software built on a foundation of AppleTalk Filing Protocol (AFP). It is popular with corporations that like to have a one vendor solution for their networks, but it does have some serious drawbacks for the systems integrator.

If you have been an Apple dealer or have purchased Apple products, it should come as no surprise that AppleShare is expensive—over four times as expensive as NetWare. Because Apple does not provide such key network services as electronic mail and print spooling as part of AppleShare, they must be purchased from Apple (if available) or third-party vendors. The Macintosh must serve as the file server on an AppleShare network, while PCs can participate as long as they run the PC AppleShare software that translates Sever Message Blocks to AppleTalk Filing Protocol calls. Figure 6-8 illustrates AppleShare PC in action. Apple offers Ethernet NICs for the Macintosh II, but it does not offer these boards for all Macintosh models. One advantage of AppleShare for schools is that it will run on Apple IIe and IIGS computers.

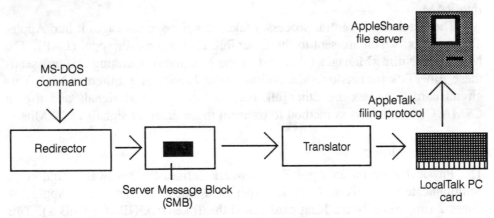

6-8 AppleShare PC in action.

AppleShare is adequate for relatively small networks that do not require elaborate security or services. Under AppleShare, for example, there are no folder-level passwords.

Other major Macintosh network options

Several other major network options for the Macintosh are covered in the following sections.

Transcendental Operating System (TOPS)

Sun's Sitka division offers TOPS (Transcendental Operating System) software. TOPS uses existing LocalTalk cabling as well as its own TOPS Filing Protocol (TFP) protocols to create a peer-to-peer network. Rather than using a centralized file server, each workstation on a TOPS network runs TOPS software and becomes a file server to other workstations on the network. Systems integrators have been attracted to TOPS because of its ability to link Sun workstations, which use Sun Computer Corporation's own *Network File System* (NSF) protocol with networked Macintosh computers; the connection is easy because Sitka TFP software for the Macintosh also contains the NSF protocol.

NSF is a service that provides transparent access to remote file systems on a network. As far as network workstations are concerned, data located anywhere on the network appears to be located on just another local hard disk drive.

Another reason TOPS networks have become so popular for systems integrators is the ease with which IBM PCs and compatibles can be integrated with Macintoshes. The company was one of the first to offer an AppleTalk NIC for PCs along with a DOS version of TOPS software. PCs on a TOPS network *publish* the files they want to share with other network users who *mount* the files they wish to access. TOPS provides a built-in conversion utility to handle IBM and Macintosh formats of popular programs such as Microsoft Word and Lotus 1-2-3.

A high-performance version of the TOPS LocalTalk NIC is known as the TOPS FlashCard. One advantage of this adapter is that it can transmit network information between PCs at 770 Kbs, three times faster than the Macintosh workstations can transmit on the same network. The Macintosh units require a FlashBox LocalTalk accelerator to run at this speed. A relatively new TOPS NIC provides FlashCard performance for microchannel architecture PS/2 models, something that many large corporations and major Macintosh sites such as General Electric have been requesting. Other TOPS features that systems integrators might find attractive include versions for Microsoft Windows and OS/2, support for TokenTalk, and gateways from its electronic mail program (Inbox) to Unix Mail and IBM's PROFS mail system.

One serious limitation of TOPS' distributed approach to file serving is that if you are using workstation B's files and that computer crashes, you could lose whatever changes you had made to your file since the last time you saved it. Also, if someone is accessing one of your files and you turn off your computer without issuing a warning, you could corrupt your version of the open file such that your system will crash the next time you try to access it.

3Com's 3+ Macintosh network software

3Com was one of the first vendors to link Macintosh workstations and PCs using Ethernet. Its 3+ Macintosh software has a number of features that make it very appealing for a systems integrator. The 3+ software and AppleShare are compatible and can coexist on the same network transparently to users and to applications that use the AppleTalk Filing Protocol (AFP). As Fig. 6-9 illustrates, 3Com's sophisticated file servers, NICs and operating system software make it possible to link Macintosh workstations on a LocalTalk network with both Token Ring and Ethernet networks.

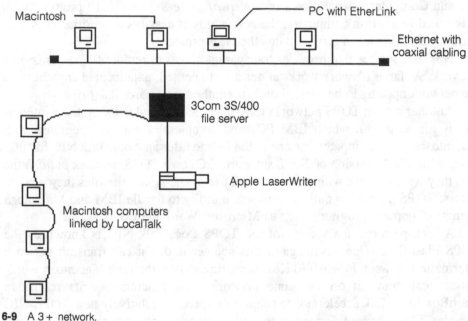

6-9 A 3+ network.

Because 3Com began operations as a pure Ethernet company, it is not surprising that XNS is its upper level protocol. 3Com packets are routed in the Transport layer using XNS's Sequenced Packet Protocol (SPP) discussed in chapter 3. You might remember that Novell took SPP and modified it to create NetWare's SPX packet format which, unfortunately, is just enough different to be incompatible with the 3Com format. 3+ software for the Macintosh also includes AppleTalk's Datagram Delivery Service which is used by AppleShare file servers to support AppleTalk bridges. Because 3+ software also includes IBM's Server Message Block (SMB) protocol, DOS and OS/2 workstations are able to share the same file simultaneously with Macintosh workstations because the network operating system understands both these two very different methods of requesting files from a file server. When a Macintosh workstation under the 3+ Macintosh network operating system issues a record lock on data in a file on the 3Com server, the 3+ software intercepts the Macintosh File Manager call to perform this task and translates it into the corresponding DOS operating system call. The file server never knows or cares whether the command is coming from a Macintosh or from a PC. Figure 6-10 reveals how 3+ software translates these File Manager requests.

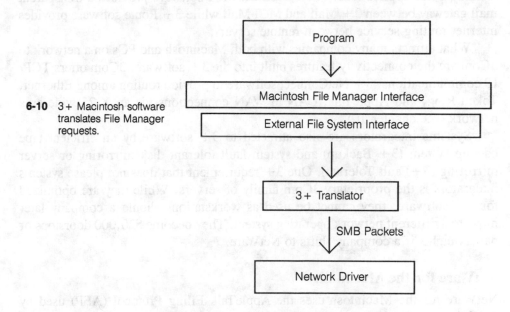

6-10 3 + Macintosh software translates File Manager requests.

Figure 6-11 reveals that the 3+ software also includes Microcom Network Protocol (MNP) at its Data Link level; this protocol has become a de facto communications standard and explains in part why 3+ software is so strong in the area of internetwork communications.

Application	XNS Name server Microsoft redirector
Presentation Session	AppleTalk file protocol XNS courier
Transport Network	XNS MINDS AppleTalk Datagram Delivery Services
Data link Physical	MNP Token Ring Ethernet

6-11 Protocols on a 3Com 3 + Open network and the OSI model.

Because 3+Mail service operates in both the DOS and Macintosh worlds, it is possible to transmit electronic mail easily and efficiently. This mail service works with the MultiFinder, so it is possible to display mail on a desktop while running other applications. The 3+ Reach/MCI software provides a transparent mail gateway between 3+ Mail and MCI Mail while 3+ Route software provides internet routing service between remote servers.

What attracts many companies with both Macintosh and PCs on a network to 3Com are the connectivity features built into the 3+ software. 3Com offers TCP/IP communications, 3+ NetConnect software to provide routing among Ethernet, Token Ring, and AppleTalk, LAN to WAN connections via an X.25 wide area network (see chapter 10).

Systems integrators are also attracted to 3+ software by an efficient tape backup system (3+ Backup) and system fault tolerant disk mirroring or server mirroring (3+Fault Tolerant). One 3+ requirement that does not please systems integrators is the proprietary 3Com family of servers. While they are optimized for 3+ software, they cannot be used as workstations should a company later move to a different network operating system. They become $20,000 doorstops or paperweights if a company shifts to NetWare.

NetWare for the Macintosh

NetWare for the Macintosh uses the AppleTalk Filing Protocol (AFP) used by Apple's own AppleShare file server. In fact, to a Macintosh workstation, the NetWare file server appears in the Chooser desk accessory as an AppleShare file server. NetWare adds many features not found under AppleShare, though, including enhanced security, better printing facilities, fault tolerance, and a transparent link with the 50−60% of corporate PC networks running NetWare.

A major advantage of NetWare for the Macintosh is that a Macintosh network can use Intel 80286 or Intel 80386 based microcomputers as servers. NetWare also can utilize 2 gigabytes of disk storage on a single file server. The prices of these AT compatibles and corresponding hard disks are far cheaper than what you will find in the Macintosh world. NetWare's print spooling is compatible with the AppleTalk Printer Access Protocol so that PC workstations can access Apple LaserWriter and ImageWriter printers.

NetWare is able to translate the AppleShare file server format to its own NetWare Control Protocol (NCP) that runs on a NetWare file server. A NetWare utility translates Macintosh file names into DOS file names since the latter are limited to 8 characters without spaces while Apple files can contain up to 31 characters.

NetWare's major strength is its security. Directory trustee rights and file attributes can be limited by the network supervisor. Directories can be hidden and users can even be restricted to certain hours on the network. The system fault tolerance includes the ability to duplicate file servers, link UPSs, and perform transaction tracking so that if the network is interrupted, transactions in midstream will not corrupt the files that are opened.

A corporate AppleTalk network in action

In 1988 an international equipment leasing firm decided to move away from its mainframe Prime computer and design a network that would use Sun workstations running the Unix operating system to run its lease-analysis program. Macintosh computers running TOPS are networked and provide all the office automation applications. The Macintosh network is connected to an Ethernet backbone at both the company's San Francisco and New York locations (see Fig. 6-12).

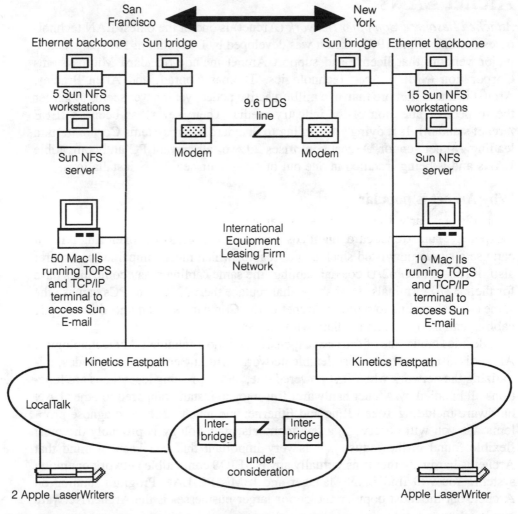

6-12 Macintosh computers networked and linked across the country.

TOPS contains the NFS (Network File System) protocol that the Sun systems use so it is easy to link the Macintosh networks to the Sun workstations. The network consultant designing this system has a choice. He can use Apple's EtherTalk network cards in the Macintosh or use lower speed Apple LocalTalk cards. A Kinetic's FastPath Ethernet-to-AppleTalk gateway provides a link to the LaserWriter printers which are linked together using LocalTalk.

A total of 50 Macintosh IIs in San Francisco and 10 Macintosh IIs in New York use a Sun workstation on the San Francisco LAN as a network file server. The TOPS terminal software enables the Macintosh workstations to emulate a Sun workstation and run files on the Sun server as well as use E-mail that connects the Sun and Macintosh worlds.

Arcnet LANs

Attached Resource Computer Network (Arcnet) is one of the oldest LAN technologies dating back to 1977 when it was developed by Datapoint in 1977; since then major vendors that license and support Arcnet include Standard Microsystems Corporation (SMC), Acer Technologies, Thomas Conrad, and Allen Bradley. Arcnet is found in more than one million active nodes, yet it never seems to garner the respect or attention of the industry media. There never has been an IEEE Arcnet standard. Is it dying? According to Standard Microsystems Corporation, a leading Arcnet vendor, Arcnet comprises 20% of all current PC and compatible LANs and is being installed in one out of every four new LAN installations.

Why Arcnet is popular

Arcnet is popular with small as well as large systems integrators because it is very inexpensive; an Arcnet card might cost one-third the price of a token ring NIC. It can use a single untwisted shielded pair cable, which most companies can spare; also, it runs on RG 62/U coaxial cabling, the same cabling many companies have for their 3270 terminals. IBM shops that replace their 3270 with PCs can use the same coaxial cabling to build an Arcnet LAN. Companies that do need fiber-optic cabling can also use this medium with Arcnet.

Besides being one of the least expensive and most reliable LAN technologies, Arcnet is also one of the most flexible networks. Adding and removing nodes, initializing the network when first powered one, and recovering lost tokens are functions all handled by Arcnet hardware. It is a joy to install compared to other LAN hardware including Token Ring and Ethernet and much easier to diagnose problems. As you will observe in a few moments, its topology is probably the most flexible found in the industry. It is very important that you keep in mind that Arcnet is hardware that runs virtually any NetBIOS compatible network operating system. You will find LAN Manager and IBM's PC LAN Program running on Arcnet, but the most popular choice for larger businesses is the Arcnet/NetWare combination.

Topology

Arcnet supports bus, star, and distributed star topologies. Each segment of an Arcnet bus can contain up to eight nodes daisy-chained together and can extend to 1000 feet. Adding an Active Link to a bus segment extends the segment's range another 1000 feet point-to-point as revealed in Fig. 6-13.

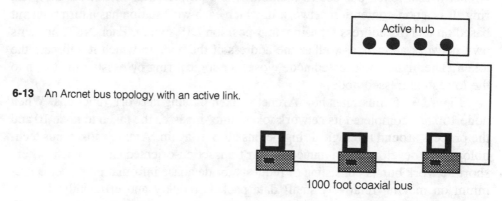

6-13 An Arcnet bus topology with an active link.

Arcnet's star topology is popular because it is the easiest arrangement to troubleshoot. Also, the failure of a single workstation does not bring down the entire network because each workstation has its own cabling connection with a hub. Up to eight workstations can be connected to a central hub with a 2000 foot maximum. Passive hubs, on the other hand, are limited to distances of 100 feet. Active hubs can be connected together to build a network with a maximum distance of four miles. Figure 6-14 illustrates a typical Arcnet star topology with both an active hub and a passive hub.

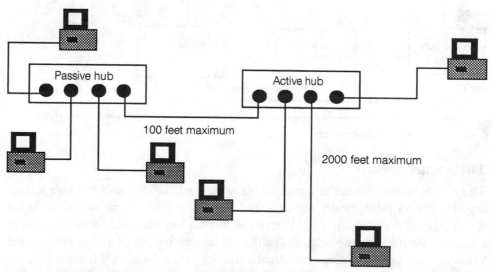

6-14 An Arcnet star with active and passive hubs.

I mentioned earlier that Arcnet's topology is extremely flexible. It is easy to connect bus segments with an Arcnet star or distributed star. Two port repeaters can connect the bus segment on one side with a star hub on the other side.

Arcnet's access method

Arcnet uses a token bus access method. It is a physical star or bus but a logical ring. It is a non-contention network in which each workstation has a turn transmit based on its NIC address set using an 8-position DIP switch. Each NIC knows its own network address as well as the address of the node to which it will pass the token. The highest-addressed node closes the logical ring by passing the token to the lowest-addressed node.

Figure 6-15 illustrates how Arcnet's token passing network functions. When node 150 has completed its network token time, it passes the token to node 10 and the process around the logical ring begins all over again. Arcnet's token bus technology was developed in a minicomputer transaction-oriented environment where short network bursts consisting of requests for database information placed a premium on moving relatively small data packets quickly and efficiently. Its low overhead and efficient non-contention token bus transmission at 2.5 Mbs makes it competitive with Ethernet under heavy traffic conditions even though it has substantially less bandwidth.

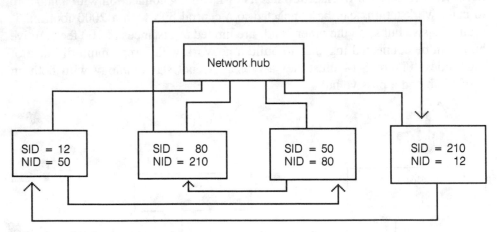

6-15 Arcnet's token bus approach.

The Arcnet packet

The major reason Arcnet is incompatible with the IEEE standards is its addressing. It uses an 8-bit locally administered station address format while the IEEE 802 LANs use a globally administered 48-bit station address. There are simply too many active Arcnet nodes to change the addressing scheme. Instead, Arcnet vendors have been fighting a political battle to persuade an ANSI committee to approve an Arcnet standard. Figure 6-16 describes the Arcnet packet format.

Alert Burst	SOH	SID	DID	DID	Count	Data	CRC	CRC

Alert Burst	Six 1-bits identify a packet
SOH	Start of Header (1 byte)
SID	Source workstation ID (1 byte)
DID	Destination workstation ID (2 bytes)
Data	1-508 bytes
CRC	Error checking (2 bytes)

6-16 The Arcnet packet format.

The Alert burst consists of six consecutive ones that identify a packet. Notice that the Source and Destination IDs are one byte and two bytes respectively, far different than the IEEE Ethernet and Token Ring formats examined earlier in the book. Notice also how relatively small the data field is; it is dwarfed by Ethernet's approximately 1500 bytes. When Ethernet has to retransmit its packets because of frequent collisions, the beauty and simplicity of Arcnet becomes apparent.

Arcnet's age is apparent, though, in the way that nodes communicate with each other using a character-oriented protocol. If node 20 wants to send a packet to node 40, it would first send a Free Buffer Enquiry (FBE) which asks if node 40 is ready to receive a transmission. Node 40 responds with an Acknowledgement (ACK) or a Negative Acknowledgement (NAK) if it declines the FBE. When node 40 receives the data packet from node 20, it checks the CRC to ensure that there was no error in transmission. It then transmits an ACK to node 20 indicating that everything arrived successfully. If it fails to send an ACK, node 20 determines that there must have been an error in transmission. Assuming the message did arrive correctly and an ACK was transmitted, node 20 would then issue an FBE to the next node scheduled to use the token.

Arcnet Plus at 20 Mbs

One of the most recent developments has been the announcement of a 20 Mbs Arcnet Plus network. Datapoint has the proprietary rights to this technology but has licensed SMC and NCR to sell products. Arcnet Plus is able to dynamically vary its data signaling rate so that it is backwardly compatible and interoperable with standard Arcnet. Network supervisors need not pull any existing Arcnet NICs or cabling but can introduce Arcnet Plus network segments selectively such as on backbones to optimize network performance.

Arcnet Plus supports packet sizes from 12.5 to 4224 bytes compared to a maximum size of 516 bytes with standard Arcnet. The network supports up to 2047 nodes per segment over standard coaxial or twisted pair wire compared to standard Arcnet's 255 nodes. This enhanced version of Arcnet will support the IEEE 802.2 48-bit addressing as well as the 802.2 media access control layer.

This will enhance compatibility with other 802 networks. Arcnet Plus will also continue to support traditional Arcnet addressing.

Network design when mixing the two Arcnet technologies might be a headache for systems integrators. Standard Arcnet NICs cannot recognize addresses above 255, so it is important to minimize communications between these two sides of a mixed network. Similarly, current hubs only transmit at 2.5Mbs; new hubs might take a while to reach the market.

Summary

Every Macintosh and Apple laser printer has a LocalTalk interface built into its hardware. While AppleTalk's transmission speed is 230.4 Kbs, AppleTalk's suite of protocols also includes drivers for Ethernet (EtherTalk) and Token Ring Network (TokenTalk). Transcendental Operating System (TOPS) offers peer-to-peer network software and hardware for the Macintosh while both NetWare and 3+ network operating systems offer sophisticated centralized file-server Macintosh networks which incorporate AppleTalk protocols and can handle Apple's own AppleShare file server packets.

Arcnet is a popular non-standard LAN technology that transmits at 2.5 Mbs with an Arcnet Plus version transmitting at 20 Mbs. Arcnet offers a variety of topologies including the star, bus, and a mix of both. Arcnet's low overhead and small-sized packets traveling under a token bus methodology results in a very efficient yet low-cost network.

7

CHAPTER

Local bridges

In this chapter, you will examine

- How bridges filter and forward frames.
- Spanning Tree bridges.
- Source Routing bridges.
- How Spanning Tree and Source Routing bridges can communicate.
- How future bridges will follow an 802.1D standard that will provide seamless linking of Spanning Tree and Source Routing bridges.

Introduction

Some industry surveys indicate that as many as 75% of Fortune 500 companies have Token Ring and Ethernet LANs they would like to link together. Bridges have become a key component of enterprise networks; they provide increased connectivity, security, and efficiency. This chapter lets you examine some of the more common types of local bridges and observe how their methods of operation differ. You will see why it is a complex process to bridge Ethernet and Token Ring networks. Finally, you will learn why a future IEEE 802 Committee standard will provide transparent bridging of these two very different networks.

The internet or enterprise network

Anyone who has followed the local area network industry over the past five years knows that large companies no longer concern themselves with linking two small LANs together. Today, companies want to know how to link together several LANs that might or might not be located at the same physical site. While the term *enterprise network* is starting to become popular, I use the traditional term *internet* to describe several networks linked together. Each individual network is known as a *subnetwork* because it is part of the larger internet.

What a local LAN bridge is

A local LAN bridge consists of the hardware and software required to link together two different LANs or subnetworks physically located at the same site into one internet. I examine remote bridges in chapter 9 when you look at wide area networks.

The simplest type of bridge examines a packet's 48-bit destination address field and compares this address with a table that lists the addresses of workstations on its network. If the address does not match any of its workstations, it forwards the packet across the bridge to the next network. These simple bridges keep forwarding packets hop by hop until they reach a network containing a workstation with the desired destination address. This process of examining address tables and forwarding packets is referred to as *Transparent Bridging*; it is a technique used by all Ethernet bridges and by some Token Ring bridges. Figure 7-1 illustrates how this type of bridge operates.

Some bridges create their own network address tables. These bridges examine the source and destination addresses in every packet transmitted onto the LANs to which it is connected. These bridges then build their own address tables that list workstation source addresses found on packets they have seen on their network with this network's corresponding number. These bridges then try to match the destination addresses of packets with one of these source addresses. When a bridge matches an address, it *filters* the packet and sends it on its way along the network where the destination workstation will recognize its own address and copy the packet to the RAM in its RAM. If no match is found, then the packet is *forwarded* and permitted to travel across the bridge to the next network. Broadcast and multicast packets are always forwarded because their destination address fields are never used as source addresses.

Bridges do not understand or concern themselves with higher level protocols. They function at the Media Access (MAC) sublayer of the OSI model's Data Link layer, far removed from the upper level protocols such as XNS or TCP/IP. As long as networks on both sides adhere to IEEE 802.2 Logical Link Control (LLC) standards, a bridge can span them regardless of differences in their media or network access method. As you will discover by reading this chapter, this means that

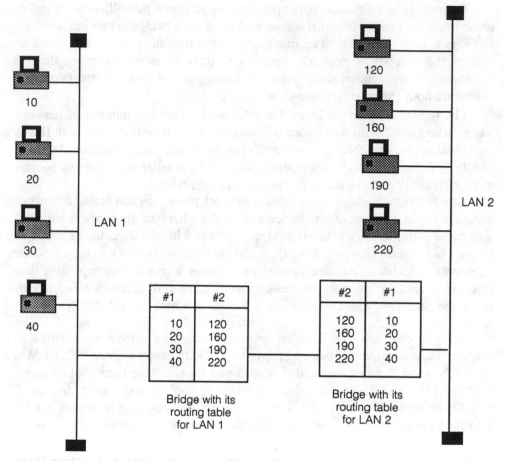

#1	#2
10	120
20	160
30	190
40	220

Bridge with its
routing table
for LAN 1

#2	#1
120	10
160	20
190	30
220	40

Bridge with its
routing table
for LAN 2

7-1 A simple bridge with transparent bridging.

it is possible for corporations to bridge their Ethernet and Token Ring networks, as well as their 802.3 LANs that might include a StarLAN, a 10BaseT Ethernet, and a thin coaxial cabled "cheapernet" network.

Why use bridges

Of a number of network design reasons for using bridges, a few include increased efficiency, security, and distance. Efficiency is usually the most often cited reasons why bridges are installed on a network. Because bridges are capable of filtering packets according to programmable criteria, a network manager could use a bridge to reduce traffic congestion and improve speed by dividing up a large network and then bridging the resulting subnets. The two smaller networks would run faster because they had less traffic.

Because larger Ethernet networks are slowed down by collisions, it makes sense to create smaller Ethernet subnetworks and use a bridge to provide such services as E-mail. Ethernet has a maximum length limitation of 2.5 Km and also restrict the number of network segments to three to avoid exceeding the 9.6 microsecond propagation delay. Network managers and systems integrators can overcome both Ethernet limitations by using bridges.

The 4 Mbs version of Token Ring Network limits the number of network workstations to 72 with unshielded twisted pair and 270 workstations with IBM's own shielded cabling. Network managers can overcome these limitations by using smaller subnetworks and then bridging them. The smaller subnetworks operate more efficiently and are easier to manage and maintain.

Another reason why bridges make a network more efficient is that a network designer can use different topologies and media wherever appropriate and then link these different networks via bridges. Offices within a department might be linked via twisted pair wire. A bridge could connect this network to the corporate fiber-optic backbone. Because twisted pair wire is so much less expensive than fiber-optic cabling, the network design saves money and increases efficiency by using the high bandwidth medium on a backbone where the most traffic is carried.

Bridges can link two similar networks that have different transmission speeds. As an example, a company might be perfectly happy with an 802.3 1 Mbs StarLAN network using unshielded twisted pair for one department but require a 10Base5 Mbs 802.3 network using thick coaxial cabling and transmitting at 10 Mbs for its manufacturing plant. A bridge buffers packets, so it is no problem for it to span packets from LANs with different transmission speeds.

Because the 802 committee developed a common Logical Link Control layer for its various network topologies, it is possible, for example, to link two Token Ring networks that are separated by an Ethernet LAN. The Ethernet LAN can forward the packets just as a mail carrier can deliver a letter written in a different language as long as the envelope (packet) follows the rules and regulations established by the IEEE 802.2 LLC standard. While added efficiency is a major reason for using bridges, bridges also can increase security. They can be programmed to forward only those packets that contain certain source or destination addresses so that only certain workstations can send information to or receive information from another subnetwork. The accounting subnetwork, for example, can have a bridge that permits only certain workstations outside this network to receive information. In addition to providing a security barrier that filters out unwarranted access, bridges also add a measure of system fault tolerance. If a single file server on a large network fails, the entire network fails. If, however, internal bridges are used so that two file servers back up each other continuously, then traffic is reduced while providing an additional measure of security in the form of a "backup" file server.

Finally, bridges can also increase the distance that a network can span. Because a bridge rebroadcasts a packet to the workstations on the receiving side, it functions like a repeater to increase the distance a packet can travel without its signal attenuating. Often bridges are *cascaded* to connect LANS sequentially as seen in Fig. 7-2.

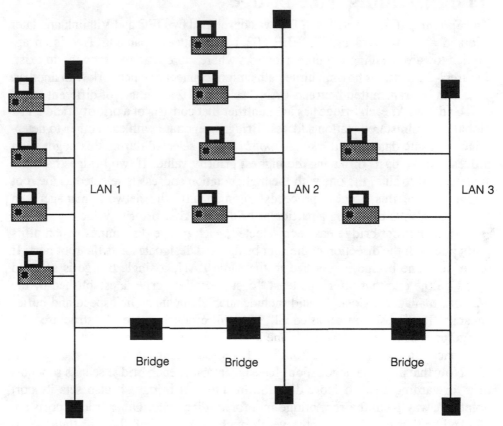

7-2 Cascaded bridges.

Intelligent bridges

All bridges have the ability to update their routing tables; that is how they keep track of which workstations have been added to the network. Intelligent bridges differ from the "simple" bridges I have been describing by offering additional capabilities. They can be programmed to filter packets based on desired criteria. I referred to an application appropriate for this type of bridge when you examined how a bridge can enhance network security by restricting traffic to and from specified subnetworks. An Ethernet segment for the accounting department might be connected to the rest of the network via a programmable bridge that only permits workstations on the corporate subnetwork to access it.

Intelligent bridges also might offer *Source Explicit Forwarding* (SEF). This feature enables network supervisors to assign internetwork access privileges by labeling specified addresses in a routing table as either accessible or inaccessible to specific users and groups.

The Spanning Tree bridge

The *Spanning Tree algorithm* (STA) was developed by DEC and Vitalink and later adopted as a standard by the IEEE 802.1 committee. Spanning Tree is an approach toward bridging multiple networks where more than one loop might exist. Figure 7-3 illustrates how multiple paths might connect one network with another. Data can be transmitted between LAN 1 and LAN 2 a number of different ways.

Under STA, each bridge has an identifier that consists of a priority field and a globally administered station address. Bridges negotiate with each other to determine the route data should take. A *root bridge* is selected during this negotiation process on the basis of having the highest priority value. If two bridges have the same priority value, the one with the higher station address is selected as the root bridge. While this process proceeds automatically, the network manager can "fix" the results by giving a particular bridge a higher priority value.

After the root bridge has been selected, each bridge determines which of its ports points in the direction of the root bridge and designates it as the root port. If more than one bridge is attached to the same LAN, a single bridge is selected based on the one that offers the least "cost" based on criteria established by the network manager. "Costs" could include such elements as line speed and buffer capacity. If all costs are set as equal, STA will produce a tree-like structure with bridge ports selected that result in the least number of hops from bridge to bridge for a packet to be transmitted from one LAN to another LAN.

Now that all these negotiations have taken place, each bridge sets its root port in a forwarding state to move data toward the root bridge. It also sets its port pointing away from the root bridge in a forwarding state. Other bridge ports are blocked so that packets cannot travel through them. As Fig. 7-4 illustrates, STA ensures that only one bridge port in each direction on a LAN is operating and that only the most efficient path is available.

What happens under STA if a bridge port goes out of service? A port that has been blocked is placed in a learning mode so that it can examine packets flowing on the network and update its database of network station addresses. The port then changes to a forwarding mode and forwards a notification of its change to the root bridge. The root bridge notifies all network bridges to update their databases to include this new bridge port.

A bridge's address database includes information on the direction to forward data for a particular workstation as well as a timer. If the timer for a particular workstation expires, then the information regarding which direction to forward data for this workstation might no longer be valid. The bridge monitors the source

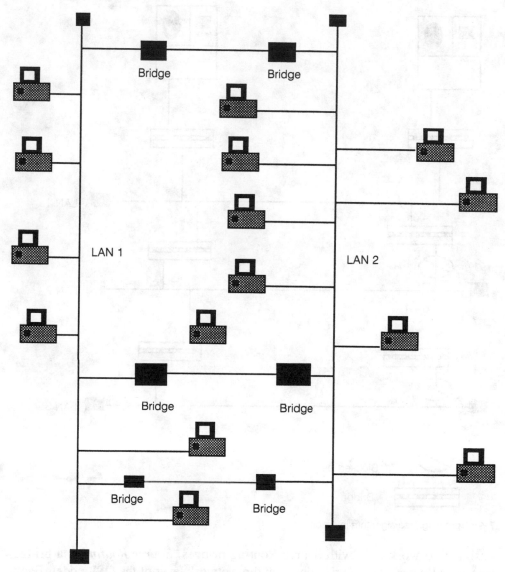

7-3 Bridging offers multiple paths between two LANs.

addresses on packets it receives and updates its address table. If a new network topology is introduced, the result might be to require a change in the direction to forward data information in a bridge's address database.

Source Routing bridges

In 1985 IBM introduced Source Routing with its Token Ring network. In fact, IBM's PC LAN program and its OS/2 Extended Edition version 1.1 are both

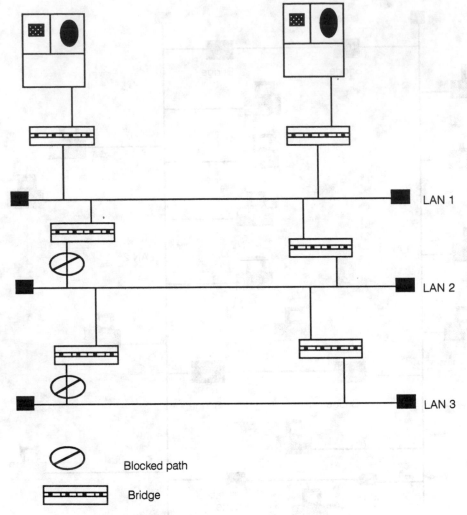

⊘   Blocked path

▭▬▭   Bridge

7-4   Spanning Tree algorithm in action.

designed to work only with Source Routing bridges. *Source Routing* is a bridge that actually performs routing duties at the Network layer of the OSI model. Each device on a LAN that uses Source Routing must have a unique six byte address. The address field's first high order bit, called the I/G bit, indicates whether there is an individual or group address. The second high order bit, the U/L bit, indicates whether the address is universally (IEEE addresses assigned to manufacturers) or locally administered.

Source Routing takes the I/G bit in the source address only and uses it as the Routing Information Indicator (RI) bit. When this bit is set to 1, it indicates the presence of additional routing information in the frame header. This additional routing information (up to 18 bytes in length) specifies the frame's complete path from source workstation to destination workstation. Figure 7-5 illustrates the location within a Token Ring frame of this critical routing information.

Broadcast	Length	Direction	Largest frame	RI1...RIn

Broadcast	Indicates whether this is a broadcast frame.
Length	Indicates the length of the routing information.
Direction	Indicates to a bridge whether this frame is traveling from source to destination or back again.
Largest frame	Indicates the largest size of the MAC information field.
RI1...RIn	Route information for each "hop" which includes a 12-bit LAN and a 4-bit bridge number.

7-5 Source routing information within a Token Ring network frame.

Each LAN ring is assigned a unique number just as an office routing slip might indicate the order in which a memo should be circulated before it reaches the file clerk for filing. If two bridges on the same LAN are parallel and can lead to the same destination, Source Routing will arbitrarily assign each of them a different number to keep the routing directions from becoming confusing. Figure 7-6 illustrates what this routing information would look like if it were translated into English.

Control (2 bytes)	RING 2	BRIDGE 1	RING 7	BRIDGE 3	RING 9	BRIDGE 0

7-6 A closer look at a source routing information field.

The length of this information field limits routing to eight ring numbers, which means a maximum of seven bridges; Source Routing bridges refer to this limitation as a seven-hop limit.

How a workstation gathers Source Routing information

A workstation gathers Source Routing information by transmitting an *all-routes broadcast frame* to all rings connected on an internet. This frame contains control information but a blank buffer that can be filled in by other workstations. Bridges fill in the numbers for the two rings they connect and their own bridge number. The destination workstation receives this broadcast frame and returns it to the source station, which now has a road map of the route that the frame took.

It is possible to use a spanning tree topology with Source Routing bridges. A special *single-route broadcast frame* is circulated once. It ensures that only certain bridges in the network are configured to pass single route type frames. Because no loops are permitted in a spanning tree topology, between any two rings only a single path can exist. Bridges will not pass a frame onto a ring if it already has circulated on that ring. A workstation uses the information it receives from its two types of broadcast frames to determine the optimal route containing the least number of hops for the frame it transmits.

The Source Routing bridge in operation

A Source Routing bridge examines every frame on each of the Token Ring Networks it links. If it sees the RI bit set to one, it then examines the routing information field to see if the two ring numbers match the two rings it connects. Assuming the routing information matches, the bridge forwards the frame across the bridge. Frames that do not have matching ring numbers are filtered.

NetWare and Source Routing

NetWare has always used a proprietary distributed routing algorithm at each of its bridges and in its file server. Novell responded to its customers who have Token Ring networks by providing a Source Routing algorithm so that NetWare bridges can communicate with Token Ring bridges on other LANs.

Current ways of linking Ethernet and Token Ring networks

Some industry surveys estimate as many as 75% of Fortune 500 companies have both Ethernet and Token Ring LANs. The accounting department might be using Ethernet to connect PCs running productivity software such as WordPerfect and Lotus 1-2-3 to their VAX computer running DEC accounting software. Other areas might be using IBM's Token Ring Network. What is a network manager or systems integrator to do in such a situation? You have already examined the differences in frame structure between the two networks and also seen that the significant differences between Spanning Tree and Source Routing approaches to routing frames.

It is absolutely critical to remember that there is a significant difference between connectivity and interoperability. *Connectivity* refers to being able to link together the two networks and transmit data while *interoperability* refers to the ability for each network to use the data transmitted to it.

Sometimes connectivity is all that is needed. Say that you have several Ethernet networks in an enterprise internet along with a 16 Mbs Token Ring network that serves primarily as a backbone, a gigantic switching station. While the 802.3 and 802.5 frames differ, they do have a common MAC layer. The Token Ring network can forward Ethernet frames through its ring and onto a bridge connected to another Ethernet network. The Token Ring Network cannot "open" the frame and understand the data contained within it, but it can understand the Source and Destination address fields. What a Token-Ring-to-Ethernet bridge does is to support Source Routing on the Token Ring side and transparent bridging on the Ethernet side.

Bridges are available today that can perform the changes in the frame required to convert an Ethernet frame to a Token Ring frame. With such bridges, workstations on the Token Ring side view the Token Ring bridge as just another bridge. Workstations on the Ethernet side, however, view the bridge as just another Ethernet workstation. Frames generated from the Token Ring side addressed to an Ethernet workstation to the bridge, where they are stripped of the Logical Link Control (LLC) protocol. They are converted into Ethernet frames and transmitted over to the Ethernet network. Frames sent from an Ethernet workstation to a Token Ring workstation must go through an additional step. The bridge must search its own address database to learn the additional routing information required for Source Routing over Token Ring networks.

The CrossComm Token Ring to Ethernet bridge family is one of the first bridges to perform this critical task. It supports higher protocols including NetWare, TCP/IP, and the 802.3 LLC protocol. As far as media, it supports thick and thin coaxial cabling, twisted pair Ethernet and StarLAN, and fiber-optic Ethernet and Token Ring. The bridge is designed to detect Ethernet packets that do not have a Source Routing information field and insert this field so that they can travel on the Token Ring side of the bridge. The actual protocol conversion that takes place is handled by CrossComm's proprietary Dynamic Conversion mode technology.

IBM's 8209 LAN Bridge can also handle the Ethernet to Token Ring protocol conversion. Because there is a significant difference in maximum frame size between Ethernet (1500 bytes) and Token Ring (approximately 5000 bytes), the 8209 bridge uses part of the Token Ring protocol to indicate to the source workstation that the maximum frame size it can use is 1500 bytes. The smaller frame sizes add overhead to the file transfer because more frames are required.

The 8209 bridge looks like a Source Routing bridge to Token Ring workstations while Ethernet workstations see all Token Ring workstations as workstations on the same Ethernet segment. Because Source Routing uses redundant parallel bridge connections while Spanning Tree permits only a single path, the 8209 bridge permits multiple connections but only one path can be active at any given time. The 8209 bridge operates in three different modes: Token Ring to Ethernet version 2, Token Ring to 802.3 LANs, and a mode in which the bridge detects the type of LAN and then switches to mode 1 or mode 2.

Source Routing Transparent bridges

Does a *Source Routing Transparent bridge* sound like a contradiction? IBM has proposed an addition to the IEEE 802.1D standard for transparent bridges that will define a Source Routing Transparent bridge (SRT). This bridge will be able to forward both Spanning Tree and Source Routing frames. IBM's proposal would seem to benefit virtually everyone in the interest of interoperability except for those customers who have already purchased IBM's own Source Routing bridges; they alone will be cut off from enterprise networking.

The Source Routing Transparent (SRT) bridge uses the routing information indicator (RI) to distinguish frames using Source Routing from those using transparent bridging. Source Routing frames set their RI indicators to one, making it easy to distinguish this group of frames.

The movement to SRT bridges will not be painless. Many industry experts point to the hardware modifications to current Source Routing bridges that will be expensive. A casualty of this new type of bridge will probably be the current solution for bridging Ethernet and Token Ring networks by performing what amounts to a protocol conversion, a transformation from one frame format to another. The future 802.1D bridges will not require anything more from the workstations on the Ethernet side because Ethernet bridges handle most of the work associated with the Spanning Tree algorithm. Workstations on the Token Ring side, however, will have to construct their routing tables and build their frames to accommodate the workstations on the Ethernet side.

A guide to selecting bridges

Bridge vendors are having a hard time differentiating their products from each other. The noise level and confusing jargon associated with bridges have grown to the point that selecting a bridge is a confusing and frustrating task even for knowledgeable systems integrators. In this section, I examine several features to look for in bridges. While you might not need specific features, this section will help you make intelligent decisions.

Packet filtering and forwarding rates

Some bridge vendors like to boast about their products' packet filtering and forwarding rates. The filtering rate in packets/second (pps) measures how quickly a bridge examines a frame, matches its address with its address table, and then decides whether to filter or forward it.

Frame sizes can vary as can network traffic. Vendors often provide information on the number of frames/second required for various frame sizes at 50% and 100% loads. With Ethernet, 100% load conditions are unrealistic because of the number of collisions under Ethernet and the subsequent dead time on the cable. Check to see if the statistics are based on the same size frames.

A network manager or systems integrator must look at how a network will be used on a day-to-day basis in order to make sense out of these statistics. Say that a network will be utilizing the TCP/IP transport protocol heavily. This protocol provides unacknowledged delivery service, which means that the network could become flooded with TCP/IP datagrams because source workstations do not have to wait for acknowledgements before sending large files.

Also, bridge vendors rarely specify the conditions under which their statistics were gathered. Just as the manufacturers of dot-matrix printers publish statistics on characters/second that fail to take into account the use of any special printing features, filtering and forwards rates for bridges rarely indicate the traffic conditions on both sides of the bridge.

Statistics on bridges for Ethernet-like half-duplex networks rarely point out that these statistics hold only for the condition in which the bridge is forwarding packets to a network with no current traffic to slow up the process. That is simply not realistic. Similarly, bridge statistics are usually based on the very simplest of bridges and ignore any programmed filtering even though that might be the precise reason why the network manager selects a specific type of bridge.

Rickert (see Bibliography) has published statistics that indicate that the key to a bridge's success could be the way it handles bursty traffic. He believes that the size of a bridge's queue or holding area for frames as critical. The queue should be large enough to handle reasonable temporary overloads, but not too large to introduce excessive delays. If a queue is too small, then frames will be lost when they back up in the queue. If the queue is too large, frames will remain in the queue past their "time-out" and still be transmitted by the bridge that is too simple to consider such circumstances. Rickert provides some valuable formulas to help the network manager or systems integrator calculate optimal queue size.

Filtering on the basis of packet length

Some bridges have the ability to filter packets based on the actual packet length. If a network has a lot of interactive traffic (short block lengths) as well as a lot of large file transfers, a network manager might want to give priority to the interactive traffic so that response time will be faster. By programming a bridge to block longer packets during heavy traffic periods, a network manager can keep response times bearable.

"Learning" bridges

Some network managers must deal with networks where some users are frequently moving from area to area while other users are being added or deleted on a daily basis. Some bridges require the network manager to modify the bridge's network address table each time there is a change. Other bridges are able to learn the locations of devices by examining the source address fields of packets they handle and then modify their own tables. These "learning" bridges are worth the additional expense when network managers spend inordinate amounts of time manually modifying bridge address tables.

Link ports

The ports on some bridges can be individually configured. In the case of the Retix Model 2265 local LAN bridge, for example, this means that one port could be configured for a standard 802.3 network (10Base5) while the other port could be configured for thin Ethernet (10Base2). This particular bridge also has a StarLAN option to link a StarLAN network with Ethernet. In the case of the Hughes 8050 Broadband/Ethernet Bridge, it is possible to link a baseband Ethernet LAN with a broadband 2 Mbs Ethernet network.

The ability to filter broadcast and multicast packets

Some bridges have the ability to filter broadcast and multicast packets. Broadcast storms consist of a packet that is broadcast and then endlessly replicated until it creates so much traffic that it brings a network to its knees. By being able to filter and restrict broadcast and multicast packets, bridges can reduce broadcast storms.

Load balancing

Load balancing makes it possible for multiple ports to carry information to the same destination. By balancing the data traffic on two 56 Kbs lines, the effect is to widen the total bandwidth transmission to 112 Kbs. Different bridge vendors have their own proprietary methods of implementing load balancing. Some bridges simply divide up all traffic evenly using a first-come-first-served approach. Others handle a specific queue first before handling a second queue. Sequencing protocols used by these bridge vendors can be important because packets might arrive out of order.

Load balancing also provides a system fault tolerance feature because the built-in redundancy means that some level of communication is maintained even if one line goes down.

Bridge management and statistical software

Some bridges come with network software that provides network management features and the ability to generate statistical reports on the bridge's activity. Most software provides information on the number of packets filtered, forwarded, refused, and rejected.

DEC's LAN Bridge 100 offers some very sophisticated statistical reports on its Ethernet bridge including network utilization and throughput, the top ten protocols used, and the top ten transmitting stations. It also provides information on which workstations transmit multicast packets. Because DEC's Local Area Transport (LAT) protocol can only be bridged and not routed, DEC network managers need this protocol information because they cannot obtain it by using routers.

Summary

Bridges link subnetworks into an enterprise-wide internet. By dividing large networks into smaller subnetworks and bridging them, network managers gain greater efficiency because there is less traffic congestion. The subnets provide greater security because of their redundancy than is possible with a single network. The Spanning Tree algorithm is used in Ethernet bridges. It requires a single path with no loops. Token Ring networks use Source Routing, an approach that places responsibility upon the source workstation to develop the complete routing path for a frame. While current Ethernet to Token Ring bridges perform protocol conversion and transform a frame from one format to the other depending upon the direction of the transmission, future bridges will be able to read a frame and transmit it in a transparent manner.

8
CHAPTER

Local routers and brouters

This chapter examines

- How a router differs from a bridge.
- Some of the major protocols associated with routing.
- Trends toward more efficient routing.
- Major router features.
- How a brouter operates.

Introduction

Chapter 7 examined how bridges link together networks at the Data Link layer of the OSI model. Bridges make connected networks look like one very large network. When large networks need to be linked together and when packets need to be routed according to their higher level protocols, a router is needed. This chapter examines how a router operates at the Network layer of the OSI model. This chapter looks at some of the major protocols used by routers to ensure safe delivery of packets. You will see the hybrid combination of a bridge and a router known as a brouter and investigate what circumstances are ideal for brouters.

What a router is

A *router* operates at the Network layer of the OSI model. Unlike Spanning Tree bridges, routers are ideally suited for large networks with several loops or redundant paths. While bridges do not concern themselves with higher level protocols, routers are protocol-specific. A router is designed to support specific protocols such as TCP/IP, XNS, NetBIOS, or DECnet and utilize the addressing schemes, error checking, and routing techniques that characterize these protocols.

Routers are particularly valuable on very large internets where the subnets might not have the same MAC layers. A 3Com 3+ LAN with TCP/IP, for example, can use a router to communicate with a VAX running TCP/IP with its VMS operating system, with an HP 3000 running TCP/IP with its UNIX operating system, and with a NetWare network running TCP/IP.

Sophisticated routers are able to handle the routing of packets to other networks even though these other networks might utilize different addressing schemes and even different error recovery schemes.

Figure 8-1 illustrates how routers operate. Unlike many bridges, routers are able to maintain several alternative paths and select the most appropriate path given certain defined conditions such as traffic congestion. In this case, a packet indicates a workstation on network XYZ as its destination address. Router 1 looks over its routing tables and determines that the optimum path is through Router 4. Unfortunately, Router 1 also realizes that the direct path to Router 4 is congested. It chooses the alternative path through Router 2 and Router 3.

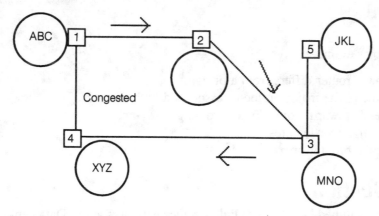

8-1 A router selects the best path.

Routers are far more intelligent than bridges. Routers use this intelligence to determine the optimum path for connecting together two LANs. A router is also "smart" enough to perform the packet segmentation and reassembly required to accommodate intermediate networks in which packet sizes are different.

Local and remote routers

Routers can be local or remote. This chapter examines local routers, devices that physically are connected to networks at the same site. I defer the discussion of remote routers to chapter 9 when I show the components of a wide area network. At that time, you will see how routers can transmit packets over high-speed lines from one part of the country to another.

Static routers

Static routers require the network manager to create routing tables. These tables remain static (unchanged) until the network manager changes them to reflect changes in network activity or node placement. Because static routers require manual operation to create and maintain routing tables, they are not desirable for larger networks where routing conditions might be changing on a minute-by-minute basis.

Dynamic routers

Dynamic routers use sophisticated algorithms to route packets along the most optimal path at the moment. Network protocol suites must have a corresponding routing protocol. Cisco Systems, for example, has a proprietary routing protocol known as Interior Gateway Routing Protocol (IGRP). IGRP considers network traffic, path reliability, and speed in selecting the optimum path.

Berkeley-derived UNIX systems use the Routing Information Protocol (RIP) to calculate how many hops through other routers different paths would encompass. They then choose the path with the fewest hops as the optimal path.

A dynamic router is constantly exchanging packets with other routers so that it can learn of any new destinations or changes in existing workstations and update its address routing tables. Dynamic routers will recognize traffic congestion and failed circuits and select an alternate route if these conditions make the usual optimal path unacceptable.

The two major internal routing algorithms are called distance vector and link state. The *distance vector* approach, sometimes also known as the *Bellman-Ford protocol*, is very common today and is used by Router Information Protocol (RIP). The distance vector approach keeps track of the route between source and destination address in terms of "hop count" or the number of routers that a packet must cross. This algorithm imposes a maximum of 15 hops for any route.

The *link state* approach requires a dynamic router to broadcast packets describing its own links to other routers. All routers on the network use these broadcast packets to assemble their own routing tables. This chapter returns to this topic later when you examine a new routing protocol known as OSPF.

Routers create "fire walls"

One major advantage that a router has over a bridge is that a router does not automatically replicate all broadcast messages. This means that if a device begins to flood a network with copies of a single packet, the routers are able to keep the problem local by presenting a "fire wall" that prevents the storm from engulfing the entire network.

Easier management of a large internet

Routers can take advantage of addressing schemes such as the one used by Internet Protocol (IP) to create subnetworks. An IP address includes a network number, subnetwork number, and host number. The XYZ Corporation might have a corporate headquarters as well as three local plants, each of which has its own subnetwork. The "host" number refers to any IP device that has an IP address; these devices can take the form of bridges, personal computers, mainframe hosts, etc.

Figure 8-2 illustrates a large company that has four major networks. The VAX is used to handle accounting, while other departments use a Banyan server running VINES, a 3Com server running 3 + Open, and a Novell file server running NetWare. Rather than concern itself with the incompatibilities of the various network operating systems, the company opted to run TCP/IP on all four networks and then link them together via routers.

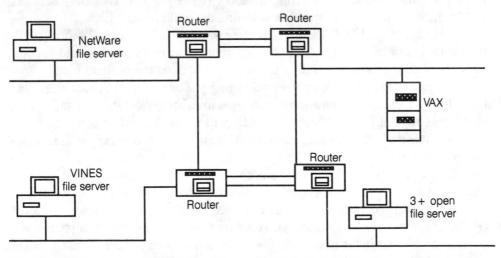

8-2   Routers link subnets together for more efficient management.

Routers can be programmed to be very selective as to the class of service they provide. This enables the company to permit electronic mail to flow and to restrict certain types of accounting information. Notice also that the routers offer a redundancy that means that if one path is blocked, packets can be routed via an alternate path.

Finally, routers make network management easier by offering network management software that monitors and controls network operations. The TCP/IP routers used in this example provide Simple Network Management Protocol (SNMP), a topic covered in chapter 12 when you look at network management systems.

Point-to-Point Protocol (PPP)
for multivendor router communications

Many examples in data communications of standards are not really very standard. The RS-232C standard is a good example; printer manufacturers never have agreed on which pins should be used for specific handshaking functions. As a result, you cannot simply substitute one printer's serial cable for a different vendor's printer cable and expect it to work.

The same sort of problem exists with routers. While TCP/IP routers use the Internet Protocol (IP) for routing their datagrams, vendors used Serial Line Internet Protocol (SLIP) as a basis for developing different ways of encapsulating IP datagrams. This has made it difficult or even impossible to mix and match TCP/IP routers on the same network. Lack of router compatibility has been a particular problem for enterprise networks in which one plant might be using a low-end router to satisfy its simple needs while another facility might be using a sophisticated router from another vendor to meet its complex needs. Recently the Internet Engineering Task Force (IETF) completed work on its Point-to-Point Protocol (PPP).

PPP replaces SLIP with a standard method for encapsulating IP datagrams. This new protocol means that systems integrators can design direct serial connections between TCP/IP routers at very high speeds ranging from 9.6 Kbs for dial up lines to T-1 and fractional T-1 service (see chapter 9 on wide area networks).

Open Shortest Path First (OSPF)

The U.S. Department of Defense's Internet Activities Board sets internet policy for TCP/IP users. The Board has created a task force known as the Internet Engineering Task Force OSPF Working Group to develop a dynamic routing protocol for TCP/IP that will provide features not offered by Routing Internet Protocol (RIP).

RIP has limitations when used with networks of more than 100 routers because of RIP's reliance on the Bellman-Ford algorithm. This approach requires the frequent broadcast of the entire routing table. On large internets with over 100 routers, routing updates take longer and longer and consume increasing amounts of bandwidth.

RIP has other limitations. Packets cannot travel through more than 15 routers from sender to receiver. This protocol selects a single path to each destination and is not capable of considering such factors as traffic congestion, delay, and bandwidth.

The Open Shortest Path First (OSPF) protocol uses a link-state and shortest-path-first algorithm. Each router broadcasts a packet that describes its own local links. Routers collect information from these broadcast packets to build their own network routing tables. Because these packets describing local links are very short, they cause far less traffic congestion than RIP's approach of broadcasting very large routing tables describing the entire network.

Another advantage of OSPF is that network managers can configure their routers to provide least-cost routing according to whatever criteria these managers define as a "cost." Unlike RIP, OSPF does not limit the number of routers that can be used nor does it limit routing to a single path; loads can be distributed over several different paths to optimize available bandwidth.

OSPF provides far more flexibility than RIP when it comes to type-of-service. This new protocol offers eight classes of service with separate paths available for each path. Network managers can program their routers so that certain types of packets (large file transfers that are not time-sensitive) are sent via satellite with delays that could stretch to several hours. Time-sensitive packets, on the other hand, can be given a class of service that will route them via more expensive phone lines.

The good news about OSPF is that the task force has developed procedures so that large networks can run both RIP and OSPF as a dual protocol stack as a temporary solution while they work on converting to the latter protocol. OSPF can route information to RIP transparently so that users are not even aware of this conversion process.

Routing features to consider

It is a jungle out there, with dozens of routers that each claim to be superior. Whether a particular feature is really beneficial or not is a decision that you will have to make as network manager or as the systems integrator designing the entire project. This section examines some of the more significant features routers offer so that you can make an informed decision.

Number/type of local and wide area network interfaces

The number of interfaces available on a router vary widely according to vendor and model. Proteon's p4200 series router, for example, offers 7 LAN ports and 14 WAN ports. Because routers are protocol specific, this particular router is designed to handle Ethernet versions 1 and 2 to IEEE 802.3 networks and IEEE 802.5 networks to Proteon's own proprietary ProNet-4 and ProNet-50 networks. Multiple WAN ports are so important because WAN links are much slower than local links and the bandwidth is much smaller. This basic difference between

WANs and LANs will become apparent in chapter 9 when you look at wide area networks.

The type of WAN interface on a router is just as important as the number of ports available. A network manager or systems integrator must select the appropriate router model for a specific network design. While many models offer RS-232-C, RS-449, and CCITT V.35 interfaces, a few also offer a fiber-optic FDDI interface. In the case of AT&T's StarTroup X.25 router, an X.25 interface to public data networks is even offered.

Network management protocols supported

On large networks it is essential to be able to gather detailed routing statistical reports as well as "fine-tune" routers for optimal performance. Routers vary widely as far as the network management software they support. Some support the IEEE 802.1 network management standard, others support Simple Network Management Protocol (SNMP), which is examined in chapter 12's discussion of network management. Some routers support only the vendor's own proprietary network management software. Systems integrators must consider long and hard whether or not they want to be locked into a specific proprietary network management scheme that probably will remain static and not grow the same way as industry supported standards.

Router performance

The number of packets per second (PPS) a router can handle is very revealing. There is a lot of overhead involved in routing decisions. The PPS figure takes into account the time required for routers to access their tables and decide on the optimum path. Unfortunately, every router vendor has a different way of measuring PPS. Are you dealing with packets traveling in both directions? Are you dealing only with packets that do not have to be segmented to travel to a network with a different packet size? How many packets are lost? What happens to speed when the router is programmed to permit only certain types of packets to pass?

Protocols supported

Because multiprotocol routers are available today, it is essential that the systems integrator consider future as well as present routing needs. TCP/IP has different broadcast formats; will the router's protocol implementation be able to support the different TCP/IP versions on an enterprise network? Similarly, while TCP/IP and its accompanying SNMP management protocol might be acceptable for the present, does the router also support the OSI suite of protocols and its CMOT management protocol? OSI protocols that could prove essential in the future for network routing include Connectionless Network Protocol (CLNP), End System to Intermediate System (ES to IS) routing, and Network Service Access Point (NSAP).

What types of networks will join the enterprise network in the future? If UNIX systems are on the drawing board, then Routing Information Protocol (RIP) is essential because it is the interior routing protocol used on Berkeley-derived UNIX systems. Will there be communication in the future with the Defense Data Network (DDN)? The DDN supports Exterior Gateway Protocol (EGP), which is also known as Request for Comment (RFC) 888 and 904. Security requirements on the Department of Defense network require an IP router that can provide datagrams that support connection to the Blacker interface for secure public data networks (X.25). Figure 8-3 lists some of the major protocols routers support along with the standard that defines them where appropriate.

Protocol	Source
IP	RFC 791, 1009
RIP – IP	RFC 1058
TCP	RFC 793
SNMP	RFC 1065, 1066, 1098
CMOT	RFC 1095
IPX	Novell
XNS	XSIS028112
RTMP	Apple
NBP	Apple
EP	Apple
ZIP	Apple

8-3 Major protocols supported by routers.

Security

Some routers offer security options that enable you to filter out packets bound for proprietary or secured systems on the basis of their IP addresses. These routers can also be programmed to filter on the basis of message type; this means that electronic mail can be permitted while file transfers can be banned.

Bridges vs. routers

While chapter 7 was devoted entirely to bridges, this chapter has dealt only with routers. One major issue confronting network managers and systems integrators is how to distinguish the need for a bridge from the need for a router. This section compares and contrasts the two types of network interoperability devices.

Bridges are ideal when two networks with different higher level protocols, but the same MAC layers need to be linked together. Bridges are relatively inexpensive and much faster than most routers. They also are much easier to install and to maintain. Once installed, bridges can automatically learn the network location of stations by listening to the source addresses of network traffic.

Bridges are not ideal, though, with large, complex networks for a variety of reasons. Because bridges pass all traffic including broadcast storms, a few NIC problems could bring down a very large internet. Also, because many bridges require a single path between networks, they lack the system fault tolerance that routers' multiple paths provide.

Because more and more networks now are running multiple protocols, a major advantage of a router is its ability to pass packets with specific protocols from one network to another. Routers using dynamic routing schemes are able to adjust to changing network conditions and provide network management functions not offered by bridges.

Another major advantage of a router over a bridge is its ability to perform packet segmentation and reassembly to accommodate intermediate networks with different packet sizes. An example of this situation might be the need to connect two Ethernet networks running NetWare via an Arcnet network running NetWare. Ethernet and Arcnet packet sizes vary considerably in size.

While they are considerably more complex and more expensive than bridges or routers, some situations might require a hybrid of the two devices called *brouters*. This next section examines this new network tool.

Brouters

While definitions vary widely by vendor, in this book I define a *brouter* as a hybrid bridge and router that is able to perform both functions. It first attempts to make a routing decision, but reverts to bridge status if unable to do so. Halley Systems' ConnectLAN 202 Local Token Ring Brouter will serve as an example how a brouter operates.

In Fig. 8-4, an IBM 9370 host uses the IBM source routing approach to communicate with an IBM Token Ring. The Token Ring is connected to another 802.5 LAN, this time with a Novell NetWare file server using the IPX protocol; the brouter uses 802.5 MAC layer procedures to pass its data transparently between these two Token Ring networks.

The NetWare Token Ring Network does not use source routing. The brouter has the ability to recognize source routed frames and forward them per the route defined in the frame. If the packet does not have its source routing information, the brouter is able to provide the best route to the destination address. In a mixed environment, this particular brouter can coexist with other vendors' source and transparent bridges so long as it is the first and last bridge in the chain as pictured in Fig. 8-4. Finally, the packet is then routed to an IBM Token Ring Network that does use source routing.

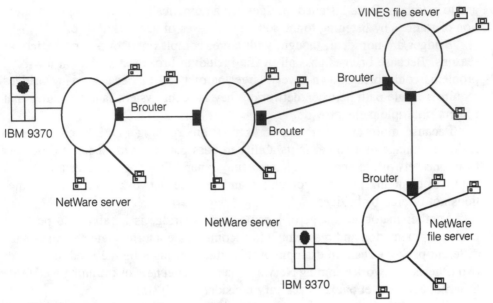

8-4 Brouters in operation.

How a brouter uses its routing tables

Figure 8-5 illustrates a brouter in action; I use RAD Network Devices' Extended Ethernet LAN to illustrate how brouters use their routing tables. This brouter is attached to an Ethernet or IEEE 802.3 LAN like any other node. Serial links connect the brouters.

RAD's brouters use a database called LAN-table to store addresses for nodes attached to their own LAN. If an address is not detected after a certain period of time, it is deleted from this table. A second database called NET-table contains all the node addresses for the extended network in terms of particular bridges. A third database called ROUTING-table contains directions for the optimal and second-best paths for routing packets to each bridge in the network. These brouters broadcast messages periodically that update everyone on the network as to which nodes have been added, deleted, or modified.

Assume that Node A wishes to send a packet to Node B. The following steps would take place:

1. Bridge #5 uses its LAN-table and NET-table to conclude that the packet has to be forwarded to a LAN connected to Bridge #4.
2. Bridge #5 uses its ROUTING-table to find out that the best path to Bridge #4 is via L7. The packet is transmitted to L7.
3. Bridge #9 uses its ROUTING-table to determine the best way to route the packet. It sends it to L4.
4. Bridge #4 receives the packet, de-encapsulates it, and then sends it to LAN3.

5. If L4 has failed, Bridge #9 is aware of this fact and uses its ROUTING-table to send the packet back to L7, which is the second best path to Bridge #4.
6. Bridge #5 receives the same packet it transmitted and will forward the packet using the second best direction—i.e., to L5.
7. Bridge #2 to L2; Bridge #3 to L3; Bridge #4 to LAN 3 completes the sequence (courtesy of RAD Network Devices).

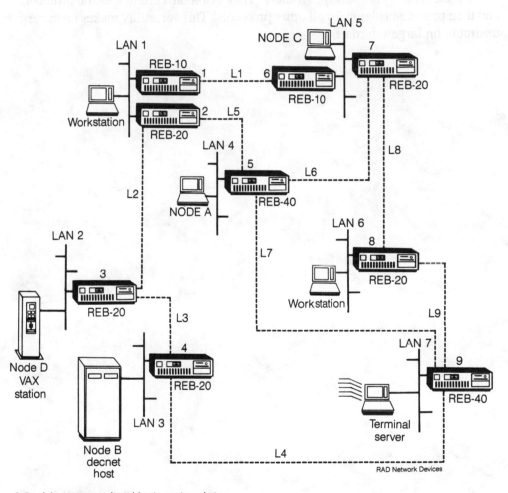

8-5 A brouter uses its tables to rout packets.

Summary

Routers function at the Network layer of the OSI model and are protocol-specific. One function they perform is the creation of "fire walls" that prevent broadcast storms on one network from sweeping across the entire internet. Routers can be programmed to provide different classes of service and to use different routes for different types of packets.

Industry committees have developed new standards such as Point-to-Point Protocol (PPP) and Open Shortest Path First (OSPF) that will make routing much more efficient. While routers differ widely when it comes to features, routing speed, protocols available, programmability, and security are important criteria to use when evaluating routing products.

Brouters are hybrid bridges/routers. They can route certain specific protocols and then provide bridging for all other protocols. This versatility makes them very desirable on large internets.

9
CHAPTER

Wide area networks

This chapter examines

- Metropolitan area networks (MANs).
- Wide area networks (WANs).
- T-1 links.
- Packet switched networks.
- SONET.

Introduction

Networks are no longer limited to one site. They may be city-wide (a metropolitan area network), or global (wide area networks). This chapter examines the nuts and bolts associated with building large networks and looks at a number of different transmission options ranging from T-1 links to packet switched networks. It concludes by looking at some evolving technologies that could dominate the next decade. This chapter is a survey. Reading it will not make you an expert on wide area networks, but it should help you understand some key concepts and learn some of the jargon associated with this complex topic.

What a metropolitan area network (MAN) is

The past several chapters have examined different types of local area networks, workstations linked together at a single site. Later, this chapter examines wide area networks, networks covering hundreds and even thousands of miles. In between LAN and WAN lies the *metropolitan area network* (MAN), a network that covers an entire city.

The IEEE 802.6 Committee has developed recommendations for a MAN that incorporate the concept of dual counter-rotating rings or buses similar to FDDI. MANs are designed to act as digital backbones that link together LANs throughout the city. They are designed to handle voice, video, and data traffic at speeds in excess of 100 Mbs and can incorporate optic fiber, coaxial cable, and even radio transmission as media.

The MAN is composed of dozens of subnetworks that communicate with each other through bridges, routers or gateways. The "glue" that makes all this work is a protocol known as *distributed queue dual bus* (DQDB). As Fig. 9-1 illustrates, DQDB consists of a dual bus topology with traffic traveling in opposite directions. Fixed length "slots" originate at the head of a bus and terminate at the end of a bus. An access unit (AU) attaches a network workstation to the dual bus cabling. The AU contains the protocol necessary to perform DQDB functions. Malfunctioning AUs are ignored by the network.

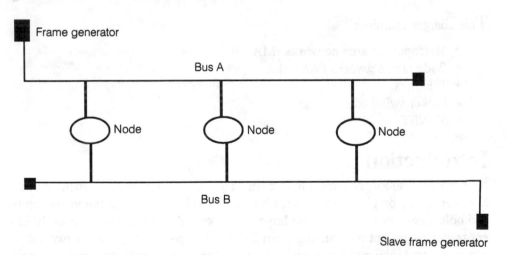

9-1   The IEEE 802.6 dual bus topology.

Nodes use a "QA slot," a packet that includes a header and a data field. Two key fields in this packet include a busy bit, which indicates whether or not a slot is empty, and a Request field, which indicates whether the slot is being queued for transmission.

Nodes set bits on QA slots traveling on one bus to reserve a slot traveling on the other bus. Nodes maintain a counter that tells them how many requests are pending in a queue; hence, they know how many empty slots a node must ignore before it becomes its turn to access the slot. The advantage of this type of approach is that the slot is constantly in use; there are always nodes with reservations waiting their turn.

To get more information on available MANs in your area, talk with your local phone company. It is the Pacific Bells, Atlantic Bells, etc., that are promoting these city-wide networks using their enormous switching capacities. This technology has already been through some beta testing of this technology by Pacific Bell, BellSouth, and Nynex in conjunction with AT&T.

Proteon and the Australian company QPSX recently announced the development of a multiprotocol router to function as an interface between 802.6 systems and FDDI. This announcement is significant because many large companies are likely to adopt FDDI as their standard for corporate network backbones. The link between FDDI and 802.6 will help to link LANs, MANs, and the WANs linking backbones together.

The 1990 Interop convention illustrated how far MANs have come. AT&T and four regional Bell operating companies demonstrated switched multimegabit data service (SMDS), which is the best known of current MAN service. Siemens demonstrated its QPSX MAN switch. Significantly, one of Siemens' demonstrations featured an Ethernet LAN connected to a MAN switch. This switch was connected to another MAN switch which, in turn, was linked to a second Ethernet LAN. Another Siemens' demo featured a Macintosh microcomputer linked to a remote mainframe computer via a MAN. The two computers ran graphics-oriented programs in a client-server environment. These demonstrations illustrated why interest in MANs is growing; they have the speed and bandwidth to link together LANs as well as incorporate host computers in city-wide networks.

What wide area networks (WANs) are

Wide area networks (WANs) link together networks located in different geographic areas. A company might have to link together its Ethernet LAN in Boston with its Token Ring network in Los Angeles. Another company might want to link together several sites so that these sites can exchange both voice and data information.

One major problem for network designers is that while PC-based local area networks and mainframe networks both routinely transmit data at several million bits/second, the transmission speeds over phone lines have lagged considerably. Linking two 10 Mbs Ethernet LANs with a 19.2 Kbs analog phone line is bound to create a serious traffic bottleneck. Some companies still struggle with 9600 bps modems. This congestion problem is becoming more manageable because of the growth of digital transmission services, as well as the development of more sophisticated types of services such as frame relay that you will consider later in this chapter.

A major problem for network managers and network designers is that WAN links are inherently less reliable than local transmission links. Error checking might not be critical on a Token Ring LAN, but it becomes a major concern when data is transmitted over phone lines that are subject to all kinds of electrical interference. When remote communications are disrupted and data has to be retransmitted, the LAN-to-WAN link becomes even more congested and inefficient.

The effect of divestiture on WANs

The breakup of the Bell system has dramatically changed the telecommunications industry and, in turn, the ways that companies transmit their voice and data on wide area networks. Prior to divestiture, a company dealt exclusively with the Bell system. Today, network managers as well as systems integrators designing wide area networks must deal with several different vendors. From the customer's premises to the closest central office (CO) is the province of the local phone company, a *local exchange company* (LEC). LECs include the Bell operating companies (Pacific Bell, Atlantic Bell, Southwest Bell, etc.) as well as a number of independent companies.

Here is where the telecommunications jargon becomes a bit oppressive, but it is important to understand who you must deal with in order to send voice or data from one network to another network. The LECs control all calls made within their geographic areas or *local area transport area* (LATA).

An LEC provides service within all the LATAs within its territory, but it cannot route a call from one to the other without going through an inter-exchange carrier's network. Within each LATA are interface points to the interLATA carriers that are known as a *Point of Presence* (POP). Each interLATA carrier such as AT&T, MCI, or Sprint have their own lists of POPs. AT&T calls its POP a *Central Office* (CO). These POPs are the only places within a LATA where an interLATA carrier can receive and deliver traffic. Figure 9-2 illustrates the route a call takes from one LATA to another LATA.

Digital signal transmission

In 1957 the Bell system installed its first T-1 trunk to carry high speed digital voice signals. Because these are digital and not analog signals, a device is needed to generate these digital signals. The digital pulses generated at a customer's site have to be filtered effectively to eliminate noise and distortion. Customers interface with the telephone company's digital network through a channel service unit (CSU) or a data service unit (DSU).

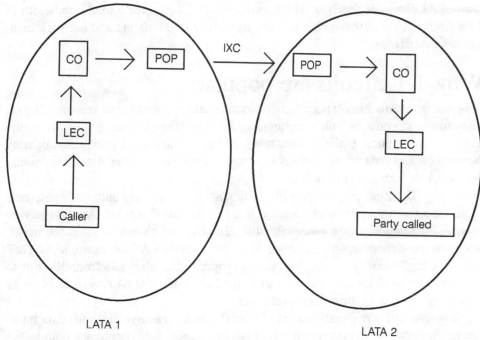

9-2 The route a call takes.

Both the CSU and the DSU function as digital modems, though the CSU also provides some line conditioning as well as some diagnostic functions. A T-1 trunk contains 24 channels. Each channel is capable of handling 64,000 bits/second. An additional 64,000 bits/second are required for error checking so that one T-1 line requires a bandwidth of 1.544 Mbs:

64,000 bps/channel $*$ 24 channels   = 1.536 Mbs
8 bps/sample $*$ 8000 samples/second = 64000 bps
Total   1.544 Mbs

This 1.544 Mbs rate is known in the telecommunications industry as *DS-1* (Digital Signal at Level 1). An entire hierarchy of digital signal bandwidth options are available:

Signal	Signal speed	Number of T-1 channels
DS-1	1.544 Mbs	1
DS-2	6.312	4
DS-3	45	28
DS-4	274	168

The T-1 (DS-1) and T-3 (DS-3) circuits are popular. The European digital hierarchy is slightly different from this North American standard. In Europe DS-1 consists of 32 channels, each of which transmits at 64 Kbs for a total bandwidth of 2.048 Mbs. Two of these channels are used only for signaling and network management functions.

Why T-1 circuits are popular

T-1 (and by extension T-3) circuits are so popular for a number of reasons. Digital transmission produces much higher quality voice signals than analog transmission. As mentioned earlier, companies can save substantially by consolidating their voice and data transmissions over the same circuit rather than maintaining two separate transmission paths.

Many T-1 multiplexers provide redundancy by offering automatic alternate routing so that other circuits are used if a path is out of service. Another advantage of T-1 service is that it is so flexible. The bandwidth can be allocated in different ways depending upon voice and data needs. As an example, AT&T Acculink multiplexers permit the user to program data channels from 300 bps to 1.5 Mbs. Voice channels can be programmed to transmit at 64 Kbs or at 24 or 32 Kbs using different compression schemes.

T-1 multiplexers usually have both synchronous and asynchronous data interfaces. A network manager with several low-speed data terminals could take advantage of a subrate multiplexer to consolidate these low-speed data sources into a single DS-0 channel. Figure 9-3 illustrates how a subrate multiplexer can

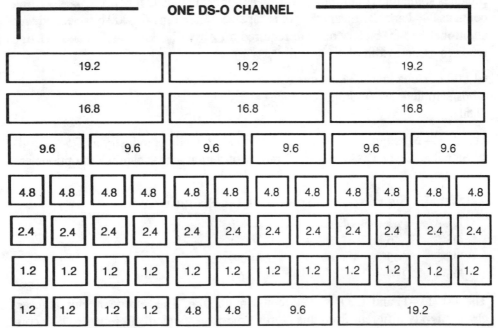

9-3 Subdividing a single DS-0 channel. CoastCom

CoastCom

fill a single DS-0 channel efficiently. Figure 9-4 illustrates how a subrate multiplexer can send information from 12 different data circuits to a T-1 multiplexer. This data stream then goes through a Digital Access and Cross Connect device (DACS) that routes it to the appropriate T-1 multiplexers to complete the journey.

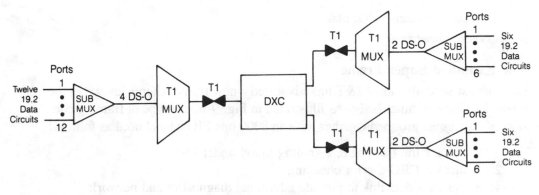

9-4 Consolidating several low-speed data streams with a subrate multiplexer. CoastCom

Another nice feature of T-1 service is that lines can be expanded easily by adding a circuit card to the T-1 multiplexers at each end of transmission. Once again using AT&T products as an example, the Dataphone II model 740 can support up to 128 lines while the model 741 Dataphone II can support up to 16 lines.

T-1 frames

A T-1 trunk carries a serial bit stream that is transmitted using time division multiplexing on a frame-by-frame basis. A frame consists of 192 bits (8 bits × 24 channels) plus one additional synchronization bit for a total of 193 bits.

Before divestiture, AT&T used T-1 lines for internal purposes, but customers were offered Voice Grade Private Lines (VGPL) for voice transmission and Dataphone Digital Service (DDS) for data transmission. When AT&T tariffed T-1 service in 1983, it became possible for corporations to combine their voice and data traffic over T-1 lines and save considerable money.

Over thirty vendors offer T-1 equipment today. In order to understand specifications for these different products, it is necessary to spend some time looking at such issues as how the data stream is framed, how error checking is performed, and the type of compression scheme (if any) used for transmitting the data.

The standard D-4 Super Frame

The telecommunications standard D-4 "super frame" framing scheme consists of creating a "super frame" of 12 separate 193-bit frames. As Fig. 9-5 illustrates, a framing bit is used to identify both the channel and the signaling frame.

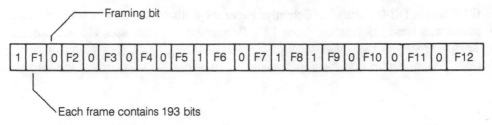

Framing bit

| 1 | F1 | 0 | F2 | 0 | F3 | 0 | F4 | 0 | F5 | 1 | F6 | 0 | F7 | 1 | F8 | 1 | F9 | 0 | F10 | 0 | F11 | 0 | F12 |

Each frame contains 193 bits

9-5 A standard superframe.

The Extended Super Frame

For the past several years AT&T has advocated a new frame scheme known as the Extended Super Frame (ESF). As illustrated in Fig. 9-6, this type of framing consists of 24 frames grouped together with an 8000 bps FE channel used as follows:

2000 bps for the framing & signaling found under D-4
2000 bps for CRC-6 error checking
4000 bps as a data link to provide additional diagnostics and network
management functions

| DL | F1 | C2 | F3 | DL | F4 | 0 | DL | F5 | C6 | F7 | DL | F8 | 0 | DL | F9 | C3 | F10 | DL | F11 | 1 | F12 | DL | F13 | C4 | F14 | DL | F15 | 0 | F16 | DL | F17 | C5 | F18 | DL | F19 | ... | F24 |

Extended Superframe = 24 frames
Sync bit pattern at head of frames 4, 8, 12, 16, 20, and 24
Six CRC bits at head of frames 2, 6, 10, 14, 18, and 22
Twelve bits in odd numbered frames (DL) not currently used

9-6 The ESF framing pattern.

The 4000 bps data link can handle the accumulation of performance data as information on logic errors. This information is stored in registers that can be accessed by the carrier or by the customer. Figure 9-7 illustrates how this network management information is accessed. The Channel Service Unit (CSU) pictured here serves as the interface between the customer's terminal equipment and the carrier. Installed at the end of each T-1 circuit, the CSU manages and monitors each of the T-1 channels. It also handles ESF framing including the CRC error checking function and the data link information. AT&T currently uses ESF to monitor and maintain its T-1 lines without charge to users.

ESF is growing in popularity because the diagnostics it provides results in less down-time. In addition, the CRC error rate indicates any degradation in transmission performance, a sure sign that repairs need to be done before conditions become worse.

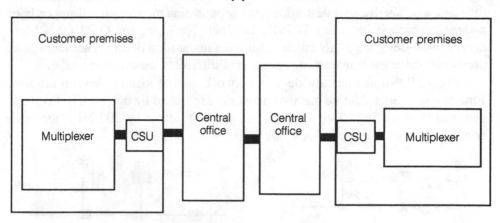

9-7 End-to-end performance monitoring with ESF.

Time division multiplexing

Data from a number of different sources feeds into each of the 24 DS-0 channels comprising a DS-1 line. This data must be placed in the appropriate superframe or extended superframe format, and then transmitted via a T-1 multiplexer using *time division multiplexing* (TDM). Time division multiplexing consolidates the data stream from each of the DS-0 channels by using an approach that guarantees a time slot for data from each of these channels. As Fig. 9-8 illustrates, a channel might not have anything to send when its turn arrives; under such circumstances, the time slot remains empty. When you look at fast packet T-1 technology later in this chapter, you will see how this new approach overcomes this TDM drawback.

Channels				
1	▓▓▓▓▓▓	Asynchronous data		▓▓▓▓▓▓
2	Synchronous data		Synchronous data	▓▓▓▓▓▓
3	▓▓▓▓▓▓	Fax	▓▓▓▓▓▓	Fax
4	Voice	Voice	▓▓▓▓▓▓	▓▓▓▓▓▓
5	Voice	Voice	Voice	Voice
6	Asynchronous data		▓▓▓▓▓▓	Asynchronous data
7	Synchronous data		Synchronous data	▓▓▓▓▓▓
8	LAN data	LAN data	▓▓▓▓▓▓	LAN data

9-8 Time division multiplexing.

Remote bridges and the WAN

Time division multiplexing is often used to build a wide area network. Sometimes a WAN consists of several LANs remotely bridged together. The major advantage of remote bridges that link together LANs located at different sites is that they can function as a single, seamless wide area network independent of all upper layer network protocols including TCP/IP, DECnet, NetWare, and OS/2 LAN Manager. A well-designed WAN might require the integration of different higher-level protocols, different transmission speeds and different transmission media.

Figure 9-9 illustrates a wide area network linking together several different Ethernet networks. Notice that two networks are linked by two 64 Kbs lines that result in load sharing. Two networks are joined together by 100 Mbs fiberoptic connections while another WAN link consists of a T-1 line.

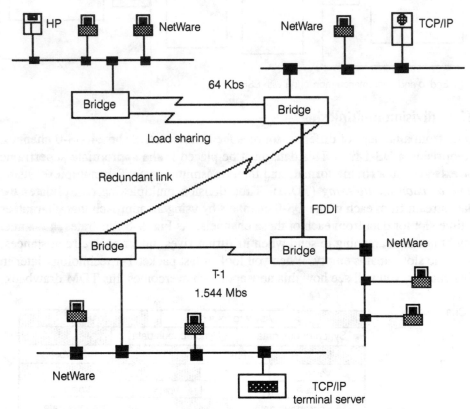

9-9 Remote bridges using a wide range of links and transmission speeds to form a WAN.

More and more products are being released to provide the remote bridging necessary to create effective wide area networks. On a NetWare file server, for example, it is now possible to install a Network Products Corporation T-1B Bridge that has a built-in data service unit (DSU) so that the T-1 multiplexer is built right into the circuit card. All a user has to do is connect an RJ-45 cable from the back of the card to the telephone closet.

Digital access and cross-connect systems (DACS)

You have seen T-1 transmission in terms of T-1 multiplexers, but in some situations a *digital access and cross-connect system* (DACS) can serve the purpose at a much lower price. The telephone company first used DACS in its central offices to switch DS-0 channels from one T-1 span (DS-1) to another. DACS was designed to break down a DS-1 stream into 24 DS-0s. These DS-0s channels then are routed to time slots on any other DS-1. The limitations of a DACS include the inability to deal with a subchannel of less than 64 Kbs, a topic you can examine when you look at fractional T-1 service. Another DACS limitation is its lack of sophistication when it comes to automatic alternate routing. A traditional DACS requires that this routing be done manually at each switch. Finally, a DACS lacks the ability to compress voice transmission; this means that a network manager cannot make efficient use of DS-0 channels by using subrate voice channels at 16 Kbs or 32 Kbs. Despite these limitations, a DACS serves a very important function. It can be used in conjunction with several T-1 multiplexers to create a wide area network, as discussed next.

The RAD Network Devices' REB-MEGAPLEX system illustrates how a DACS can be used to link IEEE 802.3 LANs to form an Ethernet T-1 WAN. The REB connects a LAN through an Ethernet transceiver on one side to the MEGA-PLEX-1 through an RS-449, V.35, or X.21 interface on the other side.

In Fig. 9-10, the REB-MEGAPLEX system is pictured linking together company offices in four different cities. Functioning at the bridge level, this WAN is completely transparent to data. It operates independently of all higher level protocols such as XNS, DECnet, and TCP/IP. Note that it is the REB-MEGAPLEX T-1 multiplexers that take the wide range of data streams pictured and place them in the traditional DS-1 format required for the DACS.

Selecting a T-1 multiplexer

T-1 multiplexers have gone through several generations; in fact, they seem to evolve almost as quickly as fruit flies. First generation multiplexers were known as channel banks. Designed strictly for superframe or extended superframe formats, these devices divided the T-1 bandwidth into 24 64 Kbs channels and did not permit any adjustment in the size of these channels.

Second-generation T-1 multiplexers added the ability to send voice information at lower rates. These schemes for adjusting the speed of voice transmission (16 Kbs, 32 Kbs, etc.) are generally proprietary so that it is not practical to try to mix and match these multiplexers. Another feature of second generation multiplexers is their ability to adjust the size of a channel according to the manufacturer's range of options. A network manager with several low-speed transmissions from terminals, for example, could send these transmissions over a T-1 line.

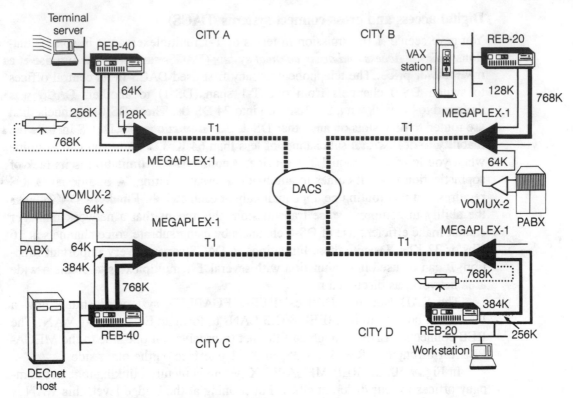

9-10 A WAN in which T-1 multiplexers are linked together by a DACs. RAD Network Devices

Third-generation T-1 multiplexers include the features found in the previous generation but add some features that make them ideally suited for large networks. One feature is the number of T-1 aggregates the multiplexer can support. An aggregate is composed of the composite data from all the channels comprising a T-1 link. Because network operations often require several data streams and multiplexers to transmit streams to a centralized multiplexer, this device must have the ability to handle such a load and keep track of all the corresponding channels.

Often data enters a T-1 multiplexer as a channel on one aggregate and must be routed to another aggregate without being absorbed by the channel side of this multiplexer. In other words, it is simply passing through the multiplexer and being rerouted to another multiplexer. This type of transmission is known as a "drop and insert." T-1 multiplexers vary in the delay time required for this rerouting.

Closely related to this delay time is the way that the T-1 multiplexer routes frames. With some multiplexers, this routing information is maintained in a central node while in other multiplexers it is distributed among nodes. The distributed approach takes longer because information must be exchanged across the network before routing can take place. The tradeoff is that when all routing information is maintained in a central node, the failure of this node means the failure of all routing capability for the multiplexer and network.

Another feature distinguishing third generation T-1 multiplexers is network management. These devices tend to support a number of network management protocols (see chapter 12) and provide graphics-oriented displays of an entire wide area network rather than the activities of the single multiplexer. This approach enables a network manager to see at a glance where a problem is located and take appropriate action.

Another significant feature to look for in a T-1 multiplexer are the protocols and standards it supports. While Super Frame and Extended Super Frame formatting is essential, the appropriate interface for Integrated Services Digital Network (ISDN) could be important in the not too distant future. Chapter 10 examines ISDN.

The type of routing performed by the T-1 multiplexer is also important. While many devices offer dynamic routing, some utilize a static routing table that the network manager must create and maintain. On a large network, this approach could prove to be inefficient and unresponsive to changing conditions.

Closely related to changing conditions on T-1 lines is the ability of a T-1 multiplexer to dynamically reroute information when a line fails. Time-sensitive applications such as those found under IBM's Systems Network Architecture (SNA) cannot maintain a session during the period of time normally required for a manual reconfiguration of a T-1 network. Lengthy rerouting of voice channels also has a negative effect. Many industry experts use five seconds as the maximum amount of time a caller will wait before hanging up.

While some T-1 multiplexers are still designed to serve only as point-to-point devices, more and more such as the IPX models from Stratacom are appearing as full-fledged network models.

Fractional T-1

A recent innovation in T-1 transmission has been the offering of fractional T-1 service (FT1). Common Carriers subdivide T-1 bandwidth into its 24-DS0 channels of 64 Kbs. The user can bundle together these channels to fit particular applications. A customer might require one-eighth (192 Kbs), one-fourth (384 Kbs), or one-half (768 Kbs) of the available bandwidth. Users only pay for the bandwidth they need.

Voice transmission can be compressed a good deal without losing any content (remember all the ahhs and uhhs in a typical conversation?). Using popular compression schemes, it is common for customers to take a 384 Kbs FT1 channel and utilize it for 20 voice lines of 16 Kbs each or perhaps 10 voice lines of 32 Kbs. Because of the efficiency of these compression schemes, no meaningful content of a conversation is lost.

While large corporations can realize tens of thousands of dollars a month in savings using FT1, they could save even more money if local phone companies would cooperate. Presently a customer must pay for a full T-1 circuit from the customer's premises to the interexchange carrier's point of presence (POP) even though the long haul portion of the circuit (POP to POP) is fractional. Figure 9-11 illustrates how fractional T-1 can be used while Fig. 9-12 lists some major fractional T-1 domestic and international offerings.

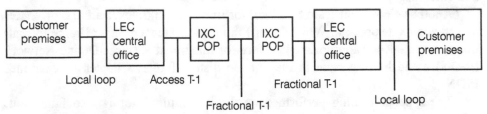

9-11 Use of fractional T-1.

International Record Carriers (RCA, Worldcom, IDB)
AT&T International Accunet
AT&T International Skynet
Sprint Meeting Service
Spectrum of Digital Services
Cable and Wireless Fractional Offering
Williams Telecommunications Fractional Offering
MCI Fractional Offering
Lightnet
Teleport
RBOCs

9-12 Some major fractional T-1 domestic and international offerings.

A WAN using fractional T-1

Imagine that you have 9 sites, each of which has a LAN, that need to be linked together in a wide area network. The higher level protocols at the various sites include NetWare's IPX, 3Com's XNS, and TCP/IP. The MAC layers of these networks are all IEEE 802.3. The corporation has looked at AT&T's 56 Kbs Dataphone Digital Service transmission but rejected it as far too expensive. The company has also priced V.35 interface cards and concluded that this solution also would be prohibitive.

One possible solution is a new type of WAN multiplexer that combines the best features of a learning bridge with T-1 and fractional T-1 service. The Codex EtherSpan bridge enables a network manager to run multiples of 64 Kbs circuits up to the maximum T-1 capacity of 1.544 Mbs. In the case of the corporation with a corporate headquarters that needs to be connected to 9 sites, EtherSpan could allocate 9 DS-0 bundles of 64 Kbs each to establish the 9 separate 64 Kbs bandwidth links. The beauty of this type of wide area network is that because it essentially is a remote bridge using fractional T-1 service, the workstations at any given site view the entire WAN as one large transparent network. Figure 9-13 illustrates how fractional T-1 service can be used in conjunction with a WAN.

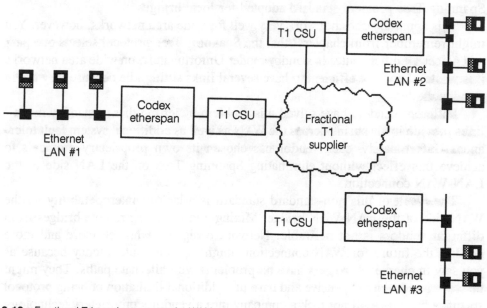

9-13 Fractional T-1 service as part of a WAN.

T-3 multiplexers

Some companies are using T-3 multiplexers to consolidate T-1 and fractional T-1 networks. Definite economies of scale are associated with using T-3 circuits rather than multiple T-1 circuits. If multiple T-1 lines are going to the same destination within a pathway, they can be combined and transmitted over a T-3 circuit. For relatively short distances, many industry experts use a 5:6 cost ratio "rule of thumb" with an 8:10 cost ratio "rule of thumb" for longer distances. This means that for relatively short distances, it becomes cost effective to use a T-3 line to replace 5−6 T-1 circuits. The added bandwidth is virtually free and can be used to carry additional voice traffic. Some companies that have traditionally used separate lines for voice and for data have consolidated these two different streams using a T-3 line.

Another use of T-3 is as a "hub" that takes a T-1 channel and switches it to another T-1 channel. Timeplex's TX3/SuperHub, for example, provides some key network management features that make it easier to manage a wide area network. A network manager can monitor and control any T-1 channel within a T-3 circuit. Test devices internal to the hub provide remote testing and monitoring.

The 802.1G committee's remote bridge standards for WANs

The IEEE 802.1G committee has been working to develop a standard for remote bridges. Perhaps because of conflicting interests by members who represent competing vendors, the committee has opted to have remote bridges use the same Spanning Tree protocol standard adopted for local bridges.

This approach does not work very well for wide area networks, however. You might remember from chapter 7 that the Spanning Tree protocol selects one path and places all other routes in standby mode. Unfortunately, on wide area networks it is wasteful and not efficient to have several links sitting idle because they are in standby mode.

Different vendors have solved this problem by letting these "standby mode" links provide load sharing across the WAN as well as additional system fault tolerance. Unfortunately, each vendor has chosen its own proprietary protocols to achieve this effect without eliminating Spanning Tree on the LAN side of the LAN-WAN connection.

The result of this non-standard standard is a lack of interoperability on the WAN side of the LAN-WAN bridge. Mixing and matching remote bridges from different vendors is not desirable. Network designers who see more and more need in the future for WAN connections might opt for routers today because as you saw in chapter 8, routers have no problems with alternate paths. They might be slower and more expensive and have the additional limitation of being protocol specific, but they will not lock a company into a vendor's proprietary technology and leave the company in that dead-end if and when a standard evolves for remote bridging.

Packet switched (X.25) networks

One of the major advantages of international standards in data communications protocols is illustrated by public data networks. These networks switch data in the form of CCITT X.25 packets across the country and around the world. The CCITT X.25 Recommendation is based on the first three layers of the OSI model discussed in chapter 3.

Typically a DTE is connected to a *Packet Assembler/Disassembler* (PAD). A PAD provides the protocol translation from a data stream's native protocol (SNA, asynchronous, etc.) to X.25 protocol. At the destination end of the transmission, a PAD translates the X.25 packets from X.25 protocol back to whatever protocol is required. These PADs help make X.25 transmission economical by concentrating the data streams from several DTEs. The PAD must place the data it receives in a packet that contains control information for error checking and sequencing. Packets have a destination address. At each stage of their transmission route, packets are checked for errors before being forwarded using the best available route at that particular moment. If a node receiving a packet detects an error, it requests the sending node to retransmit it. The path an individual packet takes is determined by the switching equipment, and no two packets will take the same route. As Fig. 9-14 illustrates, it is not just likely but probable that packets will arrive at their destination out of sequence and need to be placed back in their proper sequence. All of this activity is transparent to users. Notice that packet switched networks are usually depicted as clouds.

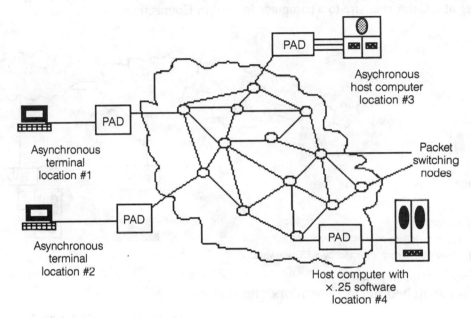

9-14 A packet switched network.

One key consideration in considering packet switched networks is that the cost of using such a network is based on the amount of information transmitted and not on the distance between locations. Cost is usually based on the number of packets sent.

X.25 networks are also appealing for companies that have geographically dispersed heterogeneous networks. A company might have an SNA network at one location, for example, and a pre-SNA network at another site comprised of pre-SNA bisynchronous 3270s, 2780/3780 remote job entry devices, and asynchronous terminals. A third site might have DEC computers running VMS. The protocol conversion required for communications among these disparate networks can be handled by an X.25 network vendor.

The X.25 standard
The CCITT X.25 standard specifies the guidelines for computers and terminals to communicate with packet switched nodes. It defines how non-packet equipment

(DTEs) can connect to packet-switched networks through the use of a packet switched node (DCE). Because this is an international standard, X.25 networks are used by many large corporations that have global communications needs. A U.S. packet switched network can exchange packets with a network in South Africa, England, or Japan using a CCITT X.75 Recommendation that defines what is required for a gateway between X.25 networks.

Figure 9-15 illustrates how a company would transmit data from a host computer at a California site to a computer located in Connecticut.

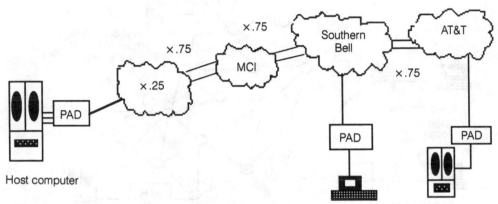

9-15   X.25 networks connected by X.75 gateways.

Packet switched network vendors and services

Telenet and Tymnet comprise approximately 85% of the U.S. packet switched network market with the remainder divided among a number of companies including AT&T and the regional Bell telephone companies. Both Telenet and Tymnet support transmission speeds ranging from 110 bps to 56 Kbs. Most packet switched data network vendors also support a number of different protocols and offer protocol conversion including 3270 Bisynchronous, SDLC, 2780, 3780, and HASP.

Choosing a public packet switched network vendor

Public X.25 network vendors offer a number of features that might help distinguish one from another. It is useful to know the right questions to ask. This section describes some of the features to consider when selecting a public packet switched network.

Throughput

Just as bridge and router vendors fudge a bit with their throughput figures, packet switched network vendors also have to be questioned closely. Do their throughput figures count only data packets, or do they include control information as well? How large are the packets? See if you can get a figure based on 128 byte packets because this is the industry norm.

Protocols supported

I touched on this topic earlier in this chapter. You or your client will know what protocols need to be supported; vendors vary very widely in what they offer. While virtually all networks support IBM's SNA/SDLC and 3270 BSC protocols, only a few support Tandem (Globenet), Uniscope (DataAmerica and Globenet), and X.400 (Telenet and Western Union).

Maximum speeds supported

Most vendors offer dial-up lines ranging from 2400 Kbs to 9600 Kbs along with dedicated lines available ranging from 19.2 Kbs to 56 Kbs. A few vendors (Telenet, Data America, Cylix) offer 1.544 Mbs transmission speed for dedicated lines.

Error correcting

All vendors offer some kind of error correcting. Some vendors provide special ports on both dial-in and private port bases that are equipped with error-correcting modems. The most popular error-correcting modems usually found in this environment are X.PC and MNP.

Network management

How far does the vendor go in providing you with tools for network management? Does the vendor let you decide what paths packets will take based on the time of day? Are you able to perform diagnostics from your own site? Can you select alternate routing based on trunk speed?

Private packet switched networks

Some companies might need a packet switched network in an area where there are no public packet switched services. It is also possible that they might have so much traffic between two sites that they could change substantial tariff charges by building their own private network. Still a third advantage to a private packet switched network is that it provides centralized management and control as well as increased security because the company has total control over all traffic on the network.

Hughes Network Systems is a major vendor of private packet switched networks. Its Integrated Packet Network (IPN) is used by a number of major corporations including Hewlett-Packard and Ford Motor Company. The Hughes packet switched network supports both terrestrial and satellite transmission links. To provide the centralized management and control functions that characterize private networks, IPN uses a Network Control System (NCS) that manages distributed databases, and coordinates administrative functions. NCS computers are designed to operate independently, yet remain fully linked for load-sharing and backup purposes. IPN offers such enhanced security features as multi-level security that restricts user access and on-board encryption.

Northern Telecom is another major player in the packet switched network industry. Its DPN-100 packet switch includes a software package called DPN Lanscope that is designed specifically to enable users to manage LANs connected over a wide area network. DPN Lanscope provides fault and performance monitoring, resource management, software distribution, and usage tracking for geographically dispersed LANs. The software is used in conjunction with DPN Advisor which resides on a UNIX workstation and provides graphic displays of the entire WAN for real-time control and fault management.

Hybrid networks

For many companies, hybrid networks represent the best of both worlds. Because public packet switched networks are traffic sensitive, some companies use these public services where they are economically beneficial to handle light traffic between sites. They then use X.75 gateways to link these networks to their own private networks which connect sites where traffic is very heavy. Figure 9-16 illustrates a typical hybrid network.

X.25 packet switching vs. T-1 multiplexing

It can be a bit confusing differentiating between the two major methods of transmitting data on a wide area network. You have seen the T-1 multiplexer and the basic technique it uses, time division multiplexing. Each channel on a time division multiplexer is allocated a portion of the bandwidth with that portion of the bandwidth totally dedicated to that particular channel. T-1 lines are cost-effective only up to a certain distance. Because a company pays for the use of a line 24 hours a day, the higher the utilization, the more cost-effective the transmission link becomes.

Packet switching uses a technique known as statistical multiplexing, which means that bandwidth is not permanently allocated to any given channel. Instead, bandwidth is dynamically allocated using statistical algorithms to each channel based on that channel's need at any given time.

This ability to dynamically allocate bandwidth is particularly efficient when dealing with "bursty" type traffic. A fax transmission, for example, might require massive amounts of bandwidth, but then that channel might remain idle for a substantial period of time.

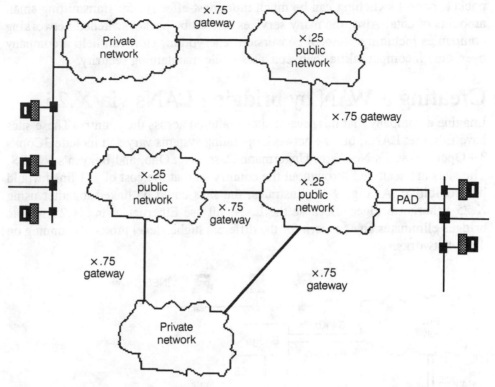

9-16 A hybrid packet switched network.

Every advantage has its price, however. In order to be able to dynamically allocate bandwidth, a packet switching statistical multiplexer must maintain constant communications with each channel to monitor what that channel's needs are. This communication requires overhead and causes some delay time.

If data flow is reasonably constant on different channels, then time division multiplexing has the edge. T-1 multiplexers were designed to handle voice traffic, and it should come as no surprise that they excel in this area. The various compression schemes used with voice traffic still require a 64 Kbs channel; they simply provide more voice conversations over this channel.

A T-1 multiplexer requires less overhead and can be considerably faster. Unlike the T-1 speed of 1.544 Mbs, packet switched networks using statistical multiplexing generally operate at a maximum speed of 64 Kbs. T-1 multiplexers are not sensitive to protocols because they simply plug their control information into a pre-assigned slot and do not worry about what protocol the data is using.

What packet switched networks do well is dynamically allocate their resources based on need and then route these packets efficiently. If a virtual circuit is tied up, packet switched networks simply route the packets along a different circuit. Because public packet switched networks generally charge by the packet, packet switching can be much more cost-effective for transmitting small amounts of data. Also, the many services offered by packet switched networking companies including protocol conversion, encryption, etc., can help a company overcome incompatibilities between sites while maintaining security.

Creating a WAN by bridging LANs via X.25

Imagine a company that has several sites scattered across the country. These sites have Ethernet LANs, but the network operating systems vary and include 3Com's 3+Open, Novell's NetWare, Ungermann-Bass's Net One, and Banyan's VINES. The sites are scattered throughout the country so that the cost of T-1 links would be prohibitive. As Fig. 9-17 illustrates, the sites could be linked together using X.25 Ethernet bridges. Because the LANs all use Ethernet, using X.25 remote bridges eliminates any concern for the different higher-level protocols running on these networks.

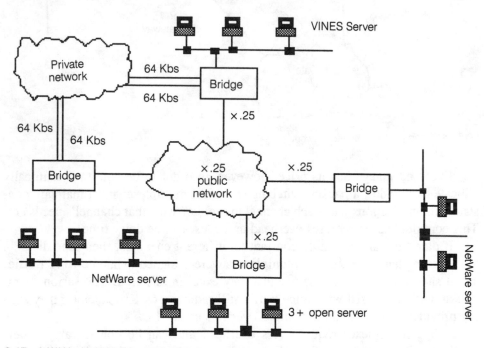

9-17 A WAN with X.25 Ethernet bridges.

Using X.25 gateways and satellite transmission to link LANs

Consider a different scenario for a WAN. Instead of all LANs having the same media access, assume a variety of different access methods but the same upper layer protocol, in this case NetWare and IPX.

A company has its corporate headquarters in Dallas, Texas, regional branches at 35 sites including New Orleans, San Francisco, Chicago, and its Canadian headquarters in Montreal. Each site has its own NetWare LAN. These LANs use whatever media access method that is cost-effective at that particular site including Ethernet, Arcnet, and Token Ring network. The company needs to link all sites together for electronic mail, LAN maintenance, and updating of key information including scheduling. A major problem for this company is that many sites do not have local public packet switched services available. As Fig. 9-18 illustrates, this particular company has combined a number of different technologies to build its WAN. Each site's NetWare LAN uses a communications server with an X.25 gateway card with the capability of transmitting up to 64 Kbs.

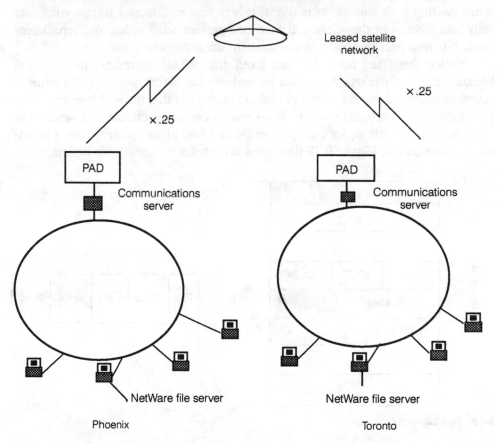

9-18 A WAN incorporating LANs and satellite transmission.

Each site uses a General DataComm MegaMux Plus multiplexer to transmit the packets to a modem which in turn transmits the signals to an RF (radio frequency) format that is transmitted to a satellite dish that uplinks the information to a leased satellite. The satellite serves as a backbone connecting all sites.

Fast packet technology

Fast packet technology is a relatively new development in T-1 transmission that combines the best features of T-1 multiplexing with some of the advantages of packet switching. Special T-1 multiplexers such as the Codex 6290 generate fast packets destined for a single channel only. The multiplexer allocates bandwidth instantaneously based on the data streams it receives. Assume that a multiplexer must handle voice, LAN traffic, and FAX transmissions. This type of data mix really benefits from a multiplexer that can allocate a single very large channel for a short period of time to expedite the transfer of a large amount of urgent data.

Besides this ability to dynamically allocate resources based on need, another reason why fast packet technology transmits packets that truly are "fast" is that when dealing with voice transmissions, this type of multiplexer frames voice bits only and filters out the silence. It then compresses what is left and repackages these bits into packets. Each packet contains an address in front.

Notice that fixed time slots and fixed channel allotments are not required because the fast packets each have an address indicating where it is destined. Another major advantage of fast packet technology is that the multiplexer can be programmed to recognize which data streams are more critical and send them first; voice information, for example, might be given higher priority than a terminal's transmission. Figure 9-19 illustrates fast packet technology in action.

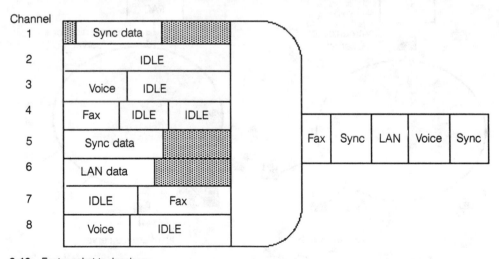

9-19 Fast packet technology.

While X.25 packet switched networks utilize layers 1, 2, and 3 of the OSI model, fast packet technology utilizes only the first layer and a portion of the second layer. Because the frames contain their own control information for source and destination addressing and error detection, the fast packet switches only need to look at the destination addresses and then pass the frames along quickly. Rather than including requests for retransmission of data with errors, the destination node simply discards data containing errors. Less processing results in increased speed. While X.25 has a maximum transmission speed of 64 Kbs, fast packet technology can provide a rate of up to 2 Mbs.

Frame relay technology

Recently a new standard has evolved for using fast packet technology more efficiently. A *frame relay* is a Data Link layer protocol that defines how variable length data frames can be assembled. Frame relay requires only 48 bits of overhead, 4 to 5 times fewer bits than required with packet switching. Frames can be sized appropriately for the data loads they need to carry. The frame relay standard provides for a Data Link Connection Identifier (DLCI), which serves as an address field to allow for multiple logical sessions per physical data link. A standard frame format is specified for each of the various packet subsystems that will receive packets. Frames are labeled with the appropriate DLCI so that when the fast packet system receives them, they can be sent to the appropriate destination. Error detection is performed only at the destination.

Fast packet technology using this frame relay approach can handle massive amounts of packets efficiently because it can allocate bandwidth dynamically.

Northern Telecom has added frame relay to its DMS SuperNode, which means that carriers will be able to offer frame relay as a service. US Sprint has announced that it will offer frame relay services the third quarter of 1991. Frame relay interfaces to bridges and routers have been announced by a number of vendors including Newbridge Networks, Vitalink, and Digital Equipment Corporation.

Cell relay technology

In the near future, it will also be possible to use fast packets with an approach known as *cell relay*. Cell relay is a very high speed switching system for public networks that is just starting to evolve. Unlike frame relay, cell relay relies on standard frames that do not change size regardless of the traffic load. Cell relay will have transmission speeds in the 150 Mbs range and is associated with two telecommunications standards, Distributed Queued Dual Bus (DQDB) and Asynchronous Transfer Mode (ATM). You saw DQDB earlier in this chapter when you examined the IEEE 802.6 specifications associated with a metropolitan area network. ATM transmits small (128K) packets over short internetwork hops. These packets or "cells" are routed by hardware platforms operating at very high speeds.

The Synchronous Optical Network (SONET)

In 1986 Bellcore proposed SONET, Synchronous Optical Network standards, to synchronize public communications networks and then tie them together via high-speed optical fiber links. The CCITT's Group XVII has drafted a SONET recommendation for Phase I and is currently working on Phase II.

What SONET offers is enormous bandwidth based on multiples of the base rate (OC-1) of 51.840 Mbs or one T-3 link. Originally the U.S. proposed a 51.84 Mbs signal while Europeans wanted a 34 Mbs signal. The two groups compromised at a basic rate of 155.52 Mbs or OC-3 to connect the two groups' signals. Figure 9-20 displays the SONET hierarchy of transmission options. Because SONET is built on the foundation of T-3, it is critical that companies thinking of purchasing T-3 multiplexers in the immediate future receive a commitment from their vendors that the multiplexer is migratable to the emerging SONET standard. The device must have sufficient backplane bandwidth to support at least SONET's OC-1, and ideally enough bandwidth to support multiples of OC-3 for future growth. While the SONET equipment already available will be used mostly for public data networks, some companies such as Apple Computer Corporation are already using SONET for their own private networks.

Optical Carrier #	Transmission Rate	T – 1s	T – 3s
OC-1	51.84	28	1
OC-3	155.52	84	3
OC-9	466.56	252	9
OC-12	622.08	336	12
OC-18	933.12	504	18
OC-24	1244.16	672	24
OC-36	1866.24	1008	36
OC-48	2488.32	1344	48

9-20 The SONET hierarchy.

SONET's Phase II will provide operational and administrative support including maintenance information on the data traveling over the links. Phase II will include involved definition of the full 7-layer OSI protocol stack including protocols associated with flow control to prevent data collisions. AT&T and MCI have already scheduled SONET testing for 1991 – 1992. MCI has indicated it will offer SONET services beginning in 1992, while many Bell operating companies are beginning to make their plans and purchase SONET equipment.

In the not too distant future, many industry experts forecast that telephone companies will offer customers dial-up 50 Mbs circuits using SONET rather than lease SONET lines. It is also likely that customers will be able to purchase fractional SONET service. Compared to the currently highest available dial-up rate of

64 Kbs, this additional bandwidth will make it economically advantageous to send video images on an as-needed basis without committing to a leased line.

Summary

Metropolitan area networks (MANs) defined by the IEEE 802.6 specifications utilize a dual bus topology with data traffic traveling in opposite directions. The protocol used by MANs is distributed queue dual bus (DQDB) protocol. MANs are designed to handle city-wide communications.

Wide area networks (WANs) link together networks located in different geographic areas. Historically WANs have been limited by the relatively slow speeds available from dial-up analog phone lines. Recently, though, new technology in the form of T-1 lines provide a 1.544 Mbs bandwidth. T-3 lines provide a signal speed of 45 Mbs.

A relatively new development has been the availability of fractional T-1 service. Users can purchase the fractional portion of a T-1 line that they need. T-1 and fractional T-1 service can be used in conjunction with remote bridges and routers to form a seamless wide area network.

Packet switched networks utilize the X.25 protocol. Public X.25 networks charge by the packet. Corporations with very heavy traffic sometimes install their own private X.25 networks. Hybrid X.25 networks represent the best of both worlds by using public networks where there is light traffic and private networks where they have heavy traffic.

Fast packet technology is much more efficient than packet switching because of its ability to dynamically allocate bandwidth as needed. Frame relay protocol is what makes fast packet technology so efficient. The future might see the growth of cell relay technology, a fiber approach that incorporates some of the same protocols associated with metropolitan area networks. Synchronous Optical Network (SONET) is a new standard for communications networks with a transmission rate of 150 Mbs. In the near future, companies might be able to purchase fractional use of SONET services on an as-needed basis.

10
CHAPTER

ISDN

In this chapter, you will examine

- ISDN's Basic Rate Interface and Primary Rate Interface.
- The significance of Signaling System 7 (SS7).
- The evolving 802.9 standard for integrated voice/data transmission.
- Why broadband ISDN seems so attractive to network managers.

Introduction

Integrated Services Digital Network (ISDN) is here. It is no longer a theory, but a high-speed digital network that can carry both voice and data information. This chapter looks at the different components or building blocks of ISDN. The chapter also looks at an evolving IEEE 802.9 standard for integrated voice/data transmission that will be ISDN compatible. Finally, it examines a broadband version of ISDN that will be capable of transmission speeds over 100 Mbs. While some of this information might have been of interest at one time only to "telephone" people, today's network manager must know enough about these new technologies to be able to consider them within the context of designing enterprise networks.

What ISDN is

Integrated Services Digital Network (ISDN) is an evolving set of international standards for connecting voice, data, and video equipment. With ISDN, a user will be able to carry on a voice call while simultaneously viewing video images or retrieving information from a computer. All these different forms of information could travel in a single ISDN interface circuit packet and be directed to an integrated voice/image/data terminal. The user will also be able to select and change whether connections are to a private voice network or a public data network. ISDN interfaces between a local exchange and the end user could replace many of the links network managers currently use including T-1 trunks, Tie trunks, WATS lines, and traditional analog trunks. In 1976 the term "ISDN" appeared in the CCITT's *Orange Book* list of terms. ISDN has taken so long to develop that skeptics have been known to refer to it as "I Still Don't Need It" or "It Still Does Nothing." Today, ISDN demonstrations at major telecommunications conferences are routine. Some companies, such as McDonald's Corporation and Hardees, are already using ISDN as beta users.

The Basic Rate Interface (BRI)

The *Basic Rate Interface* (BRI) specifies a single access point into ISDN. Known as "2B D," BRI consists of two bearer channels and one data channel. Each bearer channel operates at 64 Kbs and is a clear channel, meaning that they have no restriction on the format or type of information that passes through them. The data channel operates at 16 Kbs and is used for signaling and control information. The Basic Rate Interface is also known as the *Digital Subscriber Line* (DSL).

The Primary Rate Interface (PRI)

The *Primary Rate Interface* (PRI) is used to connect multiple users to ISDN. Also known as the *Extended Digital Subscriber Line* (EDSL), it will be used primarily to connect a PBX, LAN, or other multiuser switching device to an ISDN network. The North American standard, followed by the United States, Canada, Mexico, Japan, and South Korea, consists of 23 B channels of 64 Kbs each and one D channel of 64 Kbs. The aggregate capacity is 1.544 Mbs or the equivalent bandwidth of a T-1 facility. T-1 is intended to be the chief facility used with the North American standard PRI. The European standard for PRI consists of 30 B channels and 1 D channel for an aggregate capacity of 2.048 Mbs. Because of the greater capacity available under PRI, it supports an additional type of channel known as an H channel. Three types of H channels are specified:

H0	(384 Kbs)
H11	(1.536 Mbs)
H12	(1.920 Mbs)

The North American standard incorporates H0 and H11 channels while the European standard incorporates H0 and H12 channels.

ISDN equipment

No one said telecommunications jargon would be logical or easy to understand. The CCITT has arbitrarily defined several different types of ISDN equipment. *TE-1* equipment is ISDN compatible and can be connected directly to the network. *TE-2* equipment is not ISDN compatible and requires an interface device known as a *Terminal Adapter* (TA). A TA can convert signals from one international standard such as RS-232C to the ISDN standard. This provision for TE-2 equipment represents the CCITT's recognition of the fact companies have so much money invested in existing non-ISDN telecommunications equipment that there is no way that ISDN will grow unless existing equipment can be integrated with ISDN equipment.

Network termination equipment can take two different forms under ISDN. *NT1* describes public switched network demarcation devices such as a termination block or a registered jack. This equipment will have some built-in intelligence under ISDN because of the functions it must perform.

NT2 is the designation for customer-owned switching equipment such as a PBX or a LAN. NT2 equipment can provide additional capabilities beyond NT1 such as call switching or concentration.

There are two additional types of ISDN equipment. *Line Termination equipment* (LT) is located within the local exchange company's or common carrier's network in situations where lines must be extended beyond the normal range of the central office. *Exchange Termination equipment* (ET) terminates the Digital Subscriber Line or Extended Digital Subscriber Line in the local exchange. ET can be characterized as central office equipment, important to the phone company but nothing you need to worry about.

Network interfaces

Now that I have listed the various categories of ISDN equipment, the logical questions is how these different types of equipment can be linked to an ISDN network. Figure 10-1 illustrates how interfaces link different types of equipment to an ISDN network. An "R" interface links non-ISDN compatible equipment and terminal adapter equipment. The "S" interface links ISDN compatible equipment and network terminal equipment. A "T" interface links customer premises equipment to an ISDN network while the "U" interface ties together network termination equipment and exchange termination equipment or line termination equipment.

An example of ISDN in action

Here is a scenario that will let you see how the various ISDN components work together. Assume that a major hospital in Los Angeles uses several outside doctors

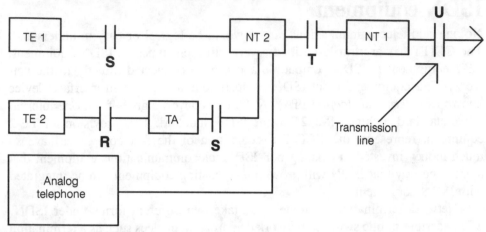

10-1 ISDN equipment types and interfaces.

as consultants. These consultants examine X-rays and then make their diagnoses. Normally a doctor is sent 12 X-rays. These X-rays are transmitted from the hospital to the doctors' offices using ISDN's Basic Rate Interface (BRI) service. Figure 10-2 illustrates how the images are transmitted from the hospital's mainframe computer via NT1 equipment. This information travels to a Pacific Bell Central Office (CO), and it then travels over the ISDN network to the appropriate doctor's office where it is received over an ISDN terminal. The doctor can study the X-rays and then transmit an analysis, which will travel at ISDN's 64 Kbs rate.

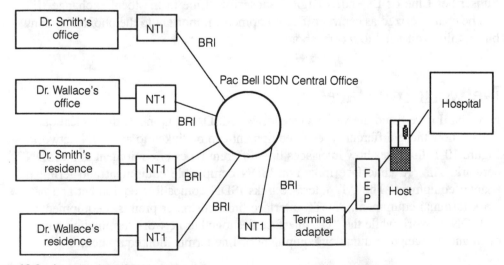

10-2 An example of ISDN in action.

Signaling System 7

ISDN requires a great deal of intelligence from the public switched network in order to format and transmit signals successfully. *Signaling System 7* (SS7) consists of a series of recommendations from the CCITT that define the content and format of signaling messages under ISDN as well as the network design parameters necessary for transferring network control information.

The three key components to SS7 are Service Switch Points, Signaling Transfer Points, and Service Control Points. The Service Switch Points, usually owned by the LECs, receive call routing and handling instructions from a Service Control Point. The Signaling Transfer Points are packet switches that transfer information between an LEC network to a common carrier network. Finally, Service Control Points are nodes containing computerized database records that provide control information to other nodes on the network. This control information could take the form of records of services to which each user subscribes or a list of toll-free 800 numbers. This information could be passed back to the appropriate node needing this information.

ISDN will provide a number of services requiring the intelligence available through SS7. Its use of out-of-band signaling conforms to ISDN's use of the D channel for signaling.

ISDN and the OSI model

The "D" channel under ISDN uses the I.450/I.451 protocols at the Network layer to recognize the type of packet as well as the type of message being transmitted. This layer covers the establishment, maintenance, and termination of calls through the network. Establishment includes setting up the call, selecting the type of service, and routing the call. Maintenance includes monitoring a call to ensure that it is not dropped or disrupted before normal termination. Termination refers to the orderly disconnection of a call.

As Fig. 10-3 illustrates, the Information field of an ISDN frame carries key Network Layer control information. The Protocol Discriminator field indicates which protocol is being used. The Call Reference field correlates the frame with the correct call. The Message Type field identifies a frame which could take the form of a setup frame, information frame, acknowledgement frame, etc. The information portion of the frame also includes control data concerning its length and the sequence of the frames.

Protocol discriminator	Call ref	Msg type	Inf element ID	Length	Information	Information element ID

10-3 Frame structure of the ISDN information field.

ISDN's Data Link Layer has a number of protocols including LAP-D, SAPI, and TEI. The LAP-D protocol, a subset of the OSI model's HDLC protocol, is used to handle the flow of frames through the D channel and provide information for detecting and controlling data flow as well as recovering errors. LAP-D is a variation of the LAP-B protocol used on the B channel. LAP-B allows only one logical link across an interface while LAP-D allows multiple logical links by permitting the address field to change from frame to frame. The flexibility to change addresses explains why a single D channel can control many B channels. Figure 10-4 reveals the format this protocol frame takes.

Flag	Address SAPI	Address TEI	Control	Control	Information	Frame check seq	Flag

10-4　The ISDN LAP-D frame.

Another key Data Link layer protocol under ISDN is the Service Access Point Identifier (SAPI), which is used to multiplex packet, signaling and management information over a single D channel while the Terminal Endpoint Identifier (TEI) is used to multiplex several logical D channels into one physical D channel. At ISDN's Physical layer, the I.430 and I.431 protocols are designed to handle BRI and PRI respectively. Figure 10-5 indicates the protocols found under ISDN at each corresponding layer of the OSI model.

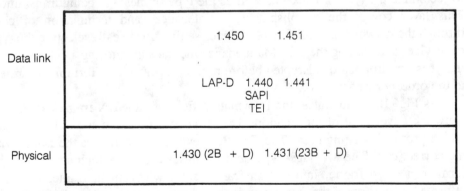

10-5　ISDN and the OSI model.

Integrated voice and data under ISDN

For several years the IEEE 802.9 committee has been working on a set of specifications for a standard that will support voice and data transmitted over a single network. The committee wants to ensure that this new standard will provide IEEE 802 MAC services while being ISDN compatible.

The 802.9 standard will cover the communication between an integrated voice/data terminal (IVDT) and a LAN where the IVDT's Access Unit (AU) provides all required services. It also will cover the situation in which the services required for an IVDT to serve as a gateway to a backbone network providing IVDT services perhaps as an 802.6 MAN using FDDI.

The 802.9 standard must be able to provide multiple access to a single wire. It does so by using time division multiplexing and assigning a block of time to each channel.

The IEEE 802.9 standard will include a P-channel protocol at the MAC layer level designed to handle packet-mode or burst data. The Link Access Procedures on the D channel (LAPD) protocol used by ISDN at the MAC layer level is also used by 802.9 networks. This protocol will ensure that 802.9 integrated voice/data networks will be able to use ISDN D channel control information.

Figure 10-6 illustrates the 802.9 MAC frame format. The flag consists of a "01111110" bit pattern that indicates a frame's start and end. The Serve Identification (SID) field indicates what kind of service is provided on the P channel. The SID field could, for example, designate ISDN's LAPD protocol or the 802.2 LLC protocol. It might even designate the X.25 packet switching protocol. The Field Control (FC) field specifies whether the frame is used for control purposes or to transmit information. It also indicates the frame's priority.

Flag	SID	FC	DA	SA	PDU	FCS	Flag

10-6   The 802.9 MAC frame format.

The Destination Address (DA) and Source Address (SA) fields are self-descriptive. The Protocol Data Unit (PDU) contains MAC control information or user data from a higher layer. Finally, the Frame Check Sequence (FCS) utilizes the CRC-32 error checking scheme.

Presently 802.9 is a Draft standard. It is likely to be adopted as an IEEE and ANSI standard in late 1991 or early 1992. The success of 802.9 is dependent upon the success of ISDN. If ISDN is successful, 802.9 will provide the "missing link" that links together a LAN's MAC layer protocols and the protocols associated with ISDN. It will be the glue that will make simultaneous voice and data transmission possible between a LAN and an ISDN integrated voice data terminal.

ISDN in action at McDonald's

The common carriers have each selected key customers as beta sites for ISDN trials. McDonald's serves as an example of how these customers are planning to use

ISDN. McDonald's Corporation has developed plans in conjunction with AT&T and Illinois Bell for a global network that utilizes ISDN. The company has indicated that it will use a combination of 2100 BRI and PRI lines at its corporate headquarters to link it with 40 domestic field offices, more than 8000 U.S. stores and 3000 overseas stores. A major advantage of ISDN for McDonald's is that it will be able to consolidate 21 existing telecommunications networks into one. A user at any ISDN terminal will be able to access database information anywhere on the network.

McDonald's has indicated that one reason that it is opting for ISDN is the services available on such a network. The company plans to use the ISDN electronic directory, including calling number identification, message waiting, and retrieval. ISDN terminals will display the number of the person calling from within the company and the caller's name. The message waiting feature will alert users when a message has been left for them, and the retrieval feature will enable them to examine a series of waiting messages by scrolling through them.

Broadband ISDN

Lately many industry experts have begun to say openly what they have been thinking for quite awhile—narrowband ISDN might have arrived too late. ISDN's individual 64 Kbs channels and its aggregate 1.5 Mbs might be insufficient for the bandwidth required by LANs and enterprise networks. *Broadband ISDN* (BISDN) raises the bandwidth threshold to over 600 Mbs and could provide the bandwidth necessary for large scale transfer of high-resolution video along with voice and data information. The CCITT has identified three "H" or high-speed channels to be used in conjunction with BISDN. Figure 10-7 reveals the CCITT ISDN hierarchy of H channels.

H Channel	Gross Bit Rate*
H11	1.544
H12	2.048
H21	34.368
H22	44.736
H4	139.264

10-7 The CCITT ISDN hierarchy of H channels.

* The Gross Bit Rate includes control data overhead

Broadband ISDN standards probably will not be adopted until 1992 or 1993. At the moment, Asynchronous Transfer Mode (ATM), the packet-oriented transport system is the leading contender. The ATM format consists of a 5 octet header cell used for error checking and a 48 octet data cell. The IEEE 802.6 committee has agreed to use this same packet structure and error checking scheme although it has added additional header information for MAN-specific functions. Proprietary ATM systems are already available today and in beta trials from the regional Bell companies. Bellcore's Switched Multimegabit Data Service (SMDS) is the leading contender at the moment for MANs. Ultimately, many industry experts predict that broadband ISDN will use the ATM format in conjunction with SONET when it becomes commercially available.

Who needs ISDN

ISDN is just one of several different communications options that a network manager must consider. Companies that today depend heavily on Centrex, large private networks, public data networks, and plan to establish global links with international branches will embrace ISDN because it will save them substantial money.

Companies that already have committed heavily to LANs and bypass technologies such as VSATs and microwave might not need ISDN. Narrowband ISDN's 64 Kbs channels and 1.544 Mbs bandwidth aggregate might be inadequate for companies that have WANs that must carry substantial amounts of information. Broadband ISDN is still too far in the distant future to serve as a practical solution to these WAN bandwidth requirements.

Summary

ISDN's Basic Rate Interface (BRI) consists of two 64 Kbs Bearer channels and one 16 Kbs Data channel. The Primary Rate Interface (PRI) is also known as "23B + D" because it consists of 23 "B" channels of 64 Kbs each and 1 64 Kbs "D" channel. ISDN equipment contains several different kinds of interfaces. TE-1 equipment is ISDN compatible while TE-2 equipment is not ISDN compatible and requires a terminal adapter. NT-1 equipment consists of public switched demarcation devices while NT-2 equipment describes customer-owned switching equipment such as a PBX.

The IEEE 802.9 committee has developed a Draft for a set of specifications for integrated voice/data transmission. This Draft's provisions are compatible with ISDN and with metropolitan area networks.

Broadband ISDN might be the answer for network managers who find narrowband ISDN inadequate for their wide area network needs. Broadband ISDN will have bandwidth in the 600 Mbs range, large enough to handle integrated voice/data/video transmission.

11
CHAPTER

Gateways to the mainframe world

This chapter examines

- Several different ways a LAN can have a gateway to the IBM mainframe world.
- How IBM's Systems Network Architecture (SNA) is changing to make it easier for peer-to-peer communications with PCs on a LAN.
- How Apple networks communicate with IBM mainframes.
- How the DEC world can be linked to LANs.

Introduction

One critical issue facing network managers is the best way to link their LANs to corporate mainframes. This chapter examines several different types of LAN gateways including a relatively new direct connection to the mainframe. You will also look at remote gateways.

In order to understand what type of gateway you need, it is helpful to review the building blocks of an IBM mainframe system including Systems Network

Architecture (SNA). This chapter looks at SNA as it is today and at some new programming interfaces that promise greater direct communication between mainframe programs and LAN programs in the future. This chapter also considers the ways that the Apple world can communicate with DEC networks and IBM mainframes. The topic of this chapter is gateways from the LAN world populated with microcomputers to the world of mainframes. The topic is a complex subject, particularly for LAN managers with little mainframe experience, so the chapter assumes no prior knowledge.

The IBM mainframe world

Before you examine the several different ways that LANs can be linked to mainframe computers, spend some time looking at the mainframe environment, particularly because you might be far more comfortable with micros and LANs than with host computer terminology. I focus initially on the IBM mainframe world since IBM controls such a significant market share.

The IBM mainframe world is a world of centralized processing dominated by the host computer. For the most part, this is a world in which the mainframe has master/slave relationships with its peripherals. This means that the host polls its various network devices to see if they want to communicate. I return later in this chapter to look at the growing movement toward peer-to-peer relationships in which devices can communicate with each other when needed as well as with the host.

Terminals and other devices communicate via *cluster controllers*, devices that serve as an interface between the host computer and its many network devices. The high-end 3175 cluster controller can support a theoretical maximum of 253 devices. Terminals dialing in from remote sites via modem communicate with a communications controller, a high-speed "traffic copy" that transmits this information to the mainframe.

The name of the game in mainframe operations is to offload as much work as possible to other processors and leave the host free to do what it does best—crunch numbers very quickly. A *front-end processor* (FEP) is a software programmable controller that relieves the host of many networking and data communications tasks. It can handle such "overhead" functions as polling devices, error checking and recovery, character code translation, and dynamic buffer control. IBM front-end processors are usually referred to by their model numbers, the most common of which are the older 3705 or the newer 3725. On an IBM mainframe network, the Network Control Program (NCP) is generated on and loaded from the host onto a front end processor. Software on the host, called Virtual Telecommunications Access Method (VTAM), communicates at a speed of approximately 2.5 Mbs with the NCP running on the FEP. The FEP also serves the role of a concentrator, concentrating several low speed data transmissions into a steady, high-speed flow of information to the host.

Generally terminals and printers are not connected directly to the FEP but are connected in clusters to control units, which are known appropriately as cluster controllers. In the IBM mainframe world, these devices are also known by their model numbers, which most often include 3174, 3274, and 3276. Figure 11-1 illustrates how these various IBM devices are linked together in a typical corporate environment.

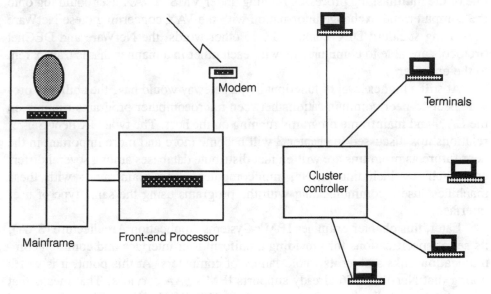

Modem

Terminals

Cluster controller

Front-end Processor

Mainframe

11-1 The basic components of a mainframe system.

The level of a gateway's functionality can vary

A *gateway* is a device that connects networks which have different network architectures. Gateways use all seven layers of the OSI model and perform the protocol conversion function at the Application layer. Typical corporate gateways connect the PC world of Token Ring, Ethernet, and AppleTalk LANs with the IBM's mainframe SNA environment, with X.25 packet switched networks, or with DEC's DECnet networks.

LAN gateways differ considerably in their functionality. At the very lowest level, a gateway provides terminal emulation so that all LAN workstations can emulate or imitate a dumb terminal. Even in this case, the level of emulation can vary considerably depending upon the gateway. Some gateways handle IBM's block data transmission approach very well and map PC keyboards so that they have the look and feel of an IBM 3270 terminal while retaining the advantage of an intelligent PC workstation by permitting easy switching from terminal emulation to PC operations with a hot key. Some gateways permit a LAN workstation to window several different host sessions and move easily from session to session.

A second level of LAN gateway functionality includes file sharing between LAN and host. Novell has licensed versions of NetWare to several minicomputer manufacturers. Shortly, you should see more and more minicomputers used as NetWare file servers. NetWare for VMS is already available, so it is possible today for a NetWare LAN user to log onto a VAX from a PC workstation, and view and access NetWare files residing on the VAX. To the LAN user, the VAX appears to be just another PC file server. Because the VAX is running NetWare as one of the multitasking processes running under VMS, a VAX user could log onto the computer and exchange information with the VAX concerning these NetWare files using standard DEC commands. In other words, the NetWare and DECnet protocols are able to communicate with each other in a manner that is transparent to the end user.

At still a higher level of functionality, a gateway would have the ability to provide peer-to-peer communications between microcomputer programs running on the LAN and mainframe programs running on the host. The type of Client-Server relationships discussed in chapter 3 will become more and more important in the near future as programs are written that distribute databases among several different machines including LANs, minicomputers, and mainframes with these machines' users communicating with the programs using the same type of user interface.

Later, this chapter examines IBM's Systems Application Architecture (SAA), its set of specifications for providing a uniform user interface and common communication links among its whole family of computers. At this point, it is worth noting that NetWare 386 already supports IBM's SAA services. That means that when programs adhering to SAA are written, Novell's NetWare 386 operating system will be able to facilitate the type of communications required for programs to exchange meaningful information.

How gateways link hosts and LANs

Before LAN gateways, companies connected PCs directly to IBM front-end processors via coaxial cabling using expensive PC 3270 emulation cards and software. Many companies invested tens or even hundreds of thousands of dollars in products such as DCA's IRMA board. With a LAN gateway, however, the micro-mainframe connection is much more cost-effective. The gateway board emulates a cluster controller so that each network workstation is seen by the mainframe as a terminal linked to the cluster controller. The gateway's multiple mainframe sessions are split among the network's workstations so that the channel rarely sits idle. Only the gateway needs to have a circuit card and the software necessary for protocol conversion and terminal emulation.

Figure 11-2 illustrates four different types of LAN connections to an IBM mainframe: Local connection between a host and a LAN gateway workstation linked via coaxial cable to a communications controller; a local connection

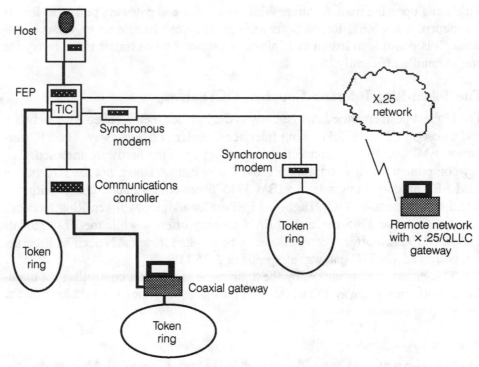

11-2 Gateways between LANs and mainframes.

between a LAN and front-end processor via a Token Ring Interface Coupler (TIC) gateway; a LAN remotely linked to a host's front-end processor via modems; and a LAN remotely linked to a mainframe's front-end processor via an X.25 network.

Local DFT coaxial gateway

With earlier IBM systems, when the host computer requested transmission of a terminal's contents, the controller, not the terminal, handled this request. This approach was known as the *Control Unit Terminal* (CUT) mode of operation. With IBM's 3174 family of controllers, the company introduced the concept of offloading this terminal processing task to programmable terminals. This approach became known as the *Distributed Function Terminal* (DFT) mode of processing. A DFT coax gateway allows a LAN workstation to emulate a Distributed Function Terminal (DFT).

The gateway PC emulates an SNA cluster controller communicating with its workstations emulating DFT terminals. Workstations on the LAN run their own software that allow them to emulate an IBM terminal. This workstation's terminal emulation software accesses the gateway via the LAN's transport protocol. The number of concurrent sessions available with these gateways varies widely depending upon the manufacturer. While some low-end gateways permit as few as 5 concurrent sessions, Rabbit Software's gateway can handle up to 40 such sessions. It is possible to install multiple coax gateways when traffic is too heavy for one to handle efficiently.

The Token Ring Interface Coupler (TIC) gateway

The highest performance LAN gateway is the link between a Token Ring network and a host's FEP via a Token Ring Interface Coupler (TIC) gateway. The TIC permits a 4 Mbs or 16 Mbs connection depending upon the hardware installed. The key component for this connection is the Token Ring Adapter, not the NIC but an IBM FEP hardware upgrade. An IBM 3745 Token Ring Adapter comes with two 802.5 connections or TICs. High-end FEPs offer additional Token Ring Network connections. The 3745 model 130 LAN gateway offers 4 while the 3745 models 210 and 410 each offer 8 connections. A non-Token Ring LAN such as Ethernet can be linked via TIC gateway at speeds of 2.35 Mbs.

The gateway PC is viewed by the mainframe as a cluster controller; the mainframe polls this gateway PC while it in turn polls all other workstations on the Token Ring network.

Remote LAN gateway

As enterprise networks and wide area networks evolve, remote LAN gateways are becoming very common. A PC on the remote site's LAN functions as a gateway and runs gateway software. This gateway PC functions as a cluster controller and communicates with a front-end processor using IBM's Synchronous Data Link Control (SDLC) protocol via synchronous modems located at both sites. Figure 11-3 illustrates a typical remote LAN gateway.

The limitation of remote gateways traditionally has been speed. The synchronous modem can dial up the front-end processor at speeds up to 64 Kbs. Companies with heavy micro-mainframe traffic might require multiple remote gateways to solve this congestion problem.

X.25 gateways

Remote LANs can also communicate with IBM mainframes via X.25 gateways. A gateway PC with an adapter card functions as a cluster controller and runs special gateway software that contains the QLLC protocol, an IBM defined protocol that runs over the X.25 protocol suite. The other LAN workstations emulate IBM 3270 terminals. The IBM host simply assumes it is communicating with a remote cluster controller.

Gateways linking together LANs

In enterprise networking, it is possible that several LANs might be linked to a company's mainframe, but they might not be linked to each other. When the need

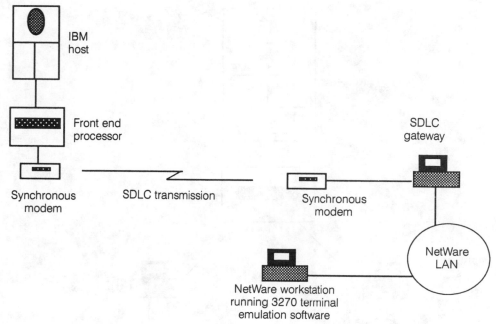

11-3 A remote LAN.

develops to link them together, a mainframe can act as a router to connect these LANs. Phase Systems has developed software for NetWare while Micro Tempus has similar software for LAN Manager that enables these LAN operating systems to run as an application under IBM's Virtual Telecommunications Access Method (VTAM) software on mainframes running VM or MVS. As Fig. 11-4 illustrates, a NetWare LAN uses its SNA gateway to send information to a mainframe. The NetWare application program running on the host under VTAM sends this information via a different gateway to its destination, a workstation on a second NetWare LAN.

Phaser Systems offers SNA routers for both NetWare 386 and NetWare 286. A major reason companies would purchase these mainframe router programs is to interconnect remote NetWare LANs and also to enable these remote LANs to be managed from a central site. The LAN traffic can piggyback on top of the LAN-to-host communications and eliminate a company's need to purchase expensive routers and bridges for remote communications as part of a wide area network.

Systems Network Architecture (SNA)

Systems Network Architecture (SNA) is IBM's network architecture, its suite of layered protocols designed to facilitate data communications for an IBM computer system environment. IBM announced SNA in 1974 to provide host to terminal connections under its Synchronous Data Link Control (SDLC) protocol. Information was to be stored on the mainframe using Virtual Telecommunications Access

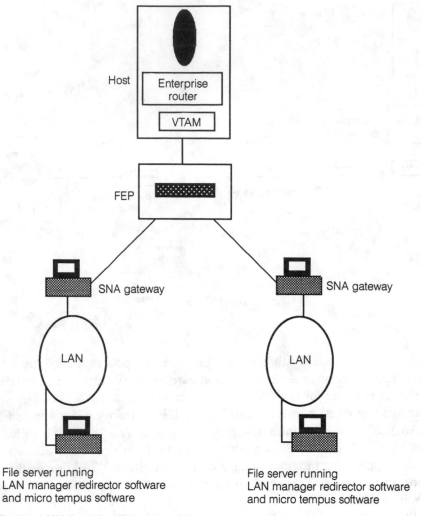

11-4 Routing LAN information through a mainframe.

Method (VTAM) while communications between the host and attached devices would be via the Network Control Program (NCP) running on a front-end processor. In this "master/slave" world, the host periodically polled the dumb terminals to see if they had information to transmit.

Network Addressable Units (NAUs)

Every component of an SNA network that can be assigned an address and receive or send information is known as a *Network Addressable Unit* (NAU). The three major types of NAUs considered here are Logical Units (LUs), Physical Units (PUs), and System Service Control Points (SSCPs). Two NAUs must establish a *session* or linkage in order to be able to communicate on the network.

Logical units (LUs)

Nobody ever said that IBM terminology was easy or even that it made any sense. The SNA world has its own terminology, so you need to go over some key terms when you consider how hosts can be linked to LANs. In the SNA environment, any device or application program that needs to use services is known as an SNA user. An SNA user accesses the network through a point of access known as a *logical unit* (LU). Think of these LUs as logical ports and not physical connections. Figure 11-5 describes the major LUs. I return to LU 6.2 later in this chapter when I cover peer-to-peer relations.

LU Type	Description
LU Type 1	Supports communication between an application program and a remote terminal.
LU Type 2	Supports communication between an application program and a 3270 terminal.
LU Type 3	Supports Type 2 communications services for keyboard/printer terminals.
LU Type 4	Supports communications between host and terminal to terminal for IBM office equipment.
LU Type 6.1	Supports communications between applications running on hosts.
LU Type 6.2	Supports program-to-program communications without the need for a host.

11-5 Major logical units (LUs) under SNA.

Physical units (PUs)

A *physical unit* (PU) refers to the actual physical device or communication link found on an SNA network. The PU actually refers to not just the physical device but also any software and microde that defines the services performed by that device. Communications processors, cluster controllers, and terminals are all defined on an SNA network as PUs. Figure 11-6 describes the key PUs.

System Service Control Points (SSCPs)

The *System Service Control Point* (SSCP) on an SNA network is defined as the network addressable unit that provides the services necessary to manage a network or a portion of a network. The SSCP resides in the *Virtual Telecommunications Access Method* (VTAM) control program on the host computer. The SSCP activates and deactivates network resources under its control or "domain" with

PU Type	Description
Type 2.0	Cluster controllers for 3270 terminals.
Type 2.1	IBM minicomputers & microcomputers. Type 2.1 nodes can communicate with each other without the host as an intermediary.
Type 4	Communications controllers functioning as front end processors.
Type 5	Host computers.

11-6 Key SNA physical units (PUs).

assistance from the *Network Control Program* (NCP), a physical unit running on a communications controller (front-end processor). Before NAUs can communicate with each other, their physical and logical connections must be turned on by the SSCP and the NCP loaded into the FEP. Figure 11-7 illustrates how these various NAUs work together to enable a 3278/9 terminal to access a program on the host computer.

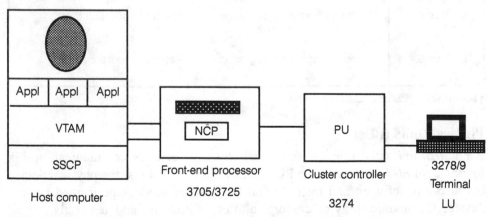

11-7 NAUs work together to enable a terminal to access a mainframe program.

SNA's layered architecture

SNA has its own layered architecture which predates the OSI model and, as Fig. 11-8 illustrates, there is no one-to-one layer correspondence between these two architectures. Despite their differences, SNA and the OSI model both enjoy the advantage of any layered architecture—the ability to modify or revise one layer's services without having to create an entirely new architecture. You have already

OSI Model Layer	SNA Layer
Application	Transaction services
Presentation	Presentation services
Session	Data flow control
Transport	Transmission control
Network	Path control
Data link	Data link control
Physical	Physical control

11-8 SNA's layered architecture.

looked at the role of the gateway that links LANs and mainframe computers; by examining the major functions performed in each SNA layer, it should become clear why micro-mainframe communications require a gateway utilizing all network layers rather than a router capable of functioning only at the Network layer.

The *Physical Control layer* corresponds the OSI model's Physical layer. It provides specifications both for serial connections between nodes and for high-speed parallel connections between host computers and front-end processors. The *Data Link Control layer* corresponds to the OSI model's layer 2. The major protocol in this layer is IBM's Synchronous Data Link Control (SDLC) although there are also protocols for IBM's own Token Ring Network as well as a high-speed parallel link protocol for IBM's S/370 hosts.

The *Path Control layer* handles routing and flow control. The protocols in this layer also handle sequencing and expedited network services. In the event that a specified route is not longer viable, this layer notifies the layer above it (Transmission Control).

The *Transmission Control layer* contains protocols that provide the pacing for data exchanges between NAUs so that information is not lost. It also handles data encryption when this is specified. This layer adds a header to an SNA frame that includes its control information.

The *Data Flow Control* layer corresponds roughly to the Session layer of the OSI model. It is responsible for the establishment of half-duplex and full-duplex network sessions. The *Presentation Services layer* is responsible for formatting, translation, and other services associated with the way the data must look. Finally, the *Transaction Services layer* corresponds to the OSI model's Application layer. Here you will find IBM's SNA Distribution Services (SNADS), which is a way of distributing data asynchronously between distributed application programs. IBM's Document Interchange Architecture (DIA), also found in this layer, provides a method of ensuring that documents can be exchanged among different application programs.

Systems Application Architecture (SAA)

Systems Application Architecture (SAA) is IBM's long-range plan and set of specifications to link together its entire computer family of products. SAA includes the Common User Access (CUA), the Common Programming Interface (CPI), and the Common Communications Services (CCS). If programmers follow the specifications for these three key interfaces, eventually it will not matter whether a user accesses a program on an IBM mainframe, minicomputer, or PS/2 running OS/2. All these programs will have the same "look and feel" and also be able to exchange information. Under pressure from large corporate customers with mixed computer vendor environments, IBM has incorporated communications standards used by other vendors' equipment as well as OSI model protocols in SAA.

Many of IBM's largest customers have been concerned whether or not SNA would ever be OSI-compatible; they feared being "locked-in" to IBM's proprietary network architecture. If a company were a 100% IBM shop, SNA would be vastly preferable to the OSI model's suite of protocols because it is optimized for IBM hardware and avoids the overhead found with OSI protocols. In a mixed environment, however, companies are planning for a time in the future when the OSI model's suite of protocols will serve as a common language connecting a company's diverse computer resources.

IBM has reassured its major customers by including OSI protocols in SAA Common Communications Support. It will offer the programming interfaces for the OSI Communications Subsystem as a feature of ACF/VTAM, the company's basic mainframe communications software. In fact, the OSI/Communications Subsystem provides the base for the SAA OSI application layer functions. OSI/ File Services implement the OSI FTAM protocol in the SAA environment. IBM has also indicated that SAA will support OSI protocols for LANs and WANs, CCITT X.400 electronic mail protocols, and CCITT X.500 protocols for a global E-mail directory.

NetWare 386 and SAA mainframe connectivity

Novell designed its NetWare 386 Communication Services for SAA to support multiple host links and up to 1000 simultaneous client sessions. The entire SNA protocol stack is incorporated into a Network Loadable Module (NLM). The NetWare 386 file server running this NLM can connect to an IBM host via a synchronous data link control (SDLC) link. It is also possible to create an indirect host-to-NetWare LAN connection by linking the file server to a Token Ring LAN via a token ring interface coupler (TIC).

Network managers have the ability to disable or enable host access to specific workstations as well as limit to users to certain types of LU sessions. Novell's Communications Services Manager enables LAN managers to monitor the performance of SAA LAN-to-host sessions and track network statistics including link efficiency and traffic patterns.

Full implementation of NetWare 386's SAA services will take a while. Third party vendors are likely to develop products that add network "hooks" to such desirable features as the Simple Network Management Protocol (SNMP). Once this protocol is available, it will be able to access all the LAN statistics gathered by NetWare 386 and make it easier to manage the network more efficiently.

A checklist for IBM mainframe gateways

Now that you have had the opportunity to examine the basic components of an IBM mainframe system as well as its network architecture and also survey the different types of gateways available, it is an appropriate time to look at specific gateway features. This section briefly describes major gateway features. From this shopping list, you should be able to formulate the questions you need to consider as a network manager or ask as a systems integrator in order to evaluate the wide range of gateways now available.

Number of simultaneous terminal sessions on a PC

Gateways provide varying numbers of simultaneous (concurrent) terminal sessions on a single PC. Is a DOS session supported separately, or is it part of the total sessions permitted a terminal in the vendor's literature? The number of terminal sessions available to a PC range from 1 to 32 among the more popular gateway products. Is there a hot key that makes it easy to switch back and forth from DOS to mainframe terminal emulation?

A gateway that emulates an IBM 3299 looks like 8 terminals to a cluster controller. If each terminal can support 5 sessions, then the gateway provides a total of 40 sessions for distribution among network workstations. The total number of concurrent sessions supported by a gateway can vary widely from less than 16 at the low end to 254 at the high end.

Terminals supported

Some gateway software packages can emulate all members of the 3178/9 and 3278/9 families of terminals; others are limited to the more common models.

Increasing numbers of LANs will require graphics terminal emulation in the near future because virtually all software is becoming more graphics-oriented. Does the software support IBM 3179 G or 3279 G graphics terminals?

File transfer capabilities

While network managers have been able to transfer binary files back and forth between mainframes and micros using a tedious record-by-record approach, they have pushed for more efficient software that would let them encode, compress and block data, calculate check sums, and then decompress, unblock and decode the files at both ends. IBM's IND$FILE protocol now has become an industry standard. Some vendors such as Data Interface Systems Corporation provide their own proprietary file transfer software as well as IND$FILE.

Some vendors improve the speed of IND$FILE by increasing the size of the PC gateway's buffer. Another key file transfer feature for gateways is to permit file transfer to take place in a host session. This ability enables multiple file transfers to take place simultaneously at each workstation. These file transfers might be taking place between a workstation and different hosts or on the same host. The gateway's ability to perform these file transfers in background mode is important for a LAN's busy gateway. If host to LAN file transfers is a major function for your proposed gateway, then it is important that you determine the file transfer protocols supported by the gateway.

Protocols supported

Virtually all gateways support IBM's Synchronous Date Link Control (SDLC) protocol. A number of gateways support Binary Synchronous Control (BSC) protocol, an older half-duplex approach still found on a significant number of mainframes. Many remote sites still use Remote Job Entry (RJE), a method of submitting work to a mainframe in batch format. Other key protocols that you might need supported include X.25, VT100 for communication with DEC systems, and Burroughs for communication with Burroughs mainframes.

Support of programming interfaces

In enterprise networks of the near future, companies will want far more connectivity than simple terminal emulation. They will want to automate logon procedures, create custom screens, automate many of the LAN to host file transfer tasks, and develop communication links between mainframe and LAN programs. Does your gateway support the necessary Application Programming Interfaces (APIs) to enable your programmers to write the necessary code? IBM's High Level Language Applications Programming Interface (HLLAPI) enables mouse support.

A gateway's support for IBM's Advanced Program-to-Program Communications (APPC) protocol for distributed processing could also be important in the future. APPC is already being used on IBM's SNA Distribution Services (SNADS) to send documents and files back and forth between two different systems. IBM's Distributed Data Management (DDM) uses APPC to transmit data between a client system and a database server. As a key component of Systems Application Architecture (SAA), APPC will be a tool for corporate programmers who want to establish links between programs running on different IBM systems.

APPC incorporates two relatively new SNA protocols. PU 2.1 permits two processors to communicate on a peer-to-peer basis, while LU 6.2 permits two application programs to have a peer-to-peer conversation. In the future, it is likely that programmers will use APPC and LU 6.2 to write code so that two programs running on different machines such as a host and a microcomputer will be able to exchange information without users needing to be aware of the how to communicate directly with the host. This information exchange will be completely transparent to the computer user. LU 6.2 will also be used to write multiple front-end applications including spreadsheets and databases running on client workstations that communicate via Structured Query Language (SQL) commands with a shared database running on a server or host.

Dedicated and pooled LUs

Some gateways permit dedicated LUs, an approach that guarantees that a given LU will be available to a LAN node when it requests one. Pooled LUs are available to all LAN nodes on a first-come, first-serve basis. On most gateways these pooled resources are freed-up and reusable once a user terminates a session.

Gateway management

The types of gateway management features supported vary widely among gateways. Some provide a gateway monitor, which enables a network manager to examine all session assignments and enable or disable devices. Some gateways let the network manager configure dedicated devices to attach to assigned devices automatically when a workstation is initiated. Dynamic device attachment logic retains prior assignments for each device and then attempts to reserve a free device for its most recent user unless or until no other device is available for another attaching user.

LAN features supported

Because gateways were available before LANs became popular, some vendors have put more effort into making their products "LAN-friendly," while other gateway vendors have provided minimal LAN functionality. Can the gateway recognize directory paths without the need to switch to the proper directory? Does the gateway communicate over NetBIOS or over Novell's IPX protocol? NetBIOS versions differ and problems could arise on a large NetWare LAN if the gateway does not support IPX. NetWare network managers also prefer gateway software that runs in a directory that can be set to Read-Only. In other words, what has the gateway vendor done to make this product easier for network users to operate?

Remote speeds supported

If your gateway is to be remote, the transmission speed it will support is critical. Some gateways still only support 19.2 Kbs modems while others support up to 64 Kbs. You might have to consider multiple remote gateways to reduce traffic congestion.

3Com's Maxess SNA Gateway as an example

3Com's Maxess SNA Gateway is a LAN SNA gateway that illustrates many of the gateway features you have been examining. The gateway workstation contains the Maxess SNA gateway coprocessor board as well as gateway software. Network workstations have far lower memory requirements because they need only run the 3270 Presentation Services and APPC transaction programs. Because applications are able to run concurrently over a single data link, one user can transfer a 3270 file while other users access programs or run LU 6.2 applications that communicate in a program-to-program mode. The program supports up to 32 concurrent sessions with each workstation able to run multiple sessions. Users have a "hot key" to switch back and forth between 3270, APPC, and DOS applications.

The Maxess SNA Gateway emulates a 3274 cluster controller while its nodes use 3278/9 terminal emulation and have the ability to define their keyboards and screens. It supports IBM IND$FILE file transfer support up to speeds of 64 Kbs.

The program is intelligent enough to be able to provide both dynamic and static LU allocation. It generates alerts when a session is not established due to a data link failure or SNA protocol violation. A Response Time Monitor accumulates information concerning the time required for a host and network to respond to terminal users. This gateway can be monitored by IBM's NetView network management program.

Apple gateways

Many Fortune 1000 companies have significant numbers of Macintosh computers which they have begun to network, usually with AppleTalk or Ethernet. In chapter 7, you saw that it is not difficult for a Macintosh on an Ethernet network to be bridged to a PC-based Ethernet LAN. What about linking the Macs to the company's IBM mainframe or perhaps to a department's VAX system? This section examines some of the Apple gateways available to the network manager or systems integrator.

Apple gateways to IBM mainframes via PC LANs

In an enterprise network, Macintosh workstations might be linked together on an AppleTalk network using these workstations' built-in LocalTalk interfaces. Because AppleTalk's suite of protocols now supports Token Ring networks with the TokenTalk protocol, Fig. 11-9 illustrates how it is possible to link an Apple-Talk network to a Token Ring network with a TokenTalk NIC serving as a bridge. The Macintosh workstations then can use the Token Ring network's gateway to the IBM mainframe.

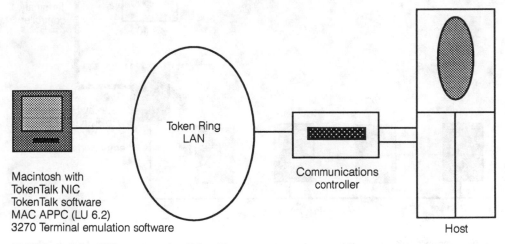

Macintosh with
TokenTalk NIC
TokenTalk software
MAC APPC (LU 6.2)
3270 Terminal emulation software

11-9 AppleTalk's SNA gateway via a Token Ring network.

Direct AppleTalk gateways to IBM mainframes

AppleTalk LANs can provide gateways to IBM mainframes in a variety of different ways. These gateways all emulate a 3174 cluster controller and distribute and manage 3270 terminal emulation sessions, but they do so in quite different ways.

DCA's MacIrmaLAN Gateway Server uses a dedicated PC or PS/2-based gateway to run either a LocalTalk PC card or an IBM Token Ring card plus AppleShare PC, IrmaLAN, and MacIrmaTalk software. Each Mac workstation runs MacIrma Workstation client software and MacIrmaTalk Startup software. Companies with a wide range of LANs including AppleTalk requiring gateways to a host might want to consider Tri-Data's Netway gateways. A Windows-based 3270 gateway supports Macintosh workstations running AppleTalk and PCs running NetWare concurrently. Tri-Data's NetWay products already support the installation of both Ethernet and Token Ring cards concurrently.

AppleTalk gateways to IBM AS/400 minicomputers

Andrew KMW Systems is the first vendor to offer an AppleTalk gateway to IBM's popular AS/400 minicomputer. This twin axial gateway supports up to a maximum of six emulation cards in a Mac II gateway. As Fig. 11-10 indicates, Macintosh AppleTalk workstations are linked to a Macintosh AS/400 gateway, which is directly connected to a terminal controller. The controller is either directly connected or connected via 9600 bps synchronous modems to the AS/400.

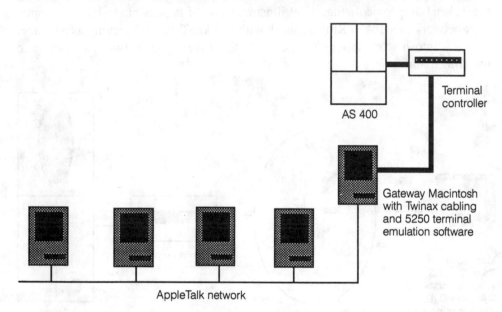

AS 400

Terminal controller

Gateway Macintosh with Twinax cabling and 5250 terminal emulation software

AppleTalk network

11-10 Connecting an AppleTalk LAN to an AS/400.

MacAPPC

Apple has developed MacAPPC, a set of programming tools that should result in more efficient Mac-to-host communications in the future. Programs written using APPCs could exchange information and pool processing power regardless of whether they were running on microcomputers, minicomputers, or hosts. MacAPPC implements SNA's LU6.2 and PU2.1, NAUs required for peer-to-peer communications under SNA. The problem with MacAPPC, though, is that it probably will be a while before you see a significant number of host programs using APPC that can interface with Mac programs that use APPC. Because of the expense of host-based programs, companies will be slow to dump these programs if they are performing adequately.

Apple also has developed MacWorkStation, a tool that lets host computer users utilize the Macintosh interface, filing, and printing features. Programmers access the Macintosh toolbox, including control over windows, pull-down menus, dialog boxes, and other features of the Macintosh user interface without having to write Macintosh applications. A company using MacWorkStation could develop applications so that its mainframe users would have a Macintosh interface.

Linking Macs to the VAX world

Digital Equipment Corporation's LanWorks for the Macintosh integrates Macintosh computers on an AppleTalk network with DEC's VAXes and DECnet/OSI network. VAXshare, the DEC file server program, looks like AppleShare on a Macintosh. DEC has agreed to change the name of the LanWorks product because it is already owned by another corporation. At the time this book is being written, the new name has not yet been determined, so I will continue to refer to this connectivity tool by its original name. This user interface makes it easy for Macintosh users to manipulate the data coming from the VAX.

LanWorks links the Macintosh micro world with the VAX world via DEC's Mailbus enterprise messaging system and All-in-1 Mail. The electronic mail package supports the CCITT's X.400 family of protocols, which means that this mail service could provide an indirect means of sending mail from an AppleTalk network to IBM's PROFS and SNADS.

Under LanWorks, the VMS server software includes VAXshare File Services and VAXshare Print Services. The file services software enables VAX computers to serve as file servers for Macintosh clients and is Apple File Protocol based. The print services package enables Macintosh and VAX users to share any DEC or Apple networked printer.

DEC has announced several related products that can be used in conjunction with LanWorks. Macintosh workstations appear to the VAX computer as Phase IV nonrouting end nodes. This means that the VAX can route packets from Macintosh workstations on Ethernet networks by encapsulating them within DECnet packets, just as it would encapsulate information from DEC workstations. DECnet management software can be used to monitor the AppleTalk communications coming from the Macintosh workstations.

Summary

LAN gateways to IBM hosts come in a number of different types, including local DFT coaxial connection, direct connection via Token Interface Coupler (TIC), remote link via modem, and X.25 connection. Mainframes can also be used as routers to link two LANs that have mainframe gateways.

In order to understand mainframe gateways, you must know something about IBM's Systems Network Architecture (SNA), its layered network architecture. Historically this has been a master/slave system with all communications initiated by the host. IBM's LU 6.2 and APPC make it possible for peer-to-peer communications in the future between LAN programs and mainframe programs.

IBM's Systems Application Architecture (SAA) is a set of specifications for consistent user interfaces and program interfaces for its entire computer family. The release of SAA-compliant services on NetWare 386 and a set of SAA tools for the Macintosh will facilitate this communication between LAN program and mainframe program.

AppleTalk LANs can communicate with IBM hosts via their own gateways or by connecting first to a Token Ring Network via TokenTalk and then using this LAN's gateway. AppleTalk LANs also can communicate with DEC VAX networks via several products developed by Apple and DEC. These products incorporate AppleTalk's suite of protocols in DECnet so that an AppleTalk user of a DEC computer's services will view a screen resembling that of AppleShare.

12
CHAPTER

Major systems integration issues

In this chapter, you will examine

- How fax servers can be incorporated in a network.
- How networks can use the CCITT X.400 and X.500 recommendations to link proprietary, non-compatible E-mail systems via gateways.
- Why SNMP has become so popular for network management.
- The major network management approaches taken by IBM, AT&T, and DEC.

Introduction

As networks evolve from single site LANs to enterprise networks that include multiple LANs as well as remote LANs with WAN links to mainframes and mini-computers, integration of basic functions such as E-mail become more difficult and the need for centralized management and control increases dramatically. This chapter examines how large multi-vendor networks can link heterogenous E-mail packages. The chapter also looks at how large networks can share fax services.

The network management issue is complex and worthy of an entire book of its own. This chapter looks at the major network management systems offered by IBM, AT&T, and DEC. By examining these different network architectures as well as the protocols running under them, you will see how your own network or the networks you are designing for clients correspond. At this point, these network management system architectures are incomplete, but they do give you some insight into the major vendors' long-term development plans.

Incorporating faxes in an enterprise network

The fax explosion the past few years has created a need for LAN managers to develop a cost-effective way that workstations can share fax services. Just having a fax available for several nodes to share is not enough, however, because it is essential that the fax blend seamlessly with existing LAN electronic mail software. When fax services are able to hide behind existing E-mail software, network users do not have to learn anything new before they can begin working efficiently. Alcom's EasyGate is a fax gateway for 3+ networks running 3+ Mail. Users can send faxes from the 3+ Mail user interface. The program contains interfaces to MCI Mail and Western Union's EasyLink. The program is able to receive faxes and forward them to the appropriate 3+ mailbox.

Fax gateways can be accessed by remote workstations. As an example, with an enterprise network that happens to be using Higgins E-mail software with Higgins 2:Fax, a user on a remote LAN can send a message through several different "hops" until it reaches a network fax gateway.

Some points to consider about fax gateways

Adding a fax gateway to a LAN does have some negative aspects. Fax services place quite a strain on a PC's processing power. While fax operations can take place in background mode, they do slow up PC processing considerably as a network document is converted into the format required for fax transmission or a document is received and its contents must be converted into a standard ASCII text file. Does a network manager really want the network congested with heavy traffic associated with fax transmission? Also, a fax server or gateway requires a scanner if the company needs to be able to send printed documents that are not on the network.

Companies that utilize compression techniques that cut 64 Kbs voice channels to 32 Kbs or 24 Kbs might not support 9.6 Kbs Group 3 faxes. The multiplexers that compress voice information are not designed to handle the variable frequency tones used by analog fax transmissions. The fax might not be able to support 9.6 Kbs traffic and automatically seek a slower speed such as 7.2 Kbs or 4.8 Kbs. Some specific multiplexers, such as Newbridge's 3600, direct fax traffic to a fax modem at speeds of 4.8 Kbs or 9.6 Kbs so that the fax traffic can be transmitted along with compressed voice information.

LAN fax features worth considering

Selecting a LAN fax also presents problems. Now CCITT Group 3 faxes are the norm; they are able to transmit a page of information in approximately one minute. Within the next few years, though, Group 4 machines will become more common. Group 4 machines are able to transmit a page of information in around ten seconds. More important, though, this type of fax is designed to work with ISDN. Companies considering ISDN or involved in ISDN beta testing might want to look at a Group 4 machine so that they will not have compatibility problems in the future. Some models offer a Group 3 converter so that these machines can communicate with the most common type of fax now in use.

Another fax feature worth considering for network managers is the type of files the fax server can handle. Assuming a network manager has standardized the LAN on a a specific word processing program or desktop publishing program, the fax server should be able to handle these types of files. If a LAN's users use graphics and want to send these pictures over a fax, then the fax server should handle such common formats as Z-Soft's PCX, Digital Research's GEM, and Cybernetics' Dr. HALO. In the near future, more LAN users might require the ability to handle Windows Paint format as well as the tagged-image file format (TIFF) used by many desktop publishing programs.

Still another feature that is essential for a fax gateway is network management. Comwave's Faxnet will serve as an example of some of the network management features a LAN manager can expect from such a product. Faxnet is a fax gateway designed to run on NetWare LANs including NetWare 386. A DOS workstation can be configured with up to eight boards with each board supporting a different fax line.

Faxnet can be programmed to prioritize outgoing faxes and store and then forward them at scheduled times. The server can be programmed to poll on-line services at scheduled times for specified data. Faxnet keeps track of each fax's destination, date, time, and duration. This information goes into a log as well as back to the source workstation.

Using FaxPress on a NetWare LAN

Look at a specific fax product designed to work with a NetWare LAN running under Ethernet, Token Ring, or Arcnet. While Castelle's FaxPress is not the only product available, it will illustrate how this whole class of products operate.

As Fig. 12-1 indicates, FaxPress is a dedicated fax server that enables a NetWare LAN to send and receive faxes from within any PC application. All fonts, graphics, and formatting are retained so that the documents sent via fax look exactly as if they were printed on an HP LaserJet. The server comes with either 2.5 or 4.5Mb of RAM and dual Motorola 68000 microprocessors. Standard CCITT Group 3 faxes are transmitted anywhere from 2400 to 9600 bps.

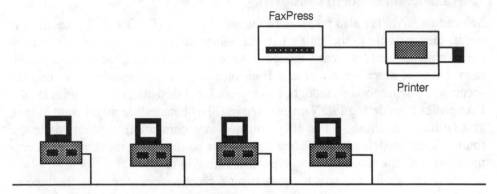

12-1   FaxPress as a NetWare print server.

What is interesting about this new technology is that it combines all the advantages of a stand-alone fax machine with a seamless integration into a NetWare environment. The four different ways that a NetWare user can send a fax are from within applications using a pop-up utility, from a menu, as an attachment to electronic mail messages, and from a command line. A user who needs a hard copy of a document and not a fax can use the HP LaserJet attached to the fax server to print a document, so that the fax server becomes just another NetWare print server when needed.

The stand-alone fax can be programmed to send messages at specified times even if the originating workstation is not in use. Conversely, a fax arriving for a workstation that is not logged onto the network can be printed on the HP LaserJet. Network management features include three levels of password security and detailed logs of all fax transmissions.

New standards to improve fax transmission

The CCITT has been working on a new standard, V.17, which modifies the existing V.33 communications standard for leased lines to work in the fax environment over conventional dial-up lines. V.17 will increase transmission speed from 9600 bps to 14,400 bps over current fax equipment by using a type of error correction (Trellis encoding) that is built right into the modulation scheme without any additional overhead. Because this new standard increases transmission speed by roughly one-third, costs should drop accordingly.

Another new standard that will affect fax transmission is EIA 578 (Asynchronous Facsimile DCE Control Standard, Service Class 1), which was approved February 1990. EIA 578 defines a standard command set that can be incorporated on the fax board in a PC by a systems integrator. The specifications for Class 1 call for the PC to handle fax compression and connection while the fax board handles all other functions.

The major importance of EIA 578 immediately is that it provides a standard set of fax drivers for systems integrators to use while writing software for programs running under Microsoft's Windows 3.0. Future classes of EIA 578 specifications will address such issues as binary file transfer and error control.

Some problems associated with network fax gateways

If a fax server is used without a link to E-mail, one problem is that a networked fax cannot know where to send an incoming file. Programs require a fax manager to scan incoming fax cover pages to decide where to route these messages. The EIA Fax Committee (TR29) is trying to develop a standard for routing incoming fax messages directly to their workstation destinations. The Committee is trying to develop a solution that will be backward compatible to the fax machines currently in the field.

What happens if an answering machine and a fax machine share the same line? Some fax machines will time out and then disconnect if they do not hear the appropriate fax tones. The CCITT Study Group VIII is working to develop standards for network fax servers that will be able to distinguish among voice, fax, and data modem calls.

Security presents still another problem when adding a fax gateway to a network. An enterprise network with several different fax gateways could present problems unless all gateways use the same proprietary encryption methods. At this time, the CCITT has not yet established standards for limiting access to networks with fax machines.

Managing electronic mail on enterprise networks

Electronic mail is probably the single-most popular network feature for many people. As long as all company networks use the same E-mail package, there are no connectivity issues. For several years, TCP/IP's Simple Mail Transfer Protocol (SMTP) provided a "bare bones" common language that enabled users to exchange messages. Because TCP/IP was not available for PC workstations until recently, a couple of generations of LAN E-mail software has developed. Unfortunately, while these packages provide far more features than SMTP, they often are unable to communicate with other LAN E-mail packages or with mail services running on larger networks. Because LANs often originated at the departmental level without MIS directive's on standardized software, this situation is not uncommon.

Now that enterprise networking is becoming a corporate goal, a problem for network managers and systems integrators is how to integrate several different company LAN E-mail packages with each other as well as with mail services running on larger computer networks, particularly with such corporate favorites as DEC's All-in-One and IBM's PROFS and SNADS. This section examines how evolving industry standards could help resolve some of these present incompatibilities.

Simple Mail Transfer Protocol (SMTP)

First there was Simple Mail Transfer Protocol (SMTP). SMTP was developed for the Defense Department's network as a "no frills" electronic messaging system that could transfer mail between two machines running on different networks, often connected via Telenet. Most UNIX systems support SMTP although it is usually not used unless the networks are running TCP/IP.

SMTP consists of only 14 different commands described in a simple document (RPC 821). It is efficient but limited. While E-mail functions have expanded dramatically the past few years, particularly in the very competitive LAN E-mail market, SMTP has remained frozen. There has been a growing movement the past few years toward an international E-mail standard, one that will serve as a common language for proprietary mail systems that need to communicate.

The X.400 standard

Incompatible E-mail systems are a major headache for any network manager charged with the responsibility of creating an enterprise network. The CCITT has established a number of standards for electronic mail that have become part of the OSI model. The original CCITT *X.400 recommendations* were adopted in 1984, and a set of updates were published in 1988 and are now undergoing testing. These 1988 changes (known in the industry as 1988 X.400) include the ability to mix text with such nontext items as spreadsheet and graphics files, audio, and video information. Each of these items is tagged by a unique object ID. Vendors must obtain object IDS for their own multimedia data formats from ANSI and then publish this information. It will be a while before these new X.400 features start to appear in E-mail products. Figure 12-2 illustrates an X.400 compliant message handling system MHS. A network user interface to the mail system is known as a *User Agent* (UA). It is this interface that enables a network user to retrieve or send mail. The User Agent constructs the X.400 "envelope" and places addressing information in the appropriate header fields. It looks up any required X.400 addresses and constructs distribution lists if they are requested. The User Agent transmits its envelope containing headers and message to a Message Transfer Agent (MTA).

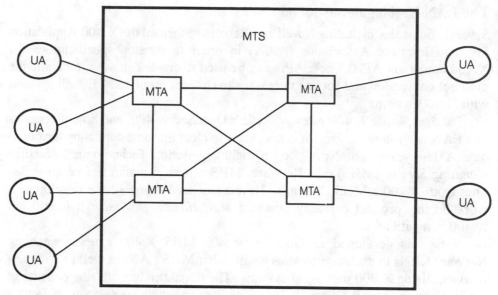

12-2 An X.400 message handling system.

Message Transfer Agents (MTAs) can be thought of as post offices that offer typical postal services for electronic messages. MTAs include the store-and-forward service of storing a message until a specified time before forwarding it to its destination. MTAs also perform error checking and ensure that the envelope and headers have been formatted correctly. The *Message Transfer System* (MTS) provides enhanced delivery services such as verified delivery or nondelivery.

The X.400 set of specifications include a P1 protocol which describes the envelope. The X.400 envelope includes a header which contains such key information as the sender, recipient, subject references, and copy lists. User Agents (UAs) communicate with Message Transfer Agents (MTAs) using the P2 protocol which specifies how the messages are structured as well as delivery instructions.

A LAN user of E-mail which is X.400 compliant or contains an X.400 gateway writes a message and attaches any additional documents required (spreadsheets, text files, etc.). The user indicates the recipient's X.400 address or the user agent looks it up. The message is transmitted via a User Agent from MTA to MTA until it reaches the recipient's MTA.

IBM offers its X.400 Open System Message Exchange (OSME) as part of its OSI Communications subsystem. This software enables IBM mainframes running under MVS or VM to act as X.400 MTAs. Because IBM also offers its X.400 PROFS Connection and DIOSS Connection packages which convert between X.400 format and PROFS and DIOSS formats, mainframe users can transmit an electronic message created under PROFS or DIOSS to an X.400 compliant E-mail system.

The LAN X.400 gateway server

Several companies including Novell and Retix have formed the X.400 Application Program Interface Association (APIA) in order to develop specifications for X.400 compliant APIs. These APIs can be used to create gateways to handle the protocol conversion and routing necessary to connect proprietary E-mail systems with X.400 systems.

I show specific X.400 gateway, Retix's OpenServer 400, and how it operates in a LAN environment. First, it is necessary to clear up some confusing terminology. A few years ago, Novell began including Action Technologies' *Message Handling Service* (MHS) with NetWare. MHS was an E-mail interface quite distinct from X.400's MHS. Recently, Novell has been doing all the development work on this product currently renamed *Mail Handling Service*; it is still not X.400 compatible.

Retix has developed an OpenServer 400 MHS X.400 gateway enabling NetWare LANs to exchange messages with other MHS LANs as well as with networks utilizing X.400 messaging systems. The initial product offering consists of a client/server model. Clients PC workstations run their own copies of Retix's user agent software as an application under Microsoft's Windows. A message is transmitted to a dedicated Message Server running the MTA software. This first version of a NetWare X.400 MHS gateway will be replaced by a much more sophisticated package running under NetWare 386.

Retix and Novell have jointly announced that Retix will develop MHS X.400 gateway software. This software will be incorporated by Novell as a Network Loadable Module (NLM) into the NetWare 386 MHS Server. Figure 12-3 illustrates how this Retix OpenServer 400 product resides on the NetWare 386 server as a gateway and uses the appropriate APIs to perform the format conversions required to go between MHS and X.400 systems.

Enterprise-wide E-mail by linking gateways

What about a situation in which a company has substantial investments not just in IBM hosts running PROFS and DIOSS, but also DEC systems running All-in-1 and VMSmail? The company wants to link mail users on these systems with LAN users as well as with UNIX users. While the Retix/Novell MHS X.400 gateway can handle a small part of this problem, it cannot solve the network manager's problem.

Touch Communications has developed a series of X.400 gateways known as WorldTalk/400. This product line enables E-mail users on AppleTalk, NetWare, and TCP/IP LANs to communicate with public messaging nets such as AT&T Mail and MCI Mail as well as with IBM's PROFS and DEC's All-in-1. Touch uses a far different approach than Retix. The two key components that it divides its messaging system into are a gateway engine residing on a UNIX-based workstation and gateway modules residing on LAN file servers or mail servers. The LAN modules perform the addressing as well as the conversion from that LAN's

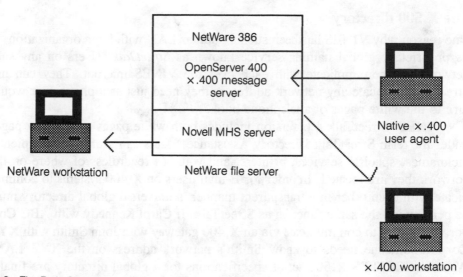

12-3 The Retix OpenServer 400 LAN X.400 MHS gateway.

E-mail's format to the X.400 format. If several different LANs are linked to a single gateway engine running on a UNIX machine, then routers are used to link together these LANs. Figure 12-4 illustrates how Touch's system works.

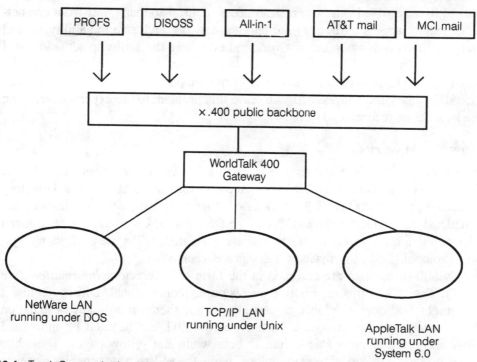

12-4 Touch Communications' WorldTalk gateway.

The X.500 directory

One reason why VINES has been such a popular LAN with large organizations is its proprietary global naming service known as *StreetTalk*. Users on any sub-network can communicate with each over the VINES internet. They can use StreetTalk to locate any network addresses they need just as a phone user would turn to the white pages of a telephone book.

VINES' StreetTalk 4.0 version includes both white pages and yellow pages under the term StreetTalk Directory Assistance. Users can search for recipients' nicknames, specific services, printers, and volumes regardless of where on the network they are located. In order for E-mail users on X.400 systems to communicate with each other in a transparent manner, a universal global directory must be performing the same function as StreetTalk. If Carol Kennedy with ABC Corporation wants to communicate via an X.400 gateway with John Smith with XYZ Corporation, she needs to know Smith's network address on the XYZ LAN. When the CCITT's X.500 set of specifications for a global directory are finally implemented, Kennedy would simply look up Smith's address on her workstation screen. Similarly, a user on XYZ's PROFS system could look up the address of another company employee who happens to be on a network using DEC's All-in-1 software.

During 1989, the CCITT finalized its *X.500 recommendation* with a complete set of CCITT recommendations scheduled to be written by 1992. One major issue still unresolved is how to restrict access control so that a user from one network cannot access a directory for another network and have the ability to read and search everything on that network and even have the ability to add additional entries or edit current entries. One real worry is that junk mail companies will be able to compile detailed information on corporate phone numbers as well as individuals' names and addresses. I will leave this problem to the experts developing the new set of recommendations.

How X.500 works

A user accesses an X.500 directory through a *Directory User Agent* (DUA). The DUA communicates using Directory Access Protocol (DAP) with a Directory System Agent (DSA). The DSA decides whether it can handle this request or must broadcast this request to other DSAs. The DSA can be distributed or centralized depending upon how the directory database is created. DSAs use a Directory System Protocol (DSP) to broadcast messages to each other.

X.500 directories are designed in the form of a *Directory Information Tree* (DIT). The root of this information tree is purely conceptional. Directly below it you might find countries, then organizations, and then virtually any designation that fits a particular company. Portions of the DIT are handled by individual DSAs. The directory is able to handle both white and yellow pages. The white pages provide name to address mappings, while the yellow pages enables a user to find another user or service by looking under specific business category attributes.

Figure 12-5 illustrates a typical DIT. Each entry has a set of attributes that can be single or multivalued. A name entry might have the required attributes of first name and last name, but other attributes including the person's photograph, phone number, or social security number might be optional.

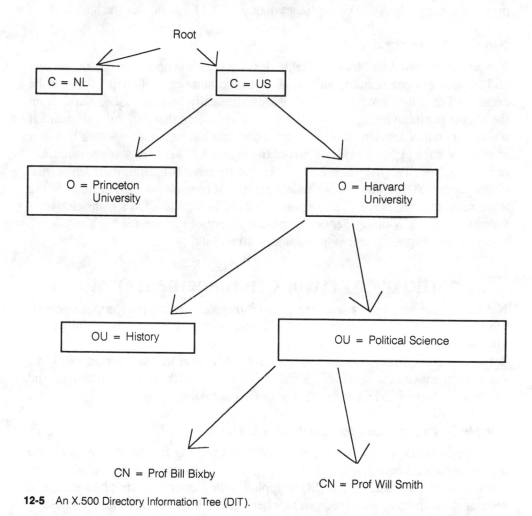

12-5 An X.500 Directory Information Tree (DIT).

3Com's directory services moving toward X.500

3Com has been positioning itself as a systems integrator, a company more concerned with enterprise networking than with selling proprietary hardware and software products. Recently the company announced its own global naming services and menuing utility for 3+ Open LAN Manager.

The 3Admin Service is an OS/2 Presentation Manager based management application that uses the naming service to enable network managers to see network resources depicted as icons. While 3+ Open Directory services using X.500 naming conventions, the software is still partially proprietary. While initial releases will first work with 3+ Open LAN Manager 1.1 and later with any LAN Manager 2.0 operating system, the company has indicated that it will make its product completely X.500 compliant when the CCITT solidifies the standard.

Novell's Name Service

Novell has released its NetWare Name Service which supports up to 400 servers and 5000 users per domain with no limit to the number of domains that can be created. The utility program NETCON automatically copies a user's name from the server in which he logs on to all the other servers in that particular domain. If a server is out of service, it is resynchronized and has its names updated before it is allowed once again to become part of the network. There are some severe limitations to Novell's first release. It lacks the hierarchical naming structure that characterizes StreetTalk. What this means is that user names cannot identify the user, division, and department because they are limited to DOS's eight-character format. Novell's Naming Service currently does not include the "white pages" and "yellow pages" services found under StreetTalk.

The battle over network management protocols

Network managers and systems integrators grapple with the problem of integrating non-compatible, proprietary networks into an enterprise network. While planning this enterprise network, however, it is absolutely critical that some way be determined to monitor, manage, and control traffic over it. This section looks at a network management protocol (SNMP) associated with TCP/IP networks and another protocol (CMIP) associated with OSI networks.

Simple Network Management Protocol (SNMP)

For several years, network managers have been waiting for the ISO to finalize a set of network management protocols. By 1987 many industry insiders had become very impatient as the ISO grappled with a document that had grown to several thousand pages and seemed nowhere near completion. A group consisting of two professors from MIT, two professors from the University of Tennessee, and two engineers from Nysernet created *Simple Network Management Protocol* (SNMP). Designed originally as the network management protocol for TCP/IP, this protocol is now able to monitor network traffic and to indicate malfunctioning equipment and performance bottlenecks on a variety of non-TCP/IP network devices including 802.1 Ethernet bridges. The Internet Activities Board that governs TCP/IP has given standards status to several elements of SNMP including the

Management Information Base-I (MIB-I), the Structure of Management Information (SMI), and the Simple Network Management Protocol (SNMP). Today over 80 vendors offer SNMP products, and work is progressing on extending SNMP so that it can handle 802.5 LANs and DECnet Phase IV devices. SNMP was developed as a connectionless protocol to reduce overhead requirements and to maintain control on the part of the user rather than have parameters handled transparently as they would be in a connection-oriented protocol.

SNMP protocol links a network management system (NMS) and a device that is being managed. This device contains an agent that communicates with the NMS. Information is stored in a *Management Information Base* (MIB). This database contains network statistics (packets transmitted, errors, etc.). Because the MIB is defined in standard terms for managing an internet router, vendors must extend the MIB so that information will be relevant for their particular device. The NMS queries agents on a regular basis and receives responses. Under SNMP, agents are very small programs because their function is simply to respond to queries with only five different types of possible messages. The majority of the processing required is done at the NMS. This arrangement encourages vendors to write the required agent software for their products so that they will work in an SNMP environment.

For devices that use proprietary protocols and are not yet SNMP compatible, it is possible to use a proxy agent. A *proxy agent* is software that acts like an agent for a device that is not SNMP compatible by translating the proprietary protocol into SNMP and vice versa. The proxy agent receives information from an agent that uses the proprietary protocol and then translates the information into SNMP format before forwarding it to the NMS.

While SNMP cannot prevent something from happening directly, it can alert a manager when traffic patterns and conditions indicate that a device is about to go bad. A network manager can set thresholds for devices ("above x number of packets retransmitted," for example) and then receive an alarm when the threshold is reached.

SNMP is a transaction-oriented protocol that permits network managers to select any particular event they want to "trap" or have a network agent initiate activity. By initiating an SNMP GET-Request, a user can view values of objects in the Management Information Base (MIB).

SNMP running under NetWare

While a number of vendors offer SNMP products today, I use one specific product to illustrate how SNMP can be incorporated into a LAN running under NetWare. Novell's LANalyzer division offers LANtern Services Manager, a product designed to monitor SNMP agents (LANtern network monitors) that collect data on activity across an Ethernet LAN running under NetWare. These SNMP agents can collect data on any device on the LAN regardless of the protocol supported.

LANtern Services Manager monitors all LANterns in real time while creating a log of network events. Alarms are displayed under Microsoft Windows. A major advantage this software has running under Windows is that a network manager can view several different LAN segments or nodes concurrently in different windows and then take corrective action when problems are detected.

What about remote monitoring? The LANtern Services Manager can receive information from multiple LANterns via serial links of speeds up to 38.4 Kbs. They also can receive information directly from bridges and routers.

Common Management Information Protocol (CMIP)

Common Management Information Protocol (CMIP) is a draft standard for network management over OSI networks. CMIP offers a much more robust set of tools for network management than SNMP. It provides six different types of services: configuration management, security management, fault management, accounting, performance management, and directory service.

A major distinction between CMIP and SNMP is that SNMP does not make a distinction between an object and its attributes. An *object* might be a device while an *attribute* might be that device's condition or a parameter describing it. What this means in practical terms is that while SNMP is easy to implement, it is difficult to maintain if a network is in a constant state of change. Under SNMP, a vendor would have to provide a different definition for each device it creates for an SNMP network, regardless of how similar these devices might be. Under CMIP, however, the vendor could let new devices use the same definitions used by other devices and simply include some additional attributes to distinguish them. The new products "inherit" the definitions of older products.

Another advantage of CMIP over SNMP is security. While work is progressing on security features for CMIP, SNMP has no security provisions. Unless network managers disable the SNMP Set command, anyone can write commands to SNMP devices and control them.

CMIP is slowly building up its own head of steam despite predictions that SNMP will dominate for several years. Digital has announced that DECnet Phase V will contain CMIP as its network management protocol. Recently British Telecommunications PLC, MCI Communications Corporation, and Telecom Canada have proposed to both the CCITT and to the OSI/Network Management Forum that CMIP be used over CCS7 (Signaling System 7). The advantage for end users is that these common carriers would be able to provide them with network management information concurrently with the data being transmitted. A gateway would provide the management data but lock users out of the internal operations of SS7.

Common management over TCP/IP (CMOT)

CMIP has not really taken off because of the small base of installed OSI networks. A network management group (known appropriately as the NetMan group) composed of such industry giants as Hewlett-Packard, Sun Microsystems, Digital Equipment Corporation, and 3Com have come up with one solution to major limitation to CMIP's growth—the lack of installed OSI networks. The *Common Management Over TCP/IP* (CMOT) protocol consists of standard CMIP with a Presentation layer that maps OSI layers 6 and below to TCP/IP.

CMOT was developed to encourage companies that are currently using TCP/IP but plan to migrate eventually to OSI networks to make the network management shift now secure in the knowledge that they will not have to change their network management software later when they make the transition to OSI.

IBM and heterogenous LAN management with OSI protocols

IBM has announced a method of dealing with the non-IBM LANs that need to be monitored on an enterprise network. Recently IBM and 3Com announced a joint effort to define a set of network management specifications for these mixed media LANs. Known as the *Heterogeneous LAN Management* (HLM) specifications, they will provide tools for network managers to monitor, control, and analyze network data.

HLM incorporates a subset of the OSI Common Management Information Protocol (CMIP) and the IEEE's 802.2 Logical Link Control (LLC). Known as CMOL, this protocol will help companies that are migrating their networks to full OSI model compliance. The two companies also will develop application programming interfaces (APIs) that will enable third-party developers to produce additional network management software.

Network management systems

You have been looking at some key network management protocols that enable agents to provide key alarm information when polled. At virtually every connectivity forum, network managers have been demanding a network management system that would take information from all the devices on all the linked together networks and provide the management and control functions. Simply monitoring resources and observing network failures is no longer enough, particularly in an enterprise network. This section examines some network management solutions offered by IBM, AT&T, and DEC.

What a network management system is

A *network management system* (NMS) is a system that manages and controls complex networks. The NMS can reconfigure the network when workstations and other resources are added or deleted. It can filter the thousands of alerts it receives and reduce the "noise" level down to where a network manager can view an uncluttered screen and see the most significant network events taking place. The NMS is able to manage bandwidth, provide cost accounting and performance measurement, and monitor security all in a user-friendly graphics environment. This is the ideal NMS described here; all the major vendors are still far from fulfilling this order, but they do have clear visions of their own ultimate NMS as well as actual products available today.

IBM's NetView

IBM's view of network management is built around its mainframe computers and its traditional view of centralized processing. The NetView program running on a mainframe serves as a *focal point*. The focal point receives information from entry points on various SNA NAUs. NetView release 2 provides an alternative LU 6.2 focal point to the mainframe program for non-SNA devices. This interface permits programmers to use APIs to create this link so that NetView can monitor non-IBM equipment.

NetView is able to communicate with LANs via key *Network Management Vector Transport* (NMVT) protocol-based code points. These alert code points are numbers that represent specific statements that appear on a NetView screen. NetView's version 2 includes an automation table containing a set of commands that can be invoked when alarms, alerts, and other messages are received from a network device. According to several recent industry reports, IBM and Novell have been cooperating so that NetView's version 2 release 2 is expected to contain several NetWare-specific NMVT code points. IBM is expected to work with other vendors so that in the future these vendors will be able to develop code points so that their networks can also be managed by NetView.

Non-IBM devices can also communicate with NetView via NetView/PC, which runs on a PC and serves as a *service point*, IBM's definition of an interface to NetView for non-IBM equipment. NetView/PC uses a systems services control point to a physical unit (SSCP-to-PU) session with the VTAM program running on the mainframe to pass control information to the NetView program. A Token Ring network running LAN Manager can transmit performance and alert data to NetView/PC, which in turn, forwards the information to NetView on the host via VTAM.

NetView can also accept voice information, particularly billing information. As Fig. 12-6 illustrates, a Call Detail Collector transmits data to the PC which forward them to the mainframe. The NetView/PC Rolm Alert Monitor sends alerts from the Rolm PBX to the NetView program running on the host.

NetView now also supports TCP/IP. IBM's TCP/IP version 2 for VM can transmit SNMP data from devices attached to an IBM host to a TCP/IP net management system.

While NetView's major strength is its ability to monitor SNA networks and IBM's own equipment, it does have a number of limitations. Companies with non-Rolm telephone equipment such as an AT&T or Northern Telecom PBX have not been able to monitor their voice networks through NetView. Similarly, NetView

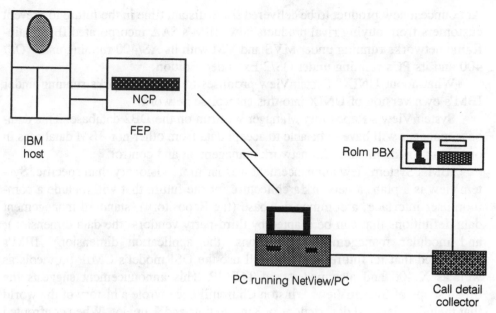

12-6 NetView collecting voice and data information.

is not able to communicate with non-IBM controllers or with LANs other than IBM's own Token Ring.

NetView and LAN Manager 2.0

IBM's own LAN Manager 2.0 (not to be confused with Microsoft's LAN Manager product) runs under OS/2 and has a direct link with NetView running on a host through the OS/2 Extended Edition 1.1 Communications Manager. The product provides NetView with alerts, LAN status, and information on bridge and adapter functions on a multi-LAN bridged network. LAN Manager enables a network manager to check on a specific workstation's adapter card or bridge as well as actually change the configuration of a network segment or a bridge.

IBM's SystemView

In September 1990 IBM announced a systems architecture strategy that eventually will give network managers a consistent end-user interface (the end-use dimension). This strategy will also share network management information across the entire IBM product line. At the heart of SystemView is a central database, a repository that will hold key systems management data collected across an enterprise network. IBM has indicated that it envisions SystemView as an open architecture that eventually will integrate SNA, SAA, OSI, TCP/IP, and AIX (IBM's UNIX) networks.

Why SystemView? Some industry experts see it as a typical IBM ploy.

Announce a new product to be delivered some distant time in the future to prevent customers from buying rival products now. IBM's SAA incorporated IBM mainframe networks running under MVS and VM with its AS/400 running under OS/400 and its PCs running under OS/2 Extended Edition.

What about UNIX? SystemView promises to bring networks running under IBM's own version of UNIX into this enterprise network.

SystemView's Repository Manager will run on the DB2 database. This database manager will have to be able to accept data from other non-IBM databases in order to provide meaningful network management and control.

IBM's SystemView announcement was far more visionary than specific. SystemView is a plan, a network architecture for the future that will include a common user interface, a common database (the Repository), standard management data definitions that can be adapted by third-party vendors (the data dimension), and modular management applications (the application dimension). IBM's announced that its future networks will use the OSI model's CMIP protocols as well as X.400 and also understand TCP/IP. This announcement suggests the broad scope of SystemView. Winston Churchill once wrote a history of the world that included detailed descriptions of King Arthur and Camelot. When confronted by a critic who questioned whether Camelot and King Arthur ever existed, Churchill replied that if they had not, they should have. I can say the same thing about SystemView; it is a necessity for large networks that need to tie together their diverse elements. If SystemView does not exist, it should.

AT&T's network management

Given its data processing roots, it is no surprise that IBM chose to approach network management from a mainframe perspective. It is also no surprise that AT&T took a completely different approach toward network management, one based on its roots in voice communications.

Unified Network Management Architecture (UNMA) stresses the voice side of network management and takes a distributed rather than centralized approach. Just as the nation's phone system is built on the foundation of standard protocols, UNMA is based on the OSI model, but incorporates a network interface known as *Network Management Protocol* (NMP) whose specifications are available to third-party vendors. NMP closely resembles the OSI suite of network management protocols.

AT&T looks at network management data coming from three distinctly different sources: customer premises, the local exchange carrier, and the interexchange carrier. Notice how this orientation encompasses both the voice and the data information transmitting over phone lines. The customer premises might include a mainframe, minicomputers, and LANs along with a private branch exchange (PBX) phone system. Each of these network components might be managed by an *Element Management System* (EMS) designed specifically for that type of equipment. Unfortunately, these EMSs are device specific and usually are unable to manage an entire network.

As Fig. 12-7 illustrates, various EMSs are linked together via network management protocol into a network management system that contains function-specific modules responsible for integrating data from different EMSs. AT&T froze the OSI model's CMIP protocols during its development and then published these specifications for other vendors' use. AT&T hopes that other vendors will develop EMSs that follow this Network Management Protocol.

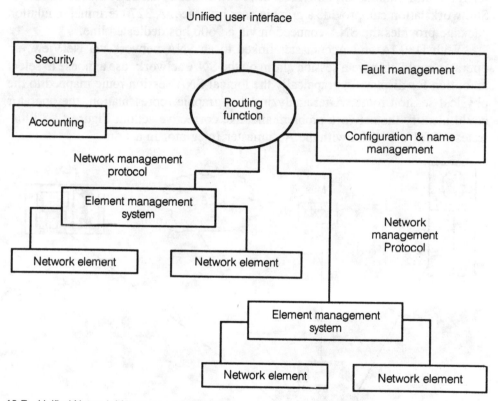

12-7 Unified Network Management Architecture.

AT&T expects the functionality of UNMA to grow as vendors develop additional products. AT&T has indicated that the nine major network management functions that its system should be able to handle are configuration management, fault management, performance management, accounting management, security management, planning capability, operations support, programmability, and integrated control.

As the originator of UNIX, AT&T has chosen predictably to build its network management system around UNIX-based workstations or minicomputers running a program known as the Accumaster Integrator.

The Accumaster collects information from all major network components including T-1 lines, LANs, PBXs and host applications. Information is filtered and then presented using a graphic interface. While the Accumaster provides a single view of an entire network with the ability to pinpoint the source of alarms, it does not control all network elements from a single location the way NetView does. Many companies with very large networks prefer this approach for security and operational reasons.

UNMA and the Accumaster work hand in hand with NetView. The Accumaster Integrator running on an AT&T 3B2/600 emulates an SNA PU 2.0 node. A Sun workstation can provide a graphic user interface. A 3270 terminal emulation package provides the SNA connection via a 9600 bps dedicated line.

With UNMA and Accumaster linked to an SNA network via NetView, an operator could observe a session alarm on the SNA network, use a mouse to select an option for displaying graphically the logical SNA session route mapped to the physical session route. After analyzing this graphic representation, the operator could identify the network problem and take corrective action. Figure 12-8 illustrates AT&T's UNMA with the Accumaster Integrator in action.

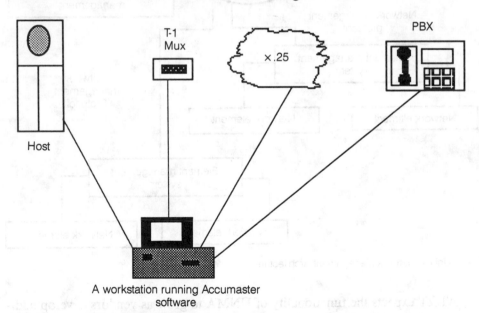

12-8 AT&T UNMA and the Accumaster Integrator.

UNMA is a developing and unfinished product. As more companies implement OSI protocols, AT&T's product will become more attractive because of its OSI-based network management protocols. As more enterprise networks develop with their emphasis on long distance lines and remote bridging, UNMA should become more popular because monitoring and controlling elements of a wide area network is AT&T's major strength.

What about UNMA and SNMP? After all, there are far more SNMP-based networks today than CIMP-based networks. AT&T has been working with Network Computing, Inc., to turn that company's LANAlert network management system for NetWare 286 file servers into a collection point for devices supporting SNMP. Alerts from SNMP devices would be translated and then transmitted via a gateway to the Accumaster.

DEC's DECnet

Digital Equipment Corporation (DEC) released its first version of DECnet back in 1975 to enable two PDP-11 minicomputers to communicate with each other. The current version of this network architecture, DECnet Phase IV, was introduced in 1982. DECnet IV supports Ethernet as its LAN protocol, the X.25 protocol for packet switched networks, and an SNA gateway in which it functions as a PU Type 2.0.

As Fig. 12-9 illustrates, DECnet IV has eight layers compared to the seven found in the OSI model. The DECnet IV Physical layer corresponds closely with its OSI model counterpart. The DECnet Data Link layer supports DEC's own Digital Data Communications Message Protocol (DDCMP) protocol, the X.25 packet switched protocol, and DEC's own Ethernet protocol, which is not compatible with the IEEE 802.3 protocol used by the OSI model.

DECnet's Routing layer uses proprietary DEC protocols to route data packets from node to node. The DECnet Transport layer corresponds roughly with its OSI

OSI Model	DNA Phase IV
Application	User Network management
Presentation	Network application
Session	DECnet session control
Transport	DECnet transport (NSP)
Network	DECnet routing (adaptive routing)
Data link	Data link
Physical	Physical link

12-9 DECnet IV and the OSI model.

model counterpart but uses its own proprietary protocols. The Session Control layer performs the traditional OSI model Session layer functions of initiating and maintaining a session, but adds additional functions such as translating DECnet node names to DECnet addresses and maintaining security by preventing unauthorized access to node resources.

DECnet's Network Application layer provides file transfer, virtual terminal service, and access to both SNA and X.25 gateways. It corresponds with the OSI model's Presentation layer. The User and Network Management layers together provide the services offered by the OSI model's Application layer.

DECnet Phase V

DECnet's Phase V has been a long time in coming. Representing DEC's commitment to OSI model protocols, it is expected to be released incrementally during 1991–1992. In its Physical layer, for example, it adds the X.21 protocol for circuit switched networks while its Data Link layer adds both High Level Data Link Control (HDLC) and OSI IEEE 802.3 protocols for Ethernet networks. Its Network layer will include ISO CMIP protocols while still supporting management of Phase IV nodes. DECnet sheds its proprietary Transport protocol and network routing protocols for ISO standard protocols. DEC's proprietary Network Information and Control Exchange (NICE) protocol for network management applications is replaced by the ISO's CMIP. While DEC has assured worried customers that upgrading from DECnet IV to DECnet V will consist of software upgrades, the change in Ethernet packet structure protocol is one concrete example of a change that will require a hardware change (the NIC). DECnet V will require DEC's own naming service, the VAX Distributed Name Service (DNS) which was introduced back in 1987. DEC has committed itself to make this naming service compatible with the X.500 directory standard when it emerges in its final form.

DEC's approach to enterprise network management

DEC has quietly been building a platform for enterprise networking based on OSI model protocols. DEC has published the specifications for its *Enterprise Management Architecture* (EMA) because vendors will have to incorporate the appropriate APIs in their network management software so these programs will be able to be a part of EMA. EMA defines management functions to include all five listed under the OSI model: configuration, fault, performance, security, and accounting.

Conceptually, the major components of DEC's Enterprise Management Architecture consists of an "Executive," access modules, functional modules, and presentation modules. The Executive provides the operating environment, the open interfaces to non-DEC as well as DEC products, and the central repository for network management information.

Access modules provide the appropriate protocol to manage network entities such as computer systems, application programs, or modems. DECnet V entities will be managed using the ISO's CMIP protocol. Functional modules are "plug-in" applications from DEC and other vendors that correspond to the five OSI management areas previously mentioned. The presentation modules integrate all EMA information through a common user interface. These modules could provide such different user interfaces as DECwindows, graphic user interfaces (GUIs), and ASCII terminals.

Unlike SystemView, which retains IBM's centralized network management and control philosophy, or UNMA with its strictly distributed management, Enterprise Management Architecture is a platform that permits either centralized or distributed network control. The key to Enterprise Management Architecture is the Director kernel. The Director runs under DEC's proprietary VMS operating system and implements APIs that enable modules on different computers to interact without knowing the precise location of each other. Under EMA you can have one Director that manages the entire network, several Directors that manage the same network entity, or several Directors that manage different network entities and communicate with each other. Developers who follow DEC guidelines can implement management modules that will interoperate under EMA.

Initially the Director is expected to support CMIP, SNMP, and DECnet Phase IV protocols. The Director draws much of its data from a centralized network management database. The database, known as the Management Information Repository, will contain real-time performance and alarm status information. This database will be consistent with the ISO's naming and addressing conventions so that its common structure for network element information can be accessed by non-DEC software.

Unlike IBM's SNA in which non-intelligent devices are controlled, DEC has a tradition of building intelligence into its devices. Its bridges and DECnet nodes have the ability to make intelligent management decisions in a distributed environment. Because DEC is building EMA to incorporate its family of products, these devices already are equipped to send network management information to each other.

DEC released its first version of EMA as DECmcc in 1990. It included the DECmcc Director, Basic Management System, Site Management Station and Enterprise Management Station. The Basic Management System includes the Director as well as DECnet-VAX software to communicate with VAX networks running under Ethernet or IEEE 802.3. The Site Management Station includes the ability to monitor the network for alarms, calculate network performance statistics (LAN Traffic Monitor), store and forward historical management data and receive notification of internal and external alarm conditions. The DEC Extended LAN Management Software (DECelms) included with the Site Management Station provides the ability to manage Ethernet/802.3 bridges and FDDI components in an extended LAN.

The Enterprise Management Station includes all software found in the Site Management Station but adds WAN management using the NMCC/DECnet Monitor for configuration, fault and performance management of WANs. An optional TCP/IP SNMP access module links the EMA network to UNIX networks as well as others using SNMP Management protocol. DEC has signed an agreement with System Center to jointly develop technology that will allow DECmcc users to monitor and control SNA networks and IBM NetView and Systems Center NET/MASTER users to control DEC systems. One major weakness of EMA so far seems to be its lack of ability to link to NetWare LANs, a major component in many enterprise networks. Another problem is that most DEC LAN management tools such as LAN Traffic Monitor run outside of EMA, although they can be combined with the Director on a workstation called NetStation.

Summary

While it is cost effective to use a fax server, some problems are associated with it. Delivering fax messages directly to the end-user's workstation is still not possible.

Linking together E-mail software running on different network platforms is becoming easier with the development of the CCITT X.400 family of E-mail protocol standards. To link together users on networks running at different locations on different file servers, a directory service is required. The CCITT has been developing an X.500 standard for directory services. IBM, AT&T, and DEC have all committed themselves to developing compatibility with both X.400 and X.500 standards.

While Simple Network Management Protocol (SNMP) has become very popular, most industry experts see it being replaced eventually by the ISO's Common Management Information Protocol (CMIP) that offers far greater functionality. A temporary measure for companies planning to migrate eventually to OSI model compatibility is Common Management Protocol Over TCP/IP (CMOT).

IBM's approach to network management, NetView, is evolving. NetView now includes direct access from Token Ring LANs and non-IBM equipment via LU 6.2. NetView can control and monitor Rolm telephone equipment (via NetView/PC) as well as SNA networks and Token Ring networks. IBM's future plans for network management (SystemView) incorporate UNIX-based computer systems and utilize standard ISO network management protocols (CMIP) while retaining the ability to use SNMP when needed.

While IBM takes a centralized approach to network management, AT&T's Unified Network Management Architecture (UNMA) uses a distributed approach. The Accumaster Integrator workstation permits network managers to monitor network conditions from a centralized location, but control is distributed. AT&T is much stronger than IBM in its ability to monitor communication links such as long distance lines.

Finally, DEC's Enterprise Network Management Architecture permits either centralized or distributed network management and control using a single Director or multiple Directors. It adheres closely to ISO standards including CMIP.

Seminars on LANs, internetworking, and enterprise networks

Internetworking is such a new field that it is hard to gather together a critical mass of information, enough to enable you to start designing enterprise networks. In this section, I list several seminar companies that offer courses that are an intensive 2, 3, or 4 days in length. I note the courses that include "hands-on" opportunities.

American Institute
437 Madison Ave.
23rd Floor
New York, NY 10022
(800) 345-8016

The American Institute offers seminars at six different technology centers (Chicago, Los Angeles, New York, San Jose, Toronto, and Herndon, Virginia). All courses are hands-on. The company has offered such relevant seminars as the following: Data Communications, Troubleshooting Datacomm Systems Networks, Hands-On OSI Featuring GOSIP For Those Migrating to OSI, Hands-On APPC, Hands-On Troubleshooting Local Area Networks, Hands-On Introduction to Novell NetWare, and Hands-On Internetworking: Using Bridges, Routers and Gateways.

Business Communications Review
950 York Rd.
Hinsdale, IL 60521-2939
(800) 227-1234

BCR offers hands-on courses on Local Area Networks (4 days), LAN Troubleshooting (2 days), Novell NetWare (3 days), Bridges, Routers, and Gateways (3 days), and Data Networks (3 days). BCR also offers telecommunications courses (its traditional area of expertise) on such topics as T-1 remote networks, introduction to telecommunications, etc.

Data-Tech Institute
Lakeview Ave.
P.O. Box 2429
Clifton, NJ 07015
(201) 478-5400

For several years this company has offered seminars on topics such as: Local Area Networks, Data Communications, Troubleshooting and Maintaining a Local Area Network, Taking Control of Novell NetWare for Administrators and Users, and Troubleshooting Novell NetWare: Fine Tuning for Optimum Network Performance. The company also offers some telecommunications seminars.

Systems Technology Forum
10201 Lee Highway, Suite 150
Fairfax, VA 22030
(800) 336-7409

STF offers courses in such areas as Network Design, Systems Network Architecture (SNA), Local Area Networks, and Introduction to Data Communications.

Technology Exchange Company
Route 128
One Jacob Way
Reading, MA 01867
(800) 333-5177

The Technology Exchange Company offers courses in such areas as UNIX, Data Communications and Networks, Local Area Networks Workshop, and Computer Network Architectures. William Stallings has taught the LAN Networks Workshop.

Technology Transfer Institute
741 Tenth St.
Santa Monica, California 90402
(213) 394-8305

TTI has always offered courses that are on the "cutting edge" of new technology. They have offered courses in such areas as LANs, network management, network performance testing, TCP/IP, and OSI protocols. The company uses well known industry figures such as James Martin and William Stallings.

Glossary

10Base2 An IEEE standard for 10 Mbs transmission of an 802.3 CSMA/CD contention network over baseband thin coaxial cable. Also known as "cheapernet."

10Base5 An IEEE standard for 10 Mbs transmission of an 802.3 CSMA/CD contention network over baseband thick coaxial cable.

10BaseT An IEEE standard for 10 Mbs transmission of an 802.3 CSMA/CD contention network over unshielded twisted pair.

10Broad36 An IEEE standard for 10 Mbs transmission of an 802.3 CSMA/CD contention network over broadband coaxial cable.

accumaster A UNIX-based workstation under AT&T's Unified Network Management Architecture that collects information from all major network components including T-1 lines, LANs, PBXs, and mainframe computers.

active monitor The workstation that assumes the role of monitor on a Token Ring network.

active star A topology in which a controller establishes active links to other star networks.

address bus The bus carrying the address of the next instruction to be executed.

Advanced Program-to-Program Communication (APPC) An IBM programming interface that enables programmers to write code allowing programs to communicate with each other.

all-routes broadcast frame A frame transmitted to all network nodes by a workstation that is gathering routing information on a source routing network.

AppleTalk Transaction Protocol A protocol that provides acknowledgement of a datagram's error free delivery.

AppleTalk Apple's suite of protocols for its local area network.

application process A program residing within a specific application.

Attached Resource Computer Network (Arcnet) A network scheme developed by DataPoint and now licensed to several other vendors that features a 2.5 Mbs token bus LAN.

autoboot ROM A ROM chip that enables diskless workstations to boot automatically from the file server.

automatic repeat request (ARQ) Techniques used for error checking.

baseband coax Coaxial cable that contains a single channel for carrying data at high speeds.

bit stuffing A technique that ensures that no more than 5 consecutive 1-bits appear in a frame. 0-bits are inserted after 5 consecutive 1-bits to ensure that a flag field is unique. A receiving station reinserts the appropriate 1-bits.

broadband coax Coaxial cable that carries multiple frequencies separated by guardbands.

Broadband ISDN (BISDN) ISDN running over broadband cabling can achieve speeds of over 600 Mbs. This new specification is still being developed.

bus mastering A technique in which the file server moves data from the network adapter cards to the disk without use of the host processor.

bus A data highway.

cache memory Very high speed RAM chips used to keep a copy of the information last accessed from disk.

Carrier Sense Multiple Access with Collision Detection (CSMA/CD) A media access method for a contention bus network.

cascaded bridges Several bridges linked together in a sequential order.

central office (CO) AT&T's term for its point of presence.

central processing unit (CPU) That portion of a computer in which instructions are interpreted and executed.

centralized Central control rests in one location.

cheapernet A term used to describe 10Base2, an 802.3 version of Ethernet on thin coaxial cabling.

client-server An arrangement in which one computer runs server software and acts as a server for a second networked computer that runs client software. The server "back end" finds the information requested and sends it (and not the entire file) back to the client "front end" that contains a user-friendly user interface.

clones A term used to describe computers that are compatible to well-known models such as the IBM AT. These clones generally offer features not found on the computer they are emulating and usually cost less. Clone manufacturers use additional features and lower prices to break down customer resistance to buying a non-brand name. Compaq, a company known for its reliable products, is an exception because its IBM clones generally sell for a higher price than the products they are emulating.

cluster controller   A mainframe device that serves as an interface between the host computer and its many peripherals. The cluster controller consolidates the many streams of data it receives from often slower transmitting devices.

Common Management Information Protocol (CMIP)   The network management protocol designed to run on an OSI network.

Common Management Over TCP/IP (CMOT)   A protocol consisting of standard CMIP with a Presentation layer that maps OSI layers 6 and below to TCP/IP.

connection-oriented service   Type 2 LANs utilize this service; it provides acknowledgments for error checking as well as flow control and error recovery.

connectionless service   Found on LANs because of their high transmission rate and high reliability. Type 1 LANs under this approach do not use the LLC layer for error checking, flow control, or error recovery. They rely on Transport layer protocols for these services.

Consultative Committee on International Telegraphy & Telephony (CCITT)   An international organization that develops telecommunications standards. European influence is quite strong, and historically voice communications have dominated over data communications as the major focus.

contention   A network in which workstations must "contend" with each other to use the network.

control bus   The bus (highway) inside a computer that carries control information.

data bus   The bus (highway) inside a computer that carries data.

Data Circuit Terminating Equipment (DCE)   An interface for the DTE to connect it to a network. A modem is an example of a DCE.

Data Flow Control layer   The SNA layer corresponding roughly to the OSI model's Session layer. It handles the establishment of half-duplex and full-duplex network sessions.

Data Stream Protocol   An AppleTalk protocol that establishes the actual communications session.

Data Terminal Equipment (DTE)   A network device such as a computer or terminal.

Datagram Delivery Protocol   An AppleTalk protocol that addresses specific logical ports to different networks to establish the route a datagram will take.

Demand Protocol Architecture (DPA)   A 3Com product that moves network transport protocols in and out of memory as needed.

Digital Access and Cross-Connect System (DACS) A device designed to switch DS-0 channels from one T-1 span to another.

direct memory access (DMA) A DMA controller determines the source and destination addresses of information to be retrieved and then orders the data bus to perform these read/write operations.

directory information tree (DIT) The form taken by X.500 directories.

directory user agent (DUA) The means by which a user accesses an X.500 global directory.

disk server A computer with a hard disk that is partitioned into volumes for each user. Programs have file locking but not record locking in this networking scheme that predates file servers.

diskless workstation A workstation that contains no disk drives. It uses an autoboot ROM to boot from the network file server.

distributed processing Workstations do their own processing rather than have processing centralized in a mainframe or minicomputer.

Distributed Queue Dual Bus (DQDB) A protocol utilized by a IEEE 802.6 MAN; it describes a dual bus topology with traffic traveling in opposite directions.

Draft International Standard (DIS) A specification that has passed both the Working Paper and Draft Proposal steps toward becoming an international standard.

Draft Proposal (DP) A specification that has passed the Working Paper stage on its road toward becoming an international standard.

Dual Attached Station (DAS) Nodes—usually more expensive multiuser and mainframe hosts—attached directly to an FDDI network.

dual protocol stack Computers contain two completely different protocol stacks so that both protocols can be run.

dynamic router A router that uses sophisticated algorithms to route packets by the optimal path at the moment.

Echo Protocol A protocol under AppleTalk that allows destination workstations to echo the contents of a datagram back to the source workstation.

Element Management System (EMS) Software designed to manage a specific network component under AT&T's Unified Network Management Architecture.

Enterprise Management Architecture (EMA) DEC's network management architecture which is built on a proprietary platform that has open interfaces to most major protocols.

Ethernet The first non-proprietary local area network hardware and software that was developed during the late 1970s through a partnership of DEC, Intel, and Xerox. It featured a 10 Mbs CSMA/CD bus network with thick coaxial cabling.

Exchange Termination Equipment (ET) Defined by ISDN as equipment that terminates the digital subscriber line or extended digital subscriber line in the local exchange. Usually this consists of central office equipment.

Extended Industry Standard Architecture (EISA) A 32-bit bus structure retaining compatibility with circuit cards for the IBM PC and AT models and compatibles. This standard was developed by a group of IBM clone manufacturers as an alternative to micro channel architecture.

Extended Super-Frame (ESF) A framing scheme advocated by AT&T which consists of 24 frames grouped together with an 8000 bps FE channel used to carry control information.

fast packet A T-1 enhancement that permits special T-1 multiplexers to allocate bandwidth dynamically.

Fiber Distributed Data Interface (FDDI) An ANSI standard for a 100Mbs fiber-optic network.

file server A computer with a hard disk used to process network commands and store network files.

File Transfer Protocol (FTP) A protocol for file transfer available with the Transmission Control Protocol/Internet Protocol suite of protocols.

File Transfer, Access, and Management (FTAM) A sophisticated file transfer program available under the Application layer of the OSI model.

FileShare Filesharing software available on a Macintosh running System 7.0 that enables network users to make all or part of their hard disk available to other users.

filter A term used to describe the way a bridge examines a packet and decides on the basis of its address tables whether or not on the packet should be forwarded.

focal point Under IBM's NetView network management program a focal point receives information from entry points located on various SNA network addressable units (NAUs).

forward A term used to describe the action a bridge takes when it sends a packet on to the next bridge toward its ultimate destination.

Fractional T-1 Service (FT1) Division of T-1 bandwidth into fractional units such as one-eighth (192 Kbs), one-fourth (384 Kbs), or one-half (768 Kbs), which are sold to customers at a much more attractive rate than full T-1 service.

frame relay A Data Link layer protocol that defines how variable length data frames can be assembled using fast packet technology.

front-end processor (FEP) A software controllable controller that offloads overhead functions such as polling devices off the host so that the host can concentrate on number crunching.

gateway A device that connects networks that have different network architectures. They use all seven layers of the OSI model and perform protocol conversion.

Go-back-N Continuous An error checking method in which a station receives several frames before replying with a NAK or an ACK. If a station sent 7 consecutive frames and an error was detected in frame 4, the sending station would retransmit frames 4 through 7.

Government OSI Profile (GOSIP) The Government Open Systems Interconnect Profile or set of protocols required so that vendors will provide the government with products that are compatible.

Heterogeneous LAN Management (HLM) A set of network management specifications developed jointly by IBM and 3Com to help network managers develop tools for monitoring, analyzing, and controlling the performance of heterogeneous LANs.

IEEE 802.3 The IEEE standard for a contention, CSMA/CD bus network.

IEEE 802.4 The IEEE standard for a non-contention token bus network that is physically a bus but logically a ring.

IEEE 802.5 The IEEE standard for a non-contention, Token Ring network.

Integrated Services Digital Network (ISDN) An evolving set of international standards for high-speed digital transmission of voice, data, and video over public phone lines at speeds up to 1.544 Mbs.

International Communications Architecture (IAC) A feature of the Macintosh System 7.0 that permits applications to send data or commands to other applications located on the same machine or on a different machine on the network.

International Standard (IS) A specification that has passed all steps and completed the process of becoming an international standard.

International Standards Organization (ISO) The organization responsible for adopting international communications standards; its Open Systems Interconnect model is an example.

Internet Protocol Exchange (IPX) The network protocol used on NetWare networks; it is derived from XNS but no longer compatible with this protocol.

internet Two or more networks linked together with a router or gateway.

jabber A condition in which a malfunctioning Ethernet node continuously transmits over the network.

jam signal A network signal generated to indicate that a collision has occurred on a local area network.

kernel The key administrative center for OS/2 responsible for scheduling, file management, memory management, and overall system coordination.

LAN Manager/X A version of LAN Manager designed to work under UNIX.

LAN Manager A network operating system designed by Microsoft to run under OS/2. Microsoft licenses this product to several companies such as 3Com, AT&T, and Hewlett Packard that develop their own versions.

Line Termination Equipment (LT) Defined by ISDN as equipment located within the local exchange company's or common carrier's network in situations in which lines must be extended beyond the normal range of a central office.

link test   A 10BaseT function that constantly scans lines between nodes and hubs as well as lines between hubs for evidence of electrical activity to ensure the line is still functioning.

lobes   The cable connecting a multistation access unit to a workstation.

Local Area Network   A group of microcomputers networked to share hardware and software resources at one physical location.

Local Area Transport Area (LATA)   The geographic area governed by a local exchange company (LEC).

Local Exchange Company (LEC)   A local phone company which might be an independent telephone company or one of the regional Bell companies.

LocalTalk   Apple's cabling system for its AppleTalk local area network.

logical unit (LU)   A logical port, a point of access that enables an SNA user to access the network.

Management Information Base (MIB)   A database containing key network management information for the SNMP protocol.

Manchester Encoding   A transmission scheme used by many networks in a negative voltage for the first half of bit time represents the value 1 while a positive voltage followed by a transition to a negative voltage represents the value 0.

Manufacturing Automation Protocol (MAP)   A suite of protocols developed specifically for a manufacturing environment that is based on the OSI model and incorporates the IEEE 802.4 standard for a token bus network. The major reason for MAP is to enable factory devices to communicate with each other and with network management tools. General Motors has been a leading advocate of MAP.

message control block (MCB)   The format used by a packet transmitted the Redirector to the NetBIOS interface.

Message Transfer Agent (MTA)   An X.400 component that provides store and forward services as well as other "post office" functions.

Message Transfer System (MTS)   An X.400 component that provides enhanced delivery services such as verified delivery or nondelivery.

metropolitan area network (MAN)   A network designed to link together diverse local networks into a city-wide net.

micro channel architecture (MCA)   An intelligent bus or data highway capable of handling high-speed traffic on an IBM PS/2 series microcomputer.

MS-Net   Microsoft original network operating system that was licensed to vendors to modify and then repackage under their own names.

Multistation Access Unit (MAU)   Wire centers with bypass circuitry found on IBM Token Ring Networks.

Name Binding Protocol A protocol under AppleTalk that matches a workstation's server names with internet addresses.

named mail slots A quick and dirty way for two processes to communicate without the need for a full duplex, error-free channel. These mail slots can be accessed by name.

Named Pipes Full duplex traffic within a computer or between two computers under OS/2. Named Pipes can be accessed like any sequential file.

NetBIOS The network interface IBM provided with its PC LAN Program. It has since become a de facto standard used by many network programs.

NetView IBM's network management program that runs on an IBM mainframe.

NetWare The leading network operating system. Novell has indicated that it wants this product to be hardware independent and serve as a platform for all the leading network protocols.

Network Addressable Unit (NAU) An SNA component capable of being assigned an address and capable of receiving or sending information to the host. NAUs include Logical Units (LUs), Physical Units (PUs), and System Service Control Points (SSCPs).

Network Control Program (NCP) A PU running on a communications controller (FEP).

Network Driver Interface Specifications (NDIS) Developed jointly by Microsoft and 3Com, this set of specifications provides an interface freeing higher level protocols running under OS/2 from any concern over a network's hardware.

Network File System (NFS) A protocol developed by Sun Computer Corporation and used on a variety of UNIX-based systems.

Network Management Protocol A suite of network management protocols based on CMIP and used by AT&T in its Unified Network Management Architecture.

Network Management System (NMS) A system that manages and controls a network and provides such features as network configuration, alerts, and traffic analysis.

Network Management Vector Transport (NMVT) The protocol by which LANs can communicate with NetView.

nodes Network workstations.

noncontention A network in which workstations do not have to contend for the right to use the network. A token bus or a token ring are examples of a non-contention network.

Open Systems Interconnect model (OSI model) A model for the interconnection of heterogeneous computer networks developed by the International Standards Organization.

Open Token Foundation (OTF) An organization of vendors formed to promote interoperability in token ring products.

operating system A group of programs that manages a computer's hardware and software resources.

OS/2 An operating system designed for Intel 80286, 80386, and 80486-based IBM microcomputers and compatibles.

Packet Assembler/Disassembler (PAD) A device that provides protocol translation from a data stream's native protocol to X.25 protocol. At the destination end of the transmission, the X.25 packets are translated to whatever protocol is required.

passive star A topology in which cables branch out of a central block. There is no repeater functionality.

Path Control layer The SNA layer that handles routing and flow control.

peer-to-peer Workstations on a network that share resources as equals in a "peer-to-peer" relationship.

Physical Control layer The SNA layer corresponding roughly to the OSI model's Physical layer. It provides specifications for serial connections between nodes as well as high-speed parallel connections between host computers and their front-end processors.

Physical Unit (PU) A physical device or communication link and its associated software and microcode found on an SNA network. Examples of PUs would include communication processors and cluster controllers.

pipe A part of memory that serves a buffer with in and out buffers. Pipes serve as channels between two programs, and the information flows serially.

Point of Presence (POP) Interface points within a LATA for an interLATA carrier such as AT&T, MCI, or Sprint.

Premises Distribution System (PDS) AT&T cabling system.

Presentation Services layer The SNA layer responsible for formatting, translation, and other services associated with the way data must look.

Printer Access Protocol An AppleTalk protocol that handles streaming tape sessions as well as streaming printer sessions.

process A single program and all the computer resources required to run it including memory areas, descriptor tables, and system support. An application is composed of many different processes.

protected mode A mode under OS/2 in which key registers and memory are protected for each program running so that a computer can be multitasking.

protocol A set of rules or conventions followed by computers so they may communicate together.

queues Memory areas serving as storage locations for information. Any process can open and write to a queue.

real mode A mode under OS/2 so that a program designed to run under MS-DOS can run. This mode limits a program to the hardware resources available under MS-DOS including a maximum of 640K of RAM and 32 megabytes of hard disk storage.

Redirector program A program that enables programmers to write to it rather than to the NetBIOS. The Redirector communicates with a file server using Server Message Blocks (SMBs).

Repository Manager The database that will hold network management information under IBM's SystemView.

ring A network topology resembling a ring that is used for non-contention networks.

root bridge Under the Spanning Tree algorithm, the bridge selected by its peers during the negotiation process as the one having the highest priority value and highest station address.

router A device that is protocol specific that connects two networks that might have completely different MAC layers.

Routing Table Maintenance Protocol (RTMP) An AppleTalk protocol that keeps track of the number of bridges that must be crossed to send a datagram from one network to another.

runts Packets that fall below the minimally acceptable packet size.

selective-repeat continuous An error checking method in which a station saves all frames in a sequence in a buffer so that if an error is detected in a particular frame (let's say frame 6), only that frame needs to be retransmitted.

semaphore A kind of flag that exists in only two states—owned or not-owned. Semaphores can signify a process is using a resource that cannot be disturbed, serve as a way of synchronizing two processes that need to communicate with each other, or signal when only one thread is in a position to monitor a particular event.

Sequenced Packet Protocol (SPP) An XNS protocol that ensures reliability above the simple datagram delivery of IDP by synchronizing sending and delivery using a full-duplex communication method. Packets are numbered so that lost or damaged packets can be requested and then retransmitted.

Server Message Block (SMB) The format used for a packet sent from the Redirector to a file server.

Service Point Under IBM's NetView, an interface to NetView from non-IBM equipment.

Session Protocol A protocol under AppleTalk that handles the correct sequencing of datagrams when they are out of order. It also takes responsibility for ensuring that datagrams are the correct size and that there are break points during conversations.

session A link between two Network Addressable Units (NAUs) under IBM's Systems Network Architecture (SNA).

shared memory A way of handling memory so that a portion of the host's memory is mapped to the NIC's memory.

Signal Quality Error (SQE) A test on a 10BaseT network that ensures that cabling is functional and workstations are able to send and receive signals.

Signaling System 7 (SS7) A series of CCITT recommendations that define the content and format of signaling messages necessary for transferring of network control information.

Simple Mail Transfer Protocol (SMTP) A mail service available under Transmission Control Protocol/Internet Protocol.

Simple Network Management Protocol (SMNP) A network management protocol designed to run on TCP/IP networks.

single attached station (SAS) A network node attached to wiring concentrators on an FDDI network.

single-route broadcast frame When spanning tree topology is used with source routing bridges, this special frame is circulated once to ensure that only certain bridges in the network are configured to pass single route type frames.

solicit successor frame A frame sent on a token bus network that is designed to determine the next user of the network.

source explicit forwarding (SEF) A feature offered by many intelligent bridges which enables a network supervisor to assign internetwork access privileges by labeling specified addresses in a routing table as either accessible or inaccessible to specific users and groups.

Source Routing Transparent Bridge A bridge cable to forward both Spanning Tree and Source Routing frames.

Source Routing An algorithm used by IBM's Token Ring networks in which bridges keep track of routing tables and know the destination address of the workstation to which they wish to route a packet.

Spanning Tree Algorithm (STA) An approach toward bridging multiple networks where more than one loop might exist. STA only permits one path to be active while alternate paths or loops are blocked.

star A network topology in which a central computer or file server has cables radiating out to each network workstation.

static router A router that requires the network manager to create routing tables. These tables remain static (unchanged) until the manager makes changes.

stop-and-wait ARQ An error checking method in which a computer transmits a frame of information and then waits to receive an acknowledgement (ACK) control code indicating that the frame arrived correctly.

StreetTalk A proprietary global naming service provided with the VINES network operating system.

subnetwork Each network that is part of a larger internet.

Super-Frame A standard DS-4 framing scheme consisting of 12 separate 193-bit frames. A framing bit identifies both the channel and the signaling frame.

Synchronous Optical Network (SONET) A set of specifications for synchronizing public communications networks and linking them together via high-speed optical fiber links.

System Service Control Point (SSCP)   The Network Addressable Unit (NAU) on an SNA network that provides the services necessary to manage a network or a portion of a network. The SSCP resides in the Virtual Telecommunications Access Method (VTAM) control program on the host computer.

Systems Application Architecture (SAA)   IBM's set of specifications for providing a common user interface and common programming interfaces for its entire line of computers.

Systems Network Architecture (SNA)   IBM's network architecture, the layered suite of protocols found on its mainframes and minicomputers.

SystemView   IBM's network architecture plan for the 1990s that includes UNIX as well as SNA, TCP/IP, OS/2.

Technical and Office Protocol (TOP)   A suite of protocols developed by Boeing and based on the OSI model. It was developed specifically to be used by the engineering, graphics, accounting, and marketing support functions in a manufacturing-oriented company such as Boeing.

Telnet   A virtual terminal service offered under Transmission Control Protocol/Internet Protocol.

terminal adapter (TA)   An interface connecting non ISDN compatible equipment to an ISDN network.

Terminal Equipment-1 (TE-1)   Equipment that is ISDN compatible and can be connected directly to an ISDN network.

Terminal Equipment-2 (TE-2)   Equipment that is not ISDN compatible and requires a terminal adapter (TA) to attach to an ISDN network.

thread   An execution path within a process under OS/2. The three priority classes for threads under OS/2 are time critical, regular, and idle time.

Time Division Multiplexing (TDM)   Multiplexing in which data streams are guaranteed a time slot whether they need it or not.

token   A specific bit pattern that indicates whether a token ring or token bus network is being used or not.

Transaction Services layer   The SNA layer corresponding roughly to the OSI model's Application layer.

Transmission Control layer   The SNA layer that provides the pacing for data exchanges between NAUs. It also handles encryption when requested.

Transmission Control Protocol/Internet Protocol(TCP/IP)   A suite of protocols designed for the Defense Department's network and now the basis of the nation's internet.

transparent bridging   A technique used by all Ethernet and some Token Ring networks in which packets are forwarded "hop-by-hop" from bridge to bridge across the network.

two-way memory interleave   A technique in which a computer accesses one bank of RAM chips while a second bank of RAM chips is being refreshed.

Unified Network Management Architecture (UNMP)   AT&T's network management architecture built on a foundation of OSI network management protocols.

UNIX   A multiuser, multitasking operating system developed by Bell Labs; it is used on many large networks, particularly for scientific and university networks.

user agent   Defined by X.400 recommendations as the component providing the X.400 envelope, all necessary headers and addresses before forwarding a message to a Message Transfer Agent.

virtual memory   A computer's ability to utilize secondary storage to handle very large programs. The computer fools the programs into thinking that there is more RAM than there really is by swapping different portions of the program from secondary storage to RAM as needed.

Virtual Telecommunications Access Method (VTAM)   This program running on an SNA network coordinates communications between teleprocessing devices and application programs and the flow of data. It also permits the network's configuration to be changed while the network is running.

virtual terminal (VT)   A virtual terminal protocol developed for the OSI model.

wait states   A computer must pause if its RAM chips are not fast enough and "wait" until these chips are refreshed and ready to receive additional information.

wide area network (WAN)   A network linking together networks located in other geographic areas.

working paper (WP)   The very first stage a specification takes on the road toward becoming an international standard.

wrapping   A procedure in which an FDDI network activates its second ring to bypass and isolate a failed node.

X.400   A series of recommendations drafted by the CCITT for protocols to provide international standards for electronic messaging.

X.500   A series of recommendations drafted by the CCITT for protocols to govern a universal directory.

Xerox Network Systems (XNS)   One of the first network protocols and the basis of the original 3Com EtherShare and Novell NetWare network protocols.

Zone Information Protocol   An AppleTalk protocol that maps the network into a series of zone names.

zone   Under AppleTalk's terminology, the logical grouping of networks on an internet.

Bibliography

AppleTalk networks

Apple. *AppleTalk Network System Overview*. Addison-Wesley, 1989.

Brief overview that does an excellent job of explaining the basic components of an AppleTalk network.

Sidhu, Gursharan, Richard Andrews, and Alan Oppenheimer. *Inside AppleTalk*. 2d ed. Addison-Wesley, 1990.

A detailed treatment of each of the protocols comprising the AppleTalk protocol suite.

Data communications

Fitzgerald, Jerry. *Business Data Communications*. 3d ed. John Wiley, 1990.

Contains very good chapters on network design fundamentals and network security and control. The references at the end of each chapter are up-to-date and useful.

Martin, James. *Data Communication Technology*. Prentice Hall, 1988.

Martin's fourth section is worth the price of this book. It contains excellent chapters on data link characteristics, data codes, contention and polling, error detection and correction, asynchronous protocols, and the binary-synchronous protocol. The chapters on Systems Network Architecture and X.25 are also excellent.

Schatt, Stan. *Data Communications for Business*. Prentice-Hall, 1991.

Thorough coverage on the latest specifications for X.400 and EDI as well as the most detailed chapter on network management. Contains the most technical treatment of microcomputers.

Stallings, William. *Business Data Communications*. Macmillan, 1990.

Excellent treatments of micro-mainframe links, flow control, multiplexing, wide area networks, and ISDN.

_____. *Handbook of Computer Communications Standards*.

Vol 1. The Open Systems Interconnection (OSI) Model and OSI-Related Standards. Macmillan, 1987.

Vol 2. Local Network Standards. Macmillan, 1987.

Vol 3. The Department of Defense (DOD) Standards Macmillan, 1987.

Volume 1 is the book to buy if you buy just one book on the OSI model. The most comprehensive and clearest treatment of this difficult subject. Volume 2 covers the IEEE 802 standards for bus token bus, and token ring as well as FDDI. The coverage on the LLC and MAC layers of the 802 standard are the best available. Volume 3 covers TCP/IP and provides detailed treatment of each of protocols comprising this popular approach to internetworking.

NetWare

Liebing, Edward. *NetWare User's Guide*. M&T Books, 1989.

Excellent examples of complex log-in scripts, a fine workstation maintenance chapter, and a good solid description of the printing process. Note that this book does not cover NetWare 386.

McCann, John T. *NetWare Supervisor's Guide*. M&T Books, 1989.

Every NetWare supervisor should have a copy of this book. It has thorough installation and workstation sections, and an excellent diagnostics and troubleshooting chapter.

Schatt, Stan. *Understanding NetWare*. Howard Sams, 1989.

Discusses NetWare within the larger framework of internetworks, so has chapters on bridges and gateways as well as on NetWare links to TCP/IP and X.25 networks. Comprehensive treatments of NetWare on the Macintosh and E-mail on a LAN.

Networks

Martin, James. *Local Area Networks: Architectures and Implementations*. Prentice Hall, 1989.

Detailed treatment of NetBIOS and APPC interfaces, the IBM Redirector, and SMB interface as well as different vendor networks (3Com, Ethernet, STARLAN, Novell, etc.).

————. *SNA: IBM's Networking Solution* Prentice Hall, 1987.

An excellent description of a very complex topic when a LAN manager has micro experience but needs to get up to speed on SNA.

McConnell, John. *Internetworking Computer Systems*. Prentice Hall, 1988.

The most detailed book on internet protocols and upper level OSI protocols. Provides the best explanation on X.400 and X.500 that I have seen.

Miller, Mark A. *LAN Protocol Handbook*. M&T Books, 1990.

If you need to know the frame structure for a specific protocol, this is the book. Covers everything from AppleTalk to XNS.

Racal Interlan. *Racal Interlan on Interoperability*. Racal Interlan, 1989.

Very readable treatment of the major issues in interoperability. An excellent introduction for beginners.

Schatt, Stan. *Understanding Local Area Networks*. 2d ed. Howard Sams, 1990.

Contains up-to-date information on IBM's LAN Server as well as NetWare 386 and VINES. Contains the most thorough treatment of Macintosh LANs as well as electronic messaging on LANs.

Stallings, William. *Local Networks*. 3d ed. Macmillan, 1990.

Excellent chapters on internetworking, network design, and the PBX. A classic that belongs in every LAN manager's library.

Tanenbaum, Andrew S. *Computer Network*. 2d ed. Prentice Hall, 1988.

The most detailed treatment of network protocol and routing schemes. An excellent reference book.

Telecommunications

Gurrie, Michael and Patrick O'Connor. *Voice/Data Telecommunications Systems*. Prentice Hall, 1986.

Very technical treatment of telecommunications. The book you need if you want to know more about PBX and station equipment as well as transmission forms and signaling.

Rowe, Stanford. *Business Telecommunications*. 2d ed. SRA, 1990.

Thorough introduction for data people who need to learn more about voice operations.

Schatt, Stan and Steve Fox. *Voice/Data Telecommunications for Business*. Prentice Hall, 1990.

Detailed treatment of AT&T, Northern Telecom, and Rolm/IBM each in their own chapter on how their PBX system integrates voice and data communications. Thorough and up-to-date chapters on ISDN and X.25. Data chapters include discussions of error checking and micro-mainframe operations.

Index

Other Bestsellers of Related Interest

WORDPERFECT® 5.1 MACROS
—Donna M. Mosich, Robert Bixby,
and Pamela Adams-Regan

Get everything you need to know about macros in any version of WordPerfect through 5.1. Create and use macros to generate form letters, automate mailing list production, index manuscripts, and more! There are more than 300 usable macros covered in this guide (and available on disk), with explanations and illustrations on how the macro command language is used. 480 pages, 162 illustrations. Book No. 3617, $26.95 paperback, $34.95 hardcover.

**BUILDING C LIBRARIES: Windows, Menus &
User Interfaces**—Len Dorfman

Improve the quality of your programs while drastically reducing development time with this new guide from expert Len Dorfman. He shows you how to use the library manager to create your own professional window, screen, and keyboard handling libraries. *Building C Libraries* emphasizes interfaces and library development. You get line after line of well-documented source code for menus, pop-up windows, Macintosh-style pull-down, bounce bars, and more. 432 pages, 198 illustrations. Book No. 3418, $26.95 paperback, $34.95 hardcover.

80386: A Programming and Design Handbook
—2nd Edition—Penn Brumm and Don Brumm

"This book has all the information you require to design, build, and program your own 80386-based system." **—Computing Magazine**

Now, with the guidance of system applications experts Penn and Don Brumm, you can exploit this advanced processor. Revised and expanded, this book explains and demonstrates such advanced features as: 32-bit instruction enhancements, memory paging functions, debugging applications, and Virtual 8086 Mode. 480 pages, 108 illustrations. Book No. 3237, $24.95 paperback, $34.95 hardcover.

**ACCPAC PLUS USER'S GUIDE,
Covers Version 5.0**—Esther Deutsch

This is the most comprehensive work available on ACCPAC PLUS, ACCPAC's hot new top-of-the-line general accounting package. The text simplifies functions through keystroke-by-keystroke instructions and sample company data in the order you will actually use the functions in practice. Plus it offers a working accounting system you can customize. You get valuable how-to-use-it data for all the major modules; general ledger, financial reporter, accounts payable, and accounts receivable. 672 pages, Illustrations. Book No. 3758, $26.95 hardcover only.

**HANDBOOK OF DATA COMMUNICATIONS AND
COMPUTER NETWORKS**—2nd Edition
—Dimitris N. Chorafas

Completely revised and updated, this results-oriented reference—with over 125 illustrations-progresses smoothly as theory is combine with concrete examples to show you how to successfully manage a dynamic information system. You'll find applications-oriented material on networks, technological advances, telecommunications technology, protocols, network design, messages and transactions, software's role, and network maintenance. 448 pages, 129 illustrations. Book No. 3690, $44.95 hardcover only.

**WORDPERFECT POWER: Word Processing Made
Easy**—2nd Edition—Jennifer de Lasala

This guide is the ultimate nontechnical learning tool. Use it to understand 5.1's new features such as optional, mouse-operated pull-down menus and equation-oriented graphics, and to find information on: commands, file management, merging, style sheets, printing, document layout, function key usage, macros, graphics, and much more. 432 pages, Illustrations. Book No. 3679, $24.95 hardcover only.

COMBATING COMPUTER CRIME:
Prevention, Detection, Investigation
—Chantico Publishing Company, Inc.

This timely handbook outlines practical solutions for identifying, preventing, and detecting computer crimes, and represents the experiences of over 2,000 participating organizations from industry, commerce, and government. Step by step, the authors show you how to establish a computer crime policy and provide a management plan of action for implementing that policy. Detailed checklists and worksheets are included. 350 pages, 100 illustrations. Book No. 3664, $39.95 hardcover only.

DISASTER RECOVERY HANDBOOK
—Chantico Publishing Company, Inc.

Could your company survive if a tornado struck today? You'll find everything you need for coping with your worst-case scenario in this book. Among the other issues covered are plan formulation and maintenance; data, communications, and microcomputer recovery procedures; emergency procedures. Action-oriented checklists and worksheets are included to help you start planning right away—before it's too late. 276 pages, 88 illustrations. Book No. 3663, $39.95 hardcover only.

ASSEMBLY LANGUAGE SUBROUTINES FOR
MS-DOS® —2nd Edition—Leo J. Scanlon

Use this collection of practical subroutines to do high-precision math, convert code, manipulate strings and lists, sort data, display prompts and messages, read user commands and responses, work with disks and files, and more. Scanlon gives you instant access to over 125 commonly needed subroutines. Never again will you waste valuable time wading through manuals or tutorials. 384 pages, 211 illustrations. Book No. 3649, $24.95 hardcover only.

ENHANCED MS-DOS® BATCH FILE
PROGRAMMING—Dan Gookin

This new guide leads you through the development of versatile batch files that incorporate the features of the latest DOS versions, commercial batch file extenders, and utilities written in high-level languages such as Pascal and C. The companion diskettes packaged with the book include all the significant batch file programs described—plus all the utilities and their source codes. 360 pages, 71 illustrations, Two 5¼" diskettes. Book No. 3641, $24.95 paperback, $34.95 hardcover.

BUILD YOUR OWN 80486 PC AND SAVE A
BUNDLE—Aubrey Pilgrim

With inexpensive third-party components and clear, step-by-step photos and assembly instructions—and without any soldering, wiring, or electronic test instruments—you can assemble a 486. This book discusses boards, monitors, hard drives, cables, printers, modems, faxes, UPSs, memory floppy disks, and more. It includes parts lists, mail order addresses, safety precautions, troubleshooting tips, and a glossary of terms. 240 pages, 62 illustrations. Book No. 3628, $16.95 paperback, $26.95 hardcover.

STRATEGY, SYSTEMS, AND INTEGRATION:
A Handbook for Information Managers
—George M. Hall

Now you can successfully plan new data processing systems and integrate existing systems. Hall shows you how you can get beyond basic strategic problems and concentrate on mastering the techniques that will meet the increasing demands of your system. From an in-depth analysis of database requirements to key management issues, you'll follow the logical order in which systems should be designed and developed. 384 pages, 118 illustrations. Book NO. 3614, $39.95 hardcover only.

BIT-MAPPED GRAPHICS—Steve Rimmer

This is one of the first books to cover specific graphic file formats used by popular paint and desktop publishing packages. It shows you how to pack and unpack bit-map image files so you can import and export them to other applications. It helps you sort through available file formats, standards, patches, and revision levels, using commercial-quality C code to explore bit-mapped graphics and effectively deal with image files. 504 pages, 131 illustrations. Book No. 3558, $38.95 hardcover only.

AUTOCAD™ Methods and Macros—2nd Edition
—Jeff Guenther and Ed Ocoboc

With 275 illustrations, this completely revised and updated guide takes you step by step through dozens of useful techniques for working through Release 11 of AutoCAD. Twenty new chapters outline object selection, lines, editing and viewing documents, inserting drawings into documents, working with text, sketching, printer plots, dialogue boxes, the new multi-purpose menu, and much more. 464 pages, 275 illustrations. Book No. 3544, $34.95 hardcover only.

MS-DOS® BATCH FILE PROGRAMMING
—2nd Edition—Ronny Richardson

Reviewer's praise of the first edition:

"By the end of this book, readers will be able to implement even the most difficult batch files, and will thoroughly understand the whole process."

—*Computer Shopper*

Now, even the novice can take advantage of batch files—simple step-saving programs that can replace complicated DOS procedures. Includes DOS 4 and the latest in batch utilities. You even get a disk that contains all the batch files. 448 pages, 339 illustrations. Book No. 3537, $36.95 hardcover only.

THE ULTIMATE DOS PROGRAMMER'S MANUAL—John Mueller and Wallace Wang

This sweeping tutorial provides you with routines that demonstrate every aspect of DOS through version 4. You get example programs using assembly language, BASIC, C, and Quick Pascal that you can study and change for your own use. In addition to providing source code examples, this book also shows you how to create programs that combine two or more languages. 904 pages, 305 illustrations. Book No. 3534, $37.95 hardcover only.

Prices Subject to Change Without Notice.

Look for These and Other TAB Books at Your Local Bookstore

To Order Call Toll Free 1-800-822-8158
(in PA, AK, and Canada call 717-794-2191)

or write to TAB Books, Blue Ridge Summit, PA 17294-0840.
